G000090760

Collins

GCSE Maths
2 tier-foundation
for Edexcel A

YEAR 10

BRIAN SPEED

KEITH GORDON

KEVIN EVANS

William Collins' dream of knowledge for all began with the publication of his first book in 1819. A self-educated mill worker, he not only enriched millions of lives, but also founded a flourishing publishing house. Today, staying true to this spirit, Collins books are packed with inspiration, innovation and a practical expertise. They place you at the centre of a world of possibility and give you exactly what you need to explore it.

Collins. Do more.

Published by Collins
An imprint of HarperCollinsPublishers
77–85 Fulham Palace Road
Hammersmith
London
W6 8JB

Browse the complete Collins catalogue at
www.collinseducation.com

ISBN-13: 978-0-000-725685-3
ISBN-10: 000-725685-X

British Library Cataloguing in Publication Data. A Catalogue record for this publication is available from the British Library.

Commissioned by Marie Taylor, Vicky Butt and Michael Cotter

Project managed by Penny Fowler

Edited by Joan Miller and Peta Abbott

Additional proof reader: Ruth Burns

Internal design by JPD

Cover design by JPD

Cover illustration by Andy Parker, JPD

Page make-up and index by Gray Publishing

Page make-up of Really Useful Maths! spreads by EMC Design

Illustrations by Gray Publishing, EMC Design, David Russel, Lazlo Veres, Lisa Alderson, Roger Wade Walker, Bob Lea, Peter Cornwell, Martin Sanders and Peters and Zabranksy

Production by Natasha Buckland

Printed and bound in Hong Kong by Printing Express Ltd.

Acknowledgements

With special thanks to Lynn and Greg Byrd

The Publishers gratefully acknowledge the following for permission to reproduce copyright material. Whilst every effort has been made to trace the copyright holders, in cases where this has been unsuccessful or if any have inadvertently been overlooked, the Publishers will be pleased to make the necessary arrangements at the first opportunity.

Edexcel material reproduced with permission of Edexcel Limited. Edexcel Ltd accepts no responsibility whatsoever for the accuracy or method of working in the answers given.

Grade bar photos © 2006 JupiterImages Corporation and Photodisc Collection / Getty Images

© 2006 JupiterImages Corporation, p1, p22 Main, p23 Middle and BR, p49, p67, p95, p143, p167, p195, p213, p257, p275

© Bernd Klumpp / Istock, p22 TL

© Karen Town / Istock, p22 TR

© David Wall / Alamy, p22 BL

© Neale Haynes/Buzz Pictures, p23 TL

© Christian Kretz / Istock, p22 TR

© PCL / Alamy, p119

© Images Etc Ltd / Alamy, p225

CONTENTS

Welcome to Collins GCSE Maths, the easiest way to learn and succeed in Mathematics. This textbook uses a stimulating approach that really appeals to students. Here are some of the key features of the textbook, to explain why.

Each chapter of the textbook begins with an **Overview**. The Overview lists the Sections you will encounter in the chapter, the key ideas you will learn, and shows how these ideas relate to, and build upon, each other. The Overview also highlights what you should already know, and if you're not sure, there is a short Quick Check activity to test yourself and recap.

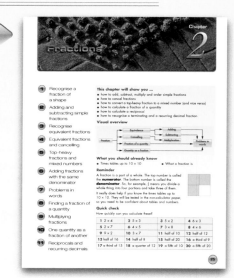

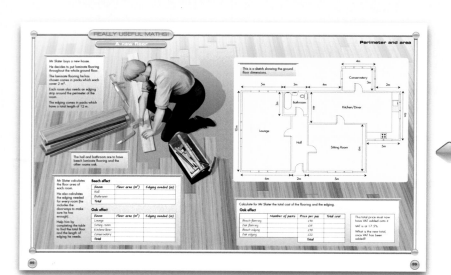

Maths can be useful to us every day of our lives, so look out for these **Really Useful Maths!** pages. These double page spreads use big, bright illustrations to depict real-life situations, and present a short series of real-world problems for you to practice your latest mathematical skills on.

Each **Section** begins first by explaining what mathematical ideas you are aiming to learn, and then lists the key words you will meet and use. The ideas are clearly explained, and this is followed by several examples showing how they can be applied to real problems. Then it's your turn to work through the exercises and improve your skills. Notice the different coloured panels along the outside of the exercise pages. These show the equivalent exam grade of the questions you are working on, so you can always tell how well you are doing.

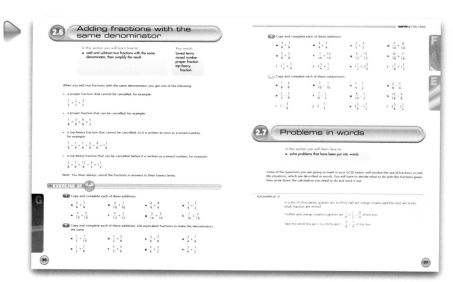

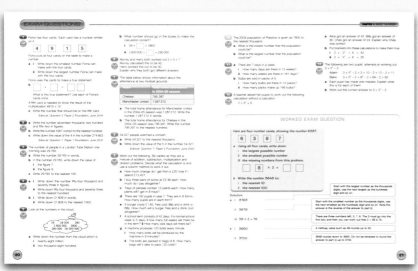

Every chapter in this textbook contains lots of **Exam Questions**. These provide ideal preparation for your examinations. Each exam question section also concludes with a fully worked example. Compare this with your own work, and pay special attention to the examiner's comments, which will ensure you understand how to score maximum marks.

Throughout the textbook you will find **Puzzles** and **Activities** – highlighted in the green panels – designed to challenge your thinking and improve your understanding.

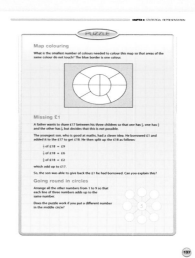

Review the **Grade Yourself** pages at the very end of the chapter. This will show what exam grade you are currently working at. Doublecheck **What you should now know** to confirm that you have the knowledge you need to progress.

Working through these sections in the right way should mean you achieve your very best in GCSE Maths. Remember though, if you get stuck, answers to all the questions are at the back of the book (except the exam question answers which your teacher has).

We do hope you enjoy using Collins GCSE Maths, and wish you every good luck in your studies!

Brian Speed, Keith Gordon, Kevin Evans

ICONS

 You may use your calculator for this question

 You should not use your calculator for this question

 Indicates a Using and Applying Mathematics question

 Indicates a Proof question

Basic number

This chapter will show you ...

- how to use basic number skills without a calculator

Visual overview

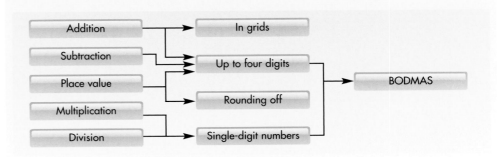

What you should already know

- Times tables up to 10×10
- Addition and subtraction of numbers less than 20
- Simple multiplication and division
- How to multiply numbers by 10 and 100

Quick check

How quickly can you complete these?

1 4×6	**2** 3×7	**3** 5×8	**4** 9×2
5 6×7	**6** $13 + 14$	**7** $15 + 15$	**8** $18 - 12$
9 $19 - 7$	**10** $11 - 6$	**11** $50 \div 5$	**12** $48 \div 6$
13 $35 \div 7$	**14** $42 \div 6$	**15** $36 \div 9$	**16** 8×10
17 9×100	**18** 3×10	**19** 14×100	**20** 17×10

1.1 Adding with grids

In this section you will learn how to:
- add and subtract single-digit numbers in a grid
- use row and column totals to find missing numbers in a grid

Key words
add
column
grid
row

ACTIVITY

Adding with grids

You need a set of cards marked 0 to 9.

0	1	2	3	4	5	6	7	8	9

Shuffle the cards and lay them out in a 3 by 3 **grid**. You will have one card left over.

3	5	0
7	6	4
8	2	9

Copy your grid onto a piece of paper. Then **add** up each **row** and each **column** and write down their totals. Finally, find the grand total and write it in the box at the bottom right.

3	5	0	8
7	6	4	17
8	2	9	19
18	13	13	44

Look out for things that help. For example:

- in the first column, 3 + 7 make 10 and 10 + 8 = 18

- in the last column, 9 + 4 = 9 + 1 + 3 = 10 + 3 = 13

Reshuffle the cards, lay them out again and copy the new grid. Copy the new grid again on a fresh sheet of paper, leaving out some of the numbers.

4	5	8
0	2	6
9	1	7

4	5	8	17
0	2	6	8
9	1	7	17
13	8	21	42

4	☐	8	17
☐	2	☐	8
9	☐	7	☐
☐	8	21	42

Pass this last grid to a friend to work out the missing numbers. You can make it quite hard because you are using only the numbers from 0 to 9. Remember: once a number has been used, it *cannot* be used again in that grid.

Example Find the numbers missing from this grid.

☐	☐	9	17
☐	2	☐	11
8	☐	☐	☐
19	3	17	☐

Clues The two numbers missing from the second column must add up to 1, so they must be 0 and 1. The two numbers missing from the first column add to 11, so they could be 7 and 4 or 6 and 5. Now, 6 or 5 won't work with 0 or 1 to give 17 across the top row. That means it has to be:

```
 7   1   9 | 17              7   1   9 | 17
 4   2  □  | 11    giving     4   2   5 | 11     as the answer.
 8   0  □  | □                8   0   3 | 11
19   3  17 | □               19   3  17 | 39
```

You can use your cards to try out your ideas.

EXERCISE 1A

1 Find the row and column totals for each of these grids.

a
```
1   3   7 | □
9   2   8 | □
6   5   4 | □
□   □   □ | □
```

b
```
0   6   7 | □
8   1   4 | □
9   5   3 | □
□   □   □ | □
```

c
```
0   8   7 | □
1   6   2 | □
9   3   4 | □
□   □   □ | □
```

d
```
2   4   6 | □
3   5   7 | □
8   9   1 | □
□   □   □ | □
```

e
```
5   9   3 | □
6   1   8 | □
2   7   4 | □
□   □   □ | □
```

f
```
0   8   3 | □
7   2   4 | □
1   6   5 | □
□   □   □ | □
```

g
```
9   4   8 | □
7   0   5 | □
1   6   3 | □
□   □   □ | □
```

h
```
0   8   6 | □
7   1   4 | □
5   9   2 | □
□   □   □ | □
```

i
```
1   8   7 | □
6   2   5 | □
0   9   3 | □
□   □   □ | □
```

2 Find the numbers missing from each of these grids. Remember: the numbers missing from each grid must be chosen from 0 to 9 without any repeats.

a
```
 1   7  □  | 16
 □   3   6 |  9
 5  □    2 | 11
 6  14  16 | 36
```

b
```
 1  □    3 |  6
 □   5   4 | 15
 7   8  □  | 24
14  15  16 | 35
```

c
```
 9   3  □  | 18
 4  □    5 |  9
 □   2   8 | 11
14   5  19 | 38
```

d
```
 □  □   □  | 16
 2  □    4 | 13
 8   5   0 | 13
19  13  10 | 42
```

e
```
 2  □    6 | 17
 □   1  □  | □
 5  □    8 | 13
11  □   17 | 38
```

f
```
 1  □   □  | 16
 □   2   4 | 12
 □   9   3 | □
12  □   15 | □
```

g
```
 0   2  □  |  3
 9  □   □  | □
 □   4   5 | 17
17  □   13 | 42
```

h
```
 □  □    3 |  4
 □   7   4 | □
 9   6  □  | 20
18  □   12 | □
```

i
```
 □  □    4 | 10
 □   2  □  | □
 8  □   □  | 15
15  □   □  | 36
```

In this section you will:

- recall and use your knowledge of times tables

ACTIVITY

Special table facts

You need a sheet of squared paper.

Start by writing in the easy tables. These are the 1 ×, 2 ×, 5 ×, 10 × and 9 × tables.

Now draw up a 10 by 10 tables square before you go any further. (Time yourself doing this and see if you can get faster.)

Once you have filled it in, shade in all the easy tables. You should be left with something like the square on the right.

×	1	2	3	4	5	6	7	8	9	10
1										
2										
3			9	12		18	21	24		
4			12	16		24	28	32		
5										
6			18	24		36	42	48		
7			21	28		42	49	56		
8			24	32		48	56	64		
9										
10										

Now cross out **one** of each pair that have the same answer, such as 3 × 4 and 4 × 3. This leaves you with:

×	1	2	3	4	5	6	7	8	9	10
1										
2										
3			9							
4			12	16						
5										
6			18	24		36				
7			21	28		42	49			
8			24	32		48	56	64		
9										
10										

Now there are just 15 table facts. Do learn them.

The rest are easy tables, so you should know all of them. But keep practising!

EXERCISE 1B

1 Write down the answer to each of the following without looking at the multiplication square.

a 4 × 5	**b** 7 × 3	**c** 6 × 4	**d** 3 × 5	**e** 8 × 2
f 3 × 4	**g** 5 × 2	**h** 6 × 7	**i** 3 × 8	**j** 9 × 2
k 5 × 6	**l** 4 × 7	**m** 3 × 6	**n** 8 × 7	**o** 5 × 5
p 5 × 9	**q** 3 × 9 ·	**r** 6 × 5	**s** 7 × 7	**t** 4 × 6
u 6 × 6	**v** 7 × 5	**w** 4 × 8	**x** 4 × 9	**y** 6 × 8

2 Write down the answer to each of the following without looking at the multiplication square.

a 10 ÷ 2	**b** 28 ÷ 7	**c** 36 ÷ 6	**d** 30 ÷ 5	**e** 15 ÷ 3
f 20 ÷ 5	**g** 21 ÷ 3	**h** 24 ÷ 4	**i** 16 ÷ 8	**j** 12 ÷ 4
k 42 ÷ 6	**l** 24 ÷ 3	**m** 18 ÷ 2	**n** 25 ÷ 5	**o** 48 ÷ 6
p 36 ÷ 4	**q** 32 ÷ 8	**r** 35 ÷ 5	**s** 49 ÷ 7	**t** 27 ÷ 3
u 45 ÷ 9	**v** 16 ÷ 4	**w** 40 ÷ 8	**x** 63 ÷ 9	**y** 54 ÷ 9

3 Write down the answer to each of the following. Look carefully at the signs, because they are a mixture of ×, +, – and ÷ .

a 5 + 7	**b** 20 − 5	**c** 3 × 7	**d** 5 + 8	**e** 24 ÷ 3
f 15 − 8	**g** 6 + 8	**h** 27 ÷ 9	**i** 6 × 5	**j** 36 ÷ 6
k 7 × 5	**l** 15 ÷ 3	**m** 24 − 8	**n** 28 ÷ 4	**o** 7 + 9
p 9 + 6	**q** 36 − 9	**r** 30 ÷ 5	**s** 8 + 7	**t** 4 × 6
u 8 × 5	**v** 42 ÷ 7	**w** 8 + 9	**x** 9 × 8	**y** 54 − 8

4 Write down the answer to each of the following.

a 3 × 10	**b** 5 × 10	**c** 8 × 10	**d** 10 × 10	**e** 12 × 10
f 18 × 10	**g** 24 × 10	**h** 4 × 100	**i** 7 × 100	**j** 9 × 100
k 10 × 100	**l** 14 × 100	**m** 24 × 100	**n** 72 × 100	**o** 100 × 100
p 20 ÷ 10	**q** 70 ÷ 10	**r** 90 ÷ 10	**s** 170 ÷ 10	**t** 300 ÷ 10
u 300 ÷ 100	**v** 800 ÷ 100	**w** 1200 ÷ 100	**x** 2900 ÷ 100	**y** 5000 ÷ 100

Order of operations and BODMAS

In this section you will learn how to:

- work out the answers to a problem with a number of different signs

Key words

brackets
operation
sequence

Suppose you have to work out the answer to $4 + 5 \times 2$. You may say the answer is 18, but the correct answer is 14.

There is an order of **operations** which you *must* follow when working out calculations like this. The $\times$ is always done *before* the +.

In $4 + 5 \times 2$ this gives $4 + 10 = 14$.

Now suppose you have to work out the answer to $(3 + 2) \times (9 - 5)$. The correct answer is 20.

You have probably realised that the parts in the **brackets** have to be done *first*, giving $5 \times 4 = 20$.

So, how do you work out a problem such as $9 \div 3 + 4 \times 2$?

To answer questions like this, you *must* follow the BODMAS rule. This tells you the **sequence** in which you *must* do the operations.

B	Brackets
O	Order (powers)
D	Division
M	Multiplication
A	Addition
S	Subtraction

For example, to work out $9 \div 3 + 4 \times 2$:

First divide:	$9 \div 3 = 3$	giving	$3 + 4 \times 2$
Then multiply:	$4 \times 2 = 8$	giving	$3 + 8$
Then add:	$3 + 8 = 11$		

And to work out $60 - 5 \times 3^2 + (4 \times 2)$:

First, work out the brackets:	$(4 \times 2) = 8$	giving	$60 - 5 \times 3^2 + 8$
Then the order (power):	$3^2 = 9$	giving	$60 - 5 \times 9 + 8$
Then multiply:	$5 \times 9 = 45$	giving	$60 - 45 + 8$
Then add:	$60 + 8 = 68$	giving	$68 - 45$
Finally, subtract:	$68 - 45 = 23$		

ACTIVITY

Dice with BODMAS

You need a sheet of squared paper and three dice.

Draw a 5 by 5 grid and write the numbers from 1 to 25 in the spaces.

The numbers can be in *any order*.

14	13	18	7	24
15	1	16	17	6
23	8	2	12	5
3	22	4	10	19
25	21	9	20	11

Now throw three dice. Record the score on each one.

Use these numbers to make up a number problem.

You must use all three numbers, and you must not put them together to make a number like 136. For example, with 1, 3 and 6 you could make:

$$1 + 3 + 6 = 10 \qquad 3 \times 6 + 1 = 19 \qquad (1 + 3) \times 6 = 24$$

$$6 \div 3 + 1 = 3 \qquad 6 + 3 - 1 = 8 \qquad 6 \div (3 \times 1) = 2$$

and so on. Remember to use **BODMAS**.

You have to make only one problem with each set of numbers.

When you have made a problem, cross the answer off on the grid and throw the dice again. Make up a problem with the next three numbers and cross that answer off the grid. Throw the dice again and so on.

The first person to make a line of five numbers across, down or diagonally is the winner.

You must write down each problem and its answer so that they can be checked.

Just put a line through each number on the grid, as you use it. Do not cross it out so that it cannot be read, otherwise your problem and its answer cannot be checked.

This might be a typical game.

14	13	18	7	24
15	1	16	17	6
23	8	2	12	5
3	22	4	10	19
25	21	9	20	11

First set (1, 3, 6) $6 \times 3 \times 1 = 18$

Second set (2, 4, 4) $4 \times 4 - 2 = 14$

Third set (3, 5, 1) $(3 - 1) \times 5 = 10$

Fourth set (3, 3, 4) $(3 + 3) \times 4 = 24$

Fifth set (1, 2, 6) $6 \times 2 - 1 = 11$

Sixth set (5, 4, 6) $(6 + 4) \div 5 = 2$

Seventh set (4, 4, 2) $2 - (4 \div 4) = 1$

EXERCISE 1C

1 Work out each of these.

   a $2 \times 3 + 5 =$ **b** $6 \div 3 + 4 =$ **c** $5 + 7 - 2 =$

   d $4 \times 6 \div 2 =$ **e** $2 \times 8 - 5 =$ **f** $3 \times 4 + 1 =$

   g $3 \times 4 - 1 =$ **h** $3 \times 4 \div 1 =$ **i** $12 \div 2 + 6 =$

   j $12 \div 6 + 2 =$ **k** $3 + 5 \times 2 =$ **l** $12 - 3 \times 3 =$

2 Work out each of the following. Remember: first work out the bracket.

   a $2 \times (3 + 5) =$ **b** $6 \div (2 + 1) =$ **c** $(5 + 7) - 2 =$

   d $5 + (7 - 2) =$ **e** $3 \times (4 \div 2) =$ **f** $3 \times (4 + 2) =$

   g $2 \times (8 - 5) =$ **h** $3 \times (4 + 1) =$ **i** $3 \times (4 - 1) =$

   j $3 \times (4 \div 1) =$ **k** $12 \div (2 + 2) =$ **l** $(12 \div 2) + 2 =$

3 Copy each of these and put a loop round the part that you do first. Then work out the answer. The first one has been done for you.

   a $(3 \times 3) - 2 = 7$ **b** $3 + 2 \times 4 =$ **c** $9 \div 3 - 2 =$

   d $9 - 4 \div 2 =$ **e** $5 \times 2 + 3 =$ **f** $5 + 2 \times 3 =$

   g $10 \div 5 - 2 =$ **h** $10 - 4 \div 2 =$ **i** $4 \times 6 - 7 =$

   j $7 + 4 \times 6 =$ **k** $6 \div 3 + 7 =$ **l** $7 + 6 \div 2 =$

4 Work out each of these.

   a $6 \times 6 + 2 =$ **b** $6 \times (6 + 2) =$ **c** $6 \div 6 + 2 =$

   d $12 \div (4 + 2) =$ **e** $12 \div 4 + 2 =$ **f** $2 \times (3 + 4) =$

   g $2 \times 3 + 4 =$ **h** $2 \times (4 - 3) =$ **i** $2 \times 4 - 3 =$

   j $17 + 5 - 3 =$ **k** $17 - 5 + 3 =$ **l** $17 - 5 \times 3 =$

   m $3 \times 5 + 5 =$ **n** $6 \times 2 + 7 =$ **o** $6 \times (2 + 7) =$

   p $12 \div 3 + 3 =$ **q** $12 \div (3 + 3) =$ **r** $14 - 7 \times 1 =$

   s $(14 - 7) \times 1 =$ **t** $2 + 6 \times 6 =$ **u** $(2 + 5) \times 6 =$

   v $12 - 6 \div 3 =$ **w** $(12 - 6) \div 3 =$ **x** $15 - (5 \times 1) =$

   y $(15 - 5) \times 1 =$ **z** $8 \times 9 \div 3 =$

5 Copy each of these and then put in brackets where necessary to make each answer true.

   a $3 \times 4 + 1 = 15$ **b** $6 \div 2 + 1 = 4$ **c** $6 \div 2 + 1 = 2$

   d $4 + 4 \div 4 = 5$ **e** $4 + 4 \div 4 = 2$ **f** $16 - 4 \div 3 = 4$

   g $3 \times 4 + 1 = 13$ **h** $16 - 6 \div 3 = 14$ **i** $20 - 10 \div 2 = 5$

   j $20 - 10 \div 2 = 15$ **k** $3 \times 5 + 5 = 30$ **l** $6 \times 4 + 2 = 36$

   m $15 - 5 \times 2 = 20$ **n** $4 \times 7 - 2 = 20$ **o** $12 \div 3 + 3 = 2$

   p $12 \div 3 + 3 = 7$ **q** $24 \div 8 - 2 = 1$ **r** $24 \div 8 - 2 = 4$

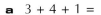

6 Three dice are thrown. They give scores of 3, 1 and 4.

A class makes the following questions with the numbers. Work them out.

a $3 + 4 + 1 =$ **b** $3 + 4 - 1 =$ **c** $4 + 3 - 1 =$

d $4 \times 3 + 1 =$ **e** $4 \times 3 - 1 =$ **f** $(4 - 1) \times 3 =$

g $4 \times 3 \times 1 =$ **h** $(3 - 1) \times 4 =$ **i** $(4 + 1) \times 3 =$

j $4 \times (3 + 1) =$ **k** $1 \times (4 - 3) =$ **l** $4 + 1 \times 3' =$

7 Three different dice give scores of 2, 3, 5. Put ×, +, ÷, – or ( ) in each sentence to make it true.

a 2   3   5 = 11   **b** 2   3   5 = 16   **c** 2   3   5 = 17

d 5   3   2 = 4   **e** 5   3   2 = 13   **f** 5   3   2 = 30

1.4 Place value and ordering numbers

In this section you will learn how to:
- identify the value of any digit in a number

Key words
digit
place value

The ordinary counting system uses **place value**, which means that the value of a **digit** depends upon its place in the number.

In the number 5348

     the 5 stands for 5 thousands or 5000

     the 3 stands for 3 hundreds or 300

     the 4 stands for 4 tens or 40

     the 8 stands for 8 units or 8

And in the number 4 073 520

     the 4 stands for 4 millions or 4 000 000

     the 73 stands for 73 thousands or 73 000

     the 5 stands for 5 hundreds or 500

     the 2 stands for 2 tens or 20

You write and say this number as:

     four million, seventy-three thousand, five hundred and twenty

Note the use of narrow spaces between groups of three digits, starting from the right. All whole and mixed numbers with five or more digits are spaced in this way.

EXAMPLE 1

Put these numbers in order with the smallest first.

7031   3071   3701   7103   7130   1730

Look at the thousands column first and then each of the other columns in turn. The correct order is:

1730   3071   3701   7031   7103   7130

EXERCISE 1D

1 Write the value of each underlined digit.

a 3<u>4</u>1	**b** 47<u>5</u>	**c** <u>1</u>86	**d** 2<u>9</u>8	**e** <u>8</u>3
f 83<u>9</u>	**g** 23<u>8</u>0	**h** 1<u>5</u>07	**i** 653<u>0</u>	**j** <u>2</u>5 436
k 29 <u>0</u>54	**l** 18 25<u>4</u>	**m** 4<u>3</u>08	**n** 52 9<u>9</u>4	**o** <u>8</u>3 205

2 Copy each of these sentences, writing the numbers in words.

a The last Olympic games in Greece had only 43 events and 200 competitors.

b The last Olympic games in Britain had 136 events and 4099 competitors.

c The last Olympic games in the USA had 271 events and 10 744 competitors.

3 Write each of the following numbers in words.

a 5 600 000   **b** 4 075 200   **c** 3 007 950   **d** 2 000 782

4 Write each of the following numbers in numerals or digits.

a Eight million, two hundred thousand and fifty-eight

b Nine million, four hundred and six thousand, one hundred and seven

c One million, five hundred and two

d Two million, seventy-six thousand and forty

5 Write these numbers in order, putting the *smallest* first.

a 21,   48,   23,   9,   15,   56,   85,   54

b 310,   86,   219,   25,   501,   62,   400,   151

c 357,   740,   2053,   888,   4366,   97,   368

6 Write these numbers in order, putting the *largest* first.

a 52,   23,   95,   34,   73,   7,   25,   89

b 65,   2,   174,   401,   80,   700,   18,   117

c 762,   2034,   395,   6227,   89,   3928,   59,   480

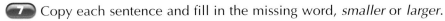

7 Copy each sentence and fill in the missing word, *smaller* or *larger*.

  a 7 is …… than 5

  c 89 is …… than 98

  e 308 is …… than 299

  g 870 is …… than 807

  i 782 is …… than 827

  b 34 is …… than 29

  d 97 is …… than 79

  f 561 is …… than 605

  h 4275 is …… than 4527

8 **a** Write as many three-digit numbers as you can using the digits 3, 6 and 8. (Only use each digit once in each number).

  b Which of your numbers is the smallest?

  c Which of your numbers is the largest?

9 Using each of the digits 0, 4 and 8 only once in each number, write as many different three-digit numbers as you can. (Do not start any number with 0.) Write your numbers down in order, smallest first.

10 Write down in order of size, smallest first, all the two-digit numbers that can be made using 3, 5 and 8. (Each digit can be repeated.)

1.5 Rounding

In this section you will learn how to:
● round a number

Key words
approximation
rounded down
rounded up

You use rounded information all the time. Look at these examples. All of these statements use rounded information. Each actual figure is either above or below the **approximation** shown here. But if the rounding is done correctly, you can find out what the maximum and the minimum figures really are. For example, if you know that the number of matches in the packet is rounded to the nearest 10,

● the smallest figure to be **rounded up** to 30 is 25, and

● the largest figure to be **rounded down** to 30 is 34 (because 35 would be rounded up to 40).

So there could actually be from 25 to 34 matches in the packet.

What about the number of runners in the marathon? If you know that the number 23 000 is rounded to the nearest 1000,

- The smallest figure to be rounded up to 23 000 is 22 500.

- The largest figure to be rounded down to 23 000 is 23 499.

So there could actually be from 22 500 to 23 499 people in the marathon.

EXERCISE 1E

1 Round each of these numbers to the nearest 10.

a 24	**b** 57	**c** 78	**d** 54	**e** 96
f 21	**g** 88	**h** 66	**i** 14	**j** 26
k 29	**l** 51	**m** 77	**n** 49	**o** 94
p 35	**q** 65	**r** 15	**s** 102	**t** 107

2 Round each of these numbers to the nearest 100.

a 240	**b** 570	**c** 780	**d** 504	**e** 967
f 112	**g** 645	**h** 358	**i** 998	**j** 1050
k 299	**l** 511	**m** 777	**n** 512	**o** 940
p 350	**q** 650	**r** 750	**s** 1020	**t** 1070

3 On the shelf of a sweetshop there are three jars like the ones below.

Jar 1   Jar 2   Jar 3

80 sweets (to the nearest 10)

120 sweets (to the nearest 10)

190 sweets (to the nearest 10)

Look at each of the numbers below and write down which jar it could be describing. (For example, 76 sweets could be in jar 1.)

a 78 sweets	**b** 119 sweets	**c** 84 sweets	**d** 75 sweets
e 186 sweets	**f** 122 sweets	**g** 194 sweets	**h** 115 sweets
i 81 sweets	**j** 79 sweets	**k** 192 sweets	**l** 124 sweets

m Which of these numbers of sweets *could not* be in jar 1: 74, 84, 81, 76?

n Which of these numbers of sweets *could not* be in jar 2: 124, 126, 120, 115?

o Which of these numbers of sweets *could not* be in jar 3: 194, 184, 191, 189?

4 Round each of these numbers to the nearest 1000.

a 2400	**b** 5700	**c** 7806	**d** 5040	**e** 9670
f 1120	**g** 6450	**h** 3499	**i** 9098	**j** 1500
k 2990	**l** 5110	**m** 7777	**n** 5020	**o** 9400
p 3500	**q** 6500	**r** 7500	**s** 1020	**t** 1770

5 Round each of these numbers to the nearest 10.

a 234	**b** 567	**c** 718	**d** 524	**e** 906
f 231	**g** 878	**h** 626	**i** 114	**j** 296
k 279	**l** 541	**m** 767	**n** 501	**o** 942
p 375	**q** 625	**r** 345	**s** 1012	**t** 1074

6 Which of these sentences could be true and which must be false?

Welcome to Elsecar
Population 800
(to the nearest 100)

Welcome to Hoyland
Population 1200
(to the nearest 100)

Welcome to Jump
Population 600
(to the nearest 100)

a There are 789 people living in Elsecar.

b There are 1278 people living in Hoyland.

c There are 550 people living in Jump.

d There are 843 people living in Elsecar.

e There are 1205 people living in Hoyland.

f There are 650 people living in Jump.

7 These were the numbers of spectators in the crowds at nine Premier Division games on a weekend in May 2005.

Aston Villa v Man City	39 645
Blackburn v Fulham	18 991
Chelsea v Charlton	42 065
C. Palace v Southampton	26 066
Everton v Newcastle	40 438
Man.Utd v West Brom	67 827
Middlesbrough v Tottenham	34 766
Norwich v Birmingham	25 477
Portsmouth v Bolton	20 188

a Which match had the largest crowd?

b Which had the smallest crowd?

c Round all the numbers to the nearest 1000.

d Round all the numbers to the nearest 100.

8 Give these cooking times to the nearest 5 minutes.

a 34 min	**b** 57 min	**c** 14 min	**d** 51 min	**e** 8 min
f 13 min	**g** 44 min	**h** 32.5 min	**i** 3 min	**j** 50 s

In this section you will learn how to:

- add and subtract numbers with more than one digit

Key words

addition
column
digit
subtract

Addition

There are three things to remember when you are adding two whole numbers.

- The answer will always be larger than the bigger number.

- Always add the units **column** first.

- When the total of the **digits** in a column is more than 9, you have to carry a digit into the next column on the left, as shown in Example 2. It is important to write down the carried digit, otherwise you may forget to include it in the **addition**.

EXAMPLE 2

Add: **a** 167 + 25   **b** 2296 + 1173

```
a      1 6 7          b       2296
    +    2 5              +  1173
       ─────                ──────
       1 9 2                 3469
          1                     1
```

Subtraction

These are four things to remember when you are subtracting two whole numbers.

- The bigger number must always be written down first.

- The answer will always be smaller than the bigger number.

- Always **subtract** the units column first.

- When you have to take a bigger digit from a smaller digit in a column, you must first remove 10 from the next column on the left and put it with the smaller digit, as shown in Example 3.

EXAMPLE 3

Subtract: **a** 874 − 215   **b** 300 − 163

```
a     8⁶7¹4          b      ²3⁹0¹0
   −  2 1 5              −   1 6 3
      ─────                 ──────
      6 5 9                  1 3 7
```

EXERCISE 1F

1 Copy and work out each of these additions.

a	365	**b**	95	**c**	4872	**d**	317	**e**	287
	+ 348		+ 56		+ 1509		416		+ 335
							+ 235		

f	483	**g**	4676	**h**	438	**i**	175	**j**	562
	+ 832		+ 3584		147		+ 276		93
					+ 233				+ 197

2 Copy and complete each of these additions.

a 128 + 518   **b** 563 + 85 + 178   **c** 3086 + 58 + 674

d 347 + 408   **e** 85 + 1852 + 659   **f** 759 + 43 + 89

g 257 + 93   **h** 605 + 26 + 2135   **i** 56 + 8407 + 395

j 89 + 752   **k** 6143 + 557 + 131   **l** 2593 + 45 + 4378

m 719 + 284   **n** 545 + 3838 + 67   **o** 5213 + 658 + 4073

3 Copy and complete each of these subtractions.

a	637	**b**	908	**c**	954	**d**	572	**e**	732
	– 187		– 345		– 472		– 158		– 447

f	673	**g**	602	**h**	638	**i**	650	**j**	580
	– 187		– 358		– 354		– 317		– 364

k	6254	**l**	8043	**m**	8432	**n**	8034	**o**	5375
	– 3362		– 3626		– 4665		– 3947		– 3547

4 Copy and complete each of these subtractions.

a 354 – 226   **b** 285 – 256   **c** 663 – 329

d 506 – 328   **e** 654 – 377   **f** 733 – 448

g 592 – 257   **h** 753 – 354   **i** 6705 – 2673

j 8021 – 3256   **k** 7002 – 3207   **l** 8700 – 3263

5 Copy each of these additions and fill in the missing digits.

a	5 3	**b**	☐ 7	**c**	4 5	**d**	4 ☐ 7
	+ 2 ☐		+ 3 ☐		+ ☐ ☐		+ ☐ 5 ☐
	☐ 9		8 4		9 3		9 3 6

G

e
$$\begin{array}{r} \square\,1\,8 \\ +\,2\,5\,\square \\ \hline 8\,\square\,7 \end{array}$$

f
$$\begin{array}{r} 5\,4\,\square \\ +\,\square\,\square\,6 \\ \hline 8\,2\,2 \end{array}$$

g
$$\begin{array}{r} 4\,6\,9 \\ +\,\square\,\square\,\square \\ \hline 7\,3\,5 \end{array}$$

h
$$\begin{array}{r} \square\,\square\,\square \\ +\,3\,4\,8 \\ \hline 8\,0\,7 \end{array}$$

i
$$\begin{array}{r} \square\,4\,\square \\ +\,3\,3\,7 \\ \hline 7\,\square\,5 \end{array}$$

j
$$\begin{array}{r} 3\,5\,7\,8 \\ +\,\square\,\square\,\square\,\square \\ \hline 8\,0\,7\,6 \end{array}$$

F

6 Copy each of these subtractions and fill in the missing digits.

a
$$\begin{array}{r} 7\,4 \\ -\,2\,\square \\ \hline \square\,1 \end{array}$$

b
$$\begin{array}{r} \square\,7 \\ -\,3\,\square \\ \hline 5\,4 \end{array}$$

c
$$\begin{array}{r} 8\,5 \\ -\,\square\,\square \\ \hline 2\,7 \end{array}$$

d
$$\begin{array}{r} 6\,7\,\square \\ -\,\square\,\square\,3 \\ \hline 1\,3\,5 \end{array}$$

e
$$\begin{array}{r} \square\,1\,4 \\ -\,2\,5\,\square \\ \hline 3\,\square\,7 \end{array}$$

f
$$\begin{array}{r} 5\,4\,\square \\ -\,\square\,\square\,6 \\ \hline 3\,2\,5 \end{array}$$

g
$$\begin{array}{r} 4\,6\,2 \\ -\,\square\,\square\,\square \\ \hline 1\,8\,5 \end{array}$$

h
$$\begin{array}{r} \square\,\square\,\square \\ -\,2\,4\,7 \\ \hline 3\,0\,9 \end{array}$$

i
$$\begin{array}{r} \square\,4\,\square \\ -\,5\,5\,8 \\ \hline 2\,\square\,5 \end{array}$$

j
$$\begin{array}{r} 8\,0\,7\,6 \\ -\,\square\,\square\,\square\,\square \\ \hline 6\,1\,8\,7 \end{array}$$

1.7 Multiplying and dividing by single-digit numbers

In this section you will learn how to:
- multiply and divide by a single-digit number

Key words
division
multiplication

Multiplication

There are two things to remember when you are multiplying two whole numbers.

- The bigger number must always be written down first.
- The answer will always be larger than the bigger number.

EXAMPLE 4

Multiply 231 by 4.

$$\begin{array}{r} 213 \\ \times\quad 4 \\ \hline 852 \\ \hline {\scriptstyle 1} \end{array}$$

Note that the first multiplication, 3×4, gives 12. So, you need to carry a digit into the next column on the left, as in the case of addition.

Division

There are two things to remember when you are dividing one whole number by another whole number:

- The answer will always be smaller than the bigger number.
- Division starts at the *left-hand side*.

EXAMPLE 5

Divide 417 by 3.

$417 \div 3$ is set out as:

$$\begin{array}{r} 1\ 3\ 9 \\ 3\ \overline{)\ 4^{1}1^{2}7} \end{array}$$

This is how the division was done:

- First, divide 3 into 4 to get 1 and remainder 1. Note where to put the 1 and the remainder 1.
- Then, divide 3 into 11 to get 3 and remainder 2. Note where to put the 3 and the remainder 2.
- Finally, divide 3 into 27 to get 9 with no remainder, giving the answer 139.

EXERCISE 1G

1 Copy and work out each of the following multiplications.

	a	b	c	d	e
	14	13	17	19	18
	× 4	× 5	× 3	× 2	× 6

	f	g	h	i	j
	23	34	42	53	85
	× 5	× 6	× 7	× 4	× 5

	k	l	m	n	o
	50	200	320	340	253
	× 3	× 4	× 3	× 4	× 6

2 Calculate each of the following multiplications by setting the work out in columns.

a 42×7 b 74×5 c 48×6

d 208×4 e 309×7 f 630×4

g 548×3 h 643×5 i 8×375

j 6×442 k 7×528 l 235×8

m 6043×9 n 5×4387 o 9×5432

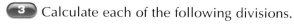

3 Calculate each of the following divisions.

    a 438 ÷ 2   **b** 634 ÷ 2   **c** 945 ÷ 3

    d 636 ÷ 6   **e** 297 ÷ 3   **f** 847 ÷ 7

    g 756 ÷ 3   **h** 846 ÷ 6   **i** 576 ÷ 4

    j 344 ÷ 4   **k** 441 ÷ 7   **l** 5818 ÷ 2

    m 3744 ÷ 9   **n** 2008 ÷ 8   **o** 7704 ÷ 6

4 By doing a suitable multiplication, answer each of these questions.

    a How many days are there in 17 weeks?

    b How many hours are there in 4 days?

    c Eggs are packed in boxes of 6. How many eggs are there in 24 boxes?

    d Joe bought 5 boxes of matches. Each box contained 42 matches. How many matches did Joe buy altogether?

    e A box of Tulip Sweets holds 35 sweets. How many sweets are there in 6 boxes?

5 By doing a suitable division, answer each of these questions.

    a How many weeks are there in 91 days?

    b How long will it take me to save £111, if I save £3 a week?

    c A rope, 215 metres long, is cut into 5 equal pieces. How long is each piece?

    d Granny has a bottle of 144 tablets. How many days will they last if she takes 4 each day?

    e I share a box of 360 sweets between 8 children. How many sweets will each child get?

Letter sets

Find the next letters in these sequences.

a O, T, T, F, F, ...   **b** T, F, S, E, T, ...

Valued letters

In the three additions below, each letter stands for a single numeral. But a letter may not necessarily stand for the same numeral when it is used in more than one sum.

a	**b**	**c**
O N E	T W O	F O U R
+ O N E	+ T W O	+ F I V E
T W O	F O U R	N I N E

Write down each addition in numbers.

Four fours

Write number sentences to give answers from 1 to 10, using only four 4s and any number of the operations +, −, × and ÷ . For example:

$1 = (4 + 4) \div (4 + 4)$ $2 = (4 \times 4) \div (4 + 4)$

Heinz 57

Pick any number in the grid on the right. Circle the number and cross out all the other numbers in the row and column containing the number you have chosen. Now circle another number that is not crossed out and cross out all the other numbers in the row and column containing this number. Repeat until you have five numbers circled. Add these numbers together. What do you get? Now do it again but start with a different number.

19	8	11	25	7
12	1	4	18	0
16	5	8	22	4
21	10	13	27	9
14	3	6	20	2

Magic squares

This is a magic square. Add the numbers in any row, column or diagonal. The answer is *always* 15.

8	1	6
3	5	7
4	9	2

Now try to complete this magic square using every number from 1 to 16.

1		14	
	6		9
8		11	
	3		16

Hints

Letter sets
Think about numbers.

Valued letters
a Try E = 3, N = 2
b Try O = 7, U = 3
c Try N = 5, O = 9
There are other answers to each sum.

1 Fiona has four cards. Each card has a number written on it.

 4 **9** **1** **5**

Fiona puts all four cards on the table to make a number.

a i Write down the smallest number Fiona can make with the four cards.

ii Write down the largest number Fiona can make with the four cards.

Fiona uses the cards to make a true statement.

b ☐ + ☐ = ☐ ☐

What is this true statement? Use each of Fiona's cards *once*.

A fifth card is needed to show the result of the multiplication 4915×10

c Write the number that should be on the fifth card.

Edexcel, Question 3, Paper 2 Foundation, June 2004

2 a Write the number seventeen thousand, two hundred and fifty-two in figures.

b Write the number 5367 correct to the nearest hundred.

c Write down the value of the 4 in the number 274 863

Edexcel, Question 1, Paper 1 Foundation, June 2005

3 The number of people in a London Tube Station one morning was 29 765.

a Write the number 29 765 in words.

b In the number 29 765, write down the value of

i the figure 7

ii the figure 9.

c Write 29 765 to the nearest 100.

4 a i Write down the number fifty-four thousand and seventy-three in figures.

ii Write down fifty-four thousand and seventy-three to the nearest hundred.

b i Write down 21 809 in words.

ii Write down 21 809 to the nearest 1000.

5 Look at the numbers in the cloud.

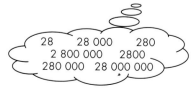

28   28 000   280
2 800 000   2800
280 000   28 000 000

a Write down the number from the cloud which is

i twenty eight million

ii two thousand eight hundred.

b What number should go in the boxes to make the calculation correct?

i $28 \times$ ☐ $= 2800$

ii $2\,800\,000 \div$ ☐ $= 280\,000$

6 Murray and Harry both worked out $2 + 4 \times 7$.
Murray calculated this to be 42.
Harry worked this out to be 30.
Explain why they both got different answers.

7 The table below shows information about the attendance at two football grounds.

Team	Total home attendance in 2004–05 season
Chelsea	795 397
Manchester United	1 287 212

a The total home attendance for Manchester United in the 2004–05 season was 1 287 212. Write the number 1 287 212 in words.

b The total home attendance for Chelsea in the 2004–05 season was 795 397. Write the number 795 397 to the nearest hundred.

8 54 327 people watched a concert.

a Write 54 327 to the nearest thousand.

b Write down the value of the 5 in the number 54 327.

Edexcel, Question 7, Paper 2 Foundation, June 2003

9 Work out the following. Be careful as they are a mixture of addition, subtraction, multiplication and division problems. Decide what the calculation is and use a column method to work it out.

a How much change do I get from a £20 note if I spend £13.45?

b I buy three pairs of socks at £2.46 each. How much do I pay altogether?

c Trays of pansies contain 12 plants each. How many plants will I get in 8 trays?

d There are 192 pupils in year 7. They are in 6 forms. How many pupils are in each form?

e A burger costs £1.65, fries cost 98p and a drink is 68p. How much will a burger, fries and a drink cost altogether?

f A school term consists of 42 days. If a normal school week is 5 days, **i** how many full weeks will there be in the term? **ii** How many odd days will there be?

g A machine produces 120 bolts every minute.

i How many bolts will be produced by the machine in 9 minutes?

ii The bolts are packed in bags of 8. How many bags will it take to pack 120 bolts?

10 The 2004 population of Plaistow is given as 7800 to the nearest thousand.

a What is the lowest number that the population could be?

b What is the largest number that the population could be?

11 **a** There are 7 days in a week.

    i How many days are there in 15 weeks?

    ii How many weeks are there in 161 days?

b Bulbs are sold in packs of 6.

    i How many bulbs are there in 12 packs?

    ii How many packs make up 186 bulbs?

12 A teacher asked her pupils to work out the following calculation without a calculator

$$2 \times 3^2 + 6$$

a Alice got an answer of 42. Billy got an answer of 30. Chas got an answer of 24. Explain why Chas was correct

b Put brackets into these calculations to make them true

    i $2 \times 3^2 + 6 = 42$

    ii $2 \times 3^2 + 6 = 30$

13 The following are two pupils' attempts at working out $3 + 5^2 - 2$

Adam $3 + 5^2 - 2 = 3 + 10 - 2 = 13 - 2 = 11$

Bekki $3 + 5^2 - 2 = 8^2 - 2 = 64 - 2 = 62$

a Each pupil has made one mistake. Explain what this is for each of them

b Work out the correct answer to $3 + 5^2 - 2$

WORKED EXAM QUESTION

Here are four number cards, showing the number 6387.

| 6 | 3 | 8 | 7 |

a Using all four cards, write down:

    i the largest possible number

    ii the smallest possible number

    iii the missing numbers from this problem.

     ☐   8   × 2 =   ☐ ☐

b Write the number 3648 to:

    i the nearest 10

    ii the nearest 100.

Solution

a i 8763

> Start with the largest number as the thousands digits, use the next largest as the hundreds digit and so on.

    ii 3678

> Start with the smallest number as the thousands digits, use the next smallest as the hundreds digit and so on. Note the answer is the reverse of the answer to part (i).

    iii 38 × 2 = 76

> There are three numbers left, 3, 7, 6. The 3 must go into the first box and then you can work out that 2 × 38 is 76.

b i 3650

> A halfway value such as 48 rounds up to 50.

    ii 3700

> 3648 rounds down to 3600. Do not be tempted to round the answer to part (i) up to 3700.

Mr and Mrs Davies, their daughter, Alice (aged 15), and their son, Joe (aged 13), decide to take an activity holiday. The family want to stay in a cottage in Wales.

The activities on offer are shown below.

Mr Davies works out the total cost of their holiday, which includes the cost of the activities, the rental for the holiday cottage (in the high season) and the cost of the petrol they will use to travel to the cottage, for trips while they are there, and to get home again.

Paragliding:
adults £99

Quad bikes:
adults £21,
children (6–15) £12.50

Horse riding:
1½ hour valley ride £28,
1½ hour beach ride £32

Windsurfing:
half day £59,
full day £79

Water-jet boat:
adults £20,
children (under 14) £10

The table shows which activities they all chose. Copy it and complete the "Totals" row. Use it to work out the total cost of the activities.

	Horse riding	Water-jet boats	Conventional boats	Kayaking	Coast jumping	Windsurfing
Mr Davies	✗	✓	✓	½ day	✗	✗
Mrs Davies	1½ hour beach ride	✓	✓	✗	✓	✗
Alice Davies	1½ hour beach ride	✓	✓	½ day	✗	½ day
Joe Davies	✗	✓	✓	✗	✓	½ day
Totals						

Coast jumping:
adults £40,
children (under 16) £25

Holiday cottage:
low season: £300
mid season: £400
high season: £550

Kayaking:
half day £29,
full day £49

Diving:
adults £38

Conventional boat:
adults £10,
children (under 14) £6

Diving	Quad bikes	Paragliding
✗	✓	✓
✓	✗	✗
✗	✓	✗
✗	✓	✗
		£99

Cost of holiday (£)	
Activities	
Cottage	
Petrol	
Total:	

It is 250 miles from their home to their holiday cottage. They drive an extra 100 miles while they are on holiday. Their car travels, on average, 50 miles to the gallon. Petrol costs £1 per litre.

1 gallon = 4.5 litres

GRADE YOURSELF

G Able to add columns and rows in grids

G Know the times tables up to 10×10

G Can use BODMAS to find the correct order of operations

G Can identify the value of digits in different places

G Able to round to the nearest 10 and 100

G Can add and subtract numbers with up to four digits

G Can multiply numbers by a single-digit number

F Able to answer problems involving multiplication or division by a single-digit number

What you should know now

- How to use BODMAS
- How to put numbers in order
- How to round to the nearest ten, hundred, thousand
- How to solve simple problems, using the four operations of arithmetic: addition, subtraction, multiplication and division

This chapter will show you ...

- how to add, subtract, multiply and order simple fractions
- how to cancel fractions
- how to convert a top-heavy fraction to a mixed number (and vice versa)
- how to calculate a fraction of a quantity
- how to calculate a reciprocal
- how to recognise a terminating and a recurring decimal fraction

Visual overview

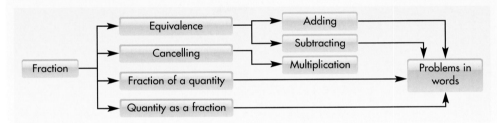

What you should already know

- Times tables up to 10×10
- What a fraction is

Reminder

A fraction is a part of a whole. The top number is called the **numerator**. The bottom number is called the **denominator**. So, for example, $\frac{3}{4}$ means you divide a whole thing into four portions and take three of them.

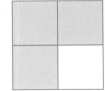

It really does help if you know the times tables up to 10×10. They will be tested in the non-calculator paper, so you need to be confident about tables and numbers.

Quick check

How quickly can you calculate these?

1 2×4	**2** 5×3	**3** 5×2	**4** 6×3
5 2×7	**6** 4×5	**7** 3×8	**8** 4×6
9 9×2	**10** 3×7	**11** half of 10	**12** half of 12
13 half of 16	**14** half of 8	**15** half of 20	**16** a third of 9
17 a third of 15	**18** a quarter of 12	**19** a fifth of 10	**20** a fifth of 20

In this section you will learn how to:

● recognise what fraction of a shape has been shaded

● shade a given simple fraction of a shape

EXERCISE 2A

1 What fraction is shaded in each of these diagrams?

a   b   c   d

e   f   g   h

i   j   k   l

m   n   o   p

2 Draw diagrams as in question **1** to show these fractions.

a $\frac{3}{4}$ b $\frac{2}{3}$ c $\frac{1}{5}$ d $\frac{5}{8}$

e $\frac{1}{6}$ f $\frac{8}{9}$ g $\frac{1}{9}$ h $\frac{1}{10}$

i $\frac{4}{5}$ j $\frac{2}{7}$ k $\frac{3}{8}$ l $\frac{5}{6}$

Adding and subtracting simple fractions

In this section you will learn how to:

- add and subtract two fractions with the same denominator

Key words

denominator
numerator

Fractions that have the same **denominator** (bottom number) can easily be added or subtracted. For example:

$$\frac{3}{10} + \frac{4}{10} = \frac{7}{10}$$

$$\frac{7}{8} - \frac{2}{8} = \frac{5}{8}$$

Just add or subtract the **numerators** (top numbers). The bottom number stays the same.

EXERCISE 2B

1 Calculate each of the following.

a $\frac{1}{4} + \frac{2}{4}$ **b** $\frac{1}{8} + \frac{3}{8}$ **c** $\frac{2}{5} + \frac{1}{5}$ **d** $\frac{3}{10} + \frac{5}{10}$

e $\frac{1}{3} + \frac{1}{3}$ **f** $\frac{2}{7} + \frac{3}{7}$ **g** $\frac{2}{9} + \frac{5}{9}$ **h** $\frac{1}{6} + \frac{4}{6}$

i $\frac{3}{5} + \frac{1}{5}$ **j** $\frac{5}{8} + \frac{2}{8}$ **k** $\frac{2}{10} + \frac{3}{10}$ **l** $\frac{4}{7} + \frac{1}{7}$

m $\frac{3}{5} + \frac{1}{5}$ **n** $\frac{2}{6} + \frac{3}{6}$ **o** $\frac{4}{9} + \frac{1}{9}$ **p** $\frac{2}{11} + \frac{5}{11}$

2 Calculate each of the following.

a $\frac{3}{4} - \frac{1}{4}$ **b** $\frac{4}{5} - \frac{1}{5}$ **c** $\frac{7}{8} - \frac{4}{8}$ **d** $\frac{8}{10} - \frac{5}{10}$

e $\frac{2}{3} - \frac{1}{3}$ **f** $\frac{5}{6} - \frac{1}{6}$ **g** $\frac{5}{7} - \frac{2}{7}$ **h** $\frac{7}{9} - \frac{2}{9}$

i $\frac{3}{5} - \frac{2}{5}$ **j** $\frac{4}{7} - \frac{1}{7}$ **k** $\frac{8}{9} - \frac{5}{9}$ **l** $\frac{9}{10} - \frac{3}{10}$

m $\frac{4}{6} - \frac{1}{6}$ **n** $\frac{5}{8} - \frac{3}{8}$ **o** $\frac{7}{11} - \frac{5}{11}$ **p** $\frac{7}{10} - \frac{3}{10}$

3 **a** Draw a diagram to show $\frac{2}{4}$

b Show on your diagram that $\frac{2}{4} = \frac{1}{2}$

c Use the above information to write down the answers to these.

i $\frac{1}{4} + \frac{1}{2}$ **ii** $\frac{3}{4} - \frac{1}{2}$

4 **a** Draw a diagram to show $\frac{5}{10}$

b Show on your diagram that $\frac{5}{10} = \frac{1}{2}$

c Use the above information to write down the answers to these.

i $\frac{1}{2} + \frac{1}{10}$ **ii** $\frac{1}{2} + \frac{3}{10}$ **iii** $\frac{1}{2} + \frac{2}{10}$

2.3 Recognise equivalent fractions

In this section you will learn how to:
- recognise equivalent fractions

Key word
equivalent

ACTIVITY

Making eighths

You need lots of squared paper and a pair of scissors.

Draw three rectangles, each 4 cm by 2 cm, on squared paper.

Each small square is called an *eighth* or $\frac{1}{8}$.

Cut one of the rectangles into halves, another into quarters and the third into eighths.

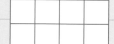

You can see that the strip equal to one half takes up 4 squares, so:

$$\frac{1}{2} = \frac{4}{8}$$

These are called **equivalent** fractions.

1 Use the strips to write down the following fractions as eighths.

a $\dfrac{1}{4}$ **b** $\dfrac{3}{4}$

2 Use the strips to work out the following problems. Leave your answers as eighths.

a $\dfrac{1}{4} + \dfrac{3}{8}$ **b** $\dfrac{3}{4} + \dfrac{1}{8}$ **c** $\dfrac{3}{8} + \dfrac{1}{2}$ **d** $\dfrac{1}{4} + \dfrac{1}{2}$

e $\dfrac{1}{8} + \dfrac{1}{8}$ **f** $\dfrac{1}{8} + \dfrac{1}{4}$ **g** $\dfrac{3}{8} + \dfrac{3}{4}$ **h** $\dfrac{3}{4} + \dfrac{1}{2}$

Making twenty-fourths

You need lots of squared paper and a pair of scissors.

Draw four rectangles, each 6 cm by 4 cm, on squared paper.

Each small square is called a *twenty-fourth* or $\frac{1}{24}$. Cut one of the rectangles into quarters, another into sixths, another into thirds and the remaining one into eighths.

You can see that the strip equal to a quarter takes up 6 squares, so:

$$\dfrac{1}{4} = \dfrac{6}{24}$$

This is another example of equivalent fractions.

This idea is used to add fractions together. For example:

$$\dfrac{1}{4} + \dfrac{1}{6}$$

can be changed into:

$$\dfrac{6}{24} + \dfrac{4}{24} = \dfrac{10}{24}$$

EXERCISE 2C

1 Use the strips to write down each of these fractions as twenty-fourths.

a $\dfrac{1}{6}$ **b** $\dfrac{1}{3}$ **c** $\dfrac{1}{8}$ **d** $\dfrac{2}{3}$ **e** $\dfrac{5}{6}$

f $\dfrac{3}{4}$ **g** $\dfrac{3}{8}$ **h** $\dfrac{5}{8}$ **i** $\dfrac{7}{8}$ **j** $\dfrac{1}{2}$

2 Use the strips to write down the answer to each of the following problems. Each answer will be in twenty-fourths.

a $\dfrac{1}{3} + \dfrac{1}{8}$ **b** $\dfrac{1}{8} + \dfrac{1}{4}$ **c** $\dfrac{1}{6} + \dfrac{1}{8}$ **d** $\dfrac{2}{3} + \dfrac{1}{8}$ **e** $\dfrac{5}{8} + \dfrac{1}{3}$

f $\dfrac{1}{8} + \dfrac{5}{6}$ **g** $\dfrac{1}{2} + \dfrac{3}{8}$ **h** $\dfrac{1}{6} + \dfrac{3}{4}$ **i** $\dfrac{5}{8} + \dfrac{1}{6}$ **j** $\dfrac{1}{3} + \dfrac{5}{8}$

3 Draw three rectangles, each 5 cm by 4 cm. Cut one into quarters, another into fifths and the last into tenths.

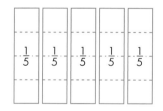
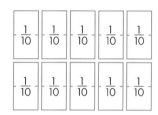

Use the strips to find the equivalent fraction in twentieths to each of the following.

a $\dfrac{1}{4}$ **b** $\dfrac{1}{5}$ **c** $\dfrac{3}{4}$ **d** $\dfrac{4}{5}$ **e** $\dfrac{1}{10}$

f $\dfrac{1}{2}$ **g** $\dfrac{3}{5}$ **h** $\dfrac{2}{5}$ **i** $\dfrac{7}{10}$ **j** $\dfrac{3}{10}$

4 Use the strips to write down the answer to each of the following.

a $\dfrac{1}{4} + \dfrac{1}{5}$ **b** $\dfrac{3}{5} + \dfrac{1}{10}$ **c** $\dfrac{3}{10} + \dfrac{1}{4}$ **d** $\dfrac{3}{4} + \dfrac{1}{5}$ **e** $\dfrac{7}{10} + \dfrac{1}{4}$

Equivalent fractions and cancelling

In this section you will learn how to:
- create equivalent fractions
- cancel fractions, where possible

Key words
denominator
lowest terms
numerator

Equivalent fractions are two or more fractions that represent the same part of a whole.

EXAMPLE 1

Complete these statements.

a $\dfrac{3}{4} \longrightarrow \dfrac{\times 4}{\times 4} = \dfrac{\square}{16}$ b $\dfrac{2}{5} = \dfrac{\square}{15}$

a Multiplying the **numerator** by 4 gives 12. This means $\frac{12}{16}$ is an equivalent fraction to $\frac{3}{4}$.

b To change the **denominator** from 5 to 15, you multiply by 3. Do the same thing to the numerator, which gives $2 \times 3 = 6$. So, $\frac{2}{5} = \frac{6}{15}$.

The basic fraction, $\frac{3}{4}$ in Example 1, is in its **lowest terms**. This means that there is no number that is a factor of both the numerator and the denominator.

EXAMPLE 2

Cancel these fractions to their lowest terms.

a $\dfrac{15}{35}$ b $\dfrac{24}{54}$

a Here is one reason why you need to know the times tables. What is the biggest number that has both 15 and 35 in its times table? You should know that this is the five times table. So, divide both top and bottom numbers by 5.

$$\frac{15}{35} = \frac{15 \div 5}{35 \div 5} = \frac{3}{7}$$

You can say that you have 'cancelled by fives'.

b The biggest number that has both 24 and 54 in its times table is 6. So, divide both the numerator and denominator by 6.

$$\frac{24}{54} = \frac{24 \div 6}{54 \div 6} = \frac{4}{9}$$

Here, you have 'cancelled by sixes'.

EXAMPLE 3

Put the following fractions in order with the smallest first.

$$\frac{5}{6}, \frac{2}{3}, \frac{3}{4}$$

First write each fraction with the same denominator by using equivalent fractions.

$$\frac{5}{6} = \frac{10}{12}$$

$$\frac{2}{3} = \frac{4}{6} = \frac{6}{9} = \frac{8}{12}$$

$$\frac{3}{4} = \frac{6}{8} = \frac{9}{12}$$

This shows that $\frac{5}{6} = \frac{10}{12}$, $\frac{2}{3} = \frac{8}{12}$ and $\frac{3}{4} = \frac{9}{12}$.

In order, the fractions are:

$$\frac{2}{3}, \frac{3}{4}, \frac{5}{6}$$

EXERCISE 2D

1 Copy and complete each of these statements.

a $\frac{2}{5} \longrightarrow \begin{matrix} \times 4 \\ \times 4 \end{matrix} = \frac{\square}{20}$

b $\frac{1}{4} \longrightarrow \begin{matrix} \times 3 \\ \times 3 \end{matrix} = \frac{\square}{12}$

c $\frac{3}{8} \longrightarrow \begin{matrix} \times 5 \\ \times 5 \end{matrix} = \frac{\square}{40}$

d $\frac{4}{5} \longrightarrow \begin{matrix} \times 3 \\ \times 3 \end{matrix} = \frac{\square}{15}$

e $\frac{5}{6} \longrightarrow \begin{matrix} \times 3 \\ \times 3 \end{matrix} = \frac{\square}{18}$

f $\frac{3}{7} \longrightarrow \begin{matrix} \times 4 \\ \times 4 \end{matrix} = \frac{\square}{28}$

g $\frac{3}{10} \longrightarrow \begin{matrix} \times \square \\ \times 2 \end{matrix} = \frac{\square}{20}$

h $\frac{1}{3} \longrightarrow \begin{matrix} \times \square \\ \times \square \end{matrix} = \frac{\square}{9}$

i $\frac{3}{5} \longrightarrow \begin{matrix} \times \square \\ \times \square \end{matrix} = \frac{\square}{20}$

j $\frac{2}{3} \longrightarrow \begin{matrix} \times \square \\ \times \square \end{matrix} = \frac{\square}{18}$

k $\frac{3}{4} \longrightarrow \begin{matrix} \times \square \\ \times \square \end{matrix} = \frac{\square}{12}$

l $\frac{5}{8} \longrightarrow \begin{matrix} \times \square \\ \times \square \end{matrix} = \frac{\square}{40}$

m $\frac{7}{10} \longrightarrow \begin{matrix} \times \square \\ \times \square \end{matrix} = \frac{\square}{20}$

n $\frac{1}{6} \longrightarrow \begin{matrix} \times \square \\ \times \square \end{matrix} = \frac{4}{\square}$

o $\frac{3}{8} \longrightarrow \begin{matrix} \times \square \\ \times \square \end{matrix} = \frac{15}{\square}$

2 Copy and complete each of these statements.

a $\frac{1}{2} = \frac{2}{\square} = \frac{3}{\square} = \frac{\square}{8} = \frac{\square}{10} = \frac{6}{\square}$

b $\frac{1}{3} = \frac{2}{\square} = \frac{3}{\square} = \frac{\square}{12} = \frac{\square}{15} = \frac{6}{\square}$

c $\frac{3}{4} = \frac{6}{\square} = \frac{9}{\square} = \frac{\square}{16} = \frac{\square}{20} = \frac{18}{\square}$

d $\frac{2}{5} = \frac{4}{\square} = \frac{6}{\square} = \frac{\square}{20} = \frac{\square}{25} = \frac{12}{\square}$

e $\frac{3}{7} = \frac{6}{\square} = \frac{9}{\square} = \frac{\square}{28} = \frac{\square}{35} = \frac{18}{\square}$

3 Copy and complete each of these statements.

a $\dfrac{10}{15} = \dfrac{10 \div 5}{15 \div 5} = \dfrac{\square}{\square}$

b $\dfrac{12}{15} = \dfrac{12 \div 3}{15 \div 3} = \dfrac{\square}{\square}$

c $\dfrac{20}{28} = \dfrac{20 \div 4}{28 \div 4} = \dfrac{\square}{\square}$

d $\dfrac{12}{18} = \dfrac{12 \div \square}{\square \div \square} = \dfrac{\square}{\square}$

e $\dfrac{15}{25} = \dfrac{15 \div 5}{\square \div \square} = \dfrac{\square}{\square}$

f $\dfrac{21}{30} = \dfrac{21 \div \square}{\square \div \square} = \dfrac{\square}{\square}$

4 Cancel each of these fractions.

a $\dfrac{4}{6}$　　b $\dfrac{5}{15}$　　c $\dfrac{12}{18}$　　d $\dfrac{6}{8}$　　e $\dfrac{3}{9}$

f $\dfrac{5}{10}$　　g $\dfrac{14}{16}$　　h $\dfrac{28}{35}$　　i $\dfrac{10}{20}$　　j $\dfrac{4}{16}$

k $\dfrac{12}{15}$　　l $\dfrac{15}{21}$　　m $\dfrac{25}{35}$　　n $\dfrac{14}{21}$　　o $\dfrac{8}{20}$

p $\dfrac{10}{25}$　　q $\dfrac{7}{21}$　　r $\dfrac{42}{60}$　　s $\dfrac{50}{200}$　　t $\dfrac{18}{12}$

u $\dfrac{6}{9}$　　v $\dfrac{18}{27}$　　w $\dfrac{36}{48}$　　x $\dfrac{21}{14}$　　y $\dfrac{42}{12}$

5 Put the following fractions in order, with the smallest first.

a $\dfrac{1}{2}, \dfrac{5}{6}, \dfrac{2}{3}$　　b $\dfrac{3}{4}, \dfrac{1}{2}, \dfrac{5}{8}$　　c $\dfrac{7}{10}, \dfrac{2}{5}, \dfrac{1}{2}$　　d $\dfrac{2}{3}, \dfrac{3}{4}, \dfrac{7}{12}$

e $\dfrac{1}{6}, \dfrac{1}{3}, \dfrac{1}{4}$　　f $\dfrac{9}{10}, \dfrac{3}{4}, \dfrac{4}{5}$　　g $\dfrac{4}{5}, \dfrac{7}{10}, \dfrac{5}{6}$　　h $\dfrac{1}{3}, \dfrac{2}{5}, \dfrac{3}{10}$

HINTS AND TIPS

Make all denominators the same, e.g. $\frac{1}{2}, \frac{5}{6}, \frac{2}{3}$ is $\frac{3}{6}, \frac{5}{6}, \frac{4}{6}$.

2.5 Top-heavy fractions and mixed numbers

In this section you will learn how to:

- change top-heavy fractions into mixed numbers
- change a mixed number into a top-heavy fraction

Key word

mixed number
proper fraction
top-heavy

A fraction such as $\frac{9}{5}$ is called **top-heavy** because the numerator (top number) is bigger than the denominator (bottom number). You may also see a top-heavy fraction called an *improper* fraction.

A fraction that is not top-heavy, such as $\frac{4}{5}$, is sometimes called a **proper fraction**. The numerator of a proper fraction is smaller than its denominator.

ACTIVITY

Converting top-heavy fractions

You need a calculator with a fraction key, which will look like this. $\boxed{a^{b/c}}$

Your calculator probably shows fractions like this. $2\lrcorner3$ or $2\ulcorner3$

This means $\frac{2}{3}$ or two-thirds.

Key the top-heavy fraction $\frac{9}{5}$ into your calculator. $\boxed{9}$ $\boxed{a^{b/c}}$ $\boxed{5}$

The display will look like this. $9\lrcorner5$

Now press the equals key $\boxed{=}$. The display will change to: $1\lrcorner4\lrcorner5$

This is the **mixed number** $1\frac{4}{5}$.

(It is called a mixed number because it is a mixture of a whole number and a proper fraction.)

Write down the result: $\dfrac{9}{5} = 1\dfrac{4}{5}$

Key the top-heavy fraction $\frac{8}{4}$ into your calculator. $\boxed{8}$ $\boxed{a^{b/c}}$ $\boxed{4}$

The display will look like this. $8\lrcorner4$

Now press the equals key $\boxed{=}$. The display will change to: 2

This represents the whole number 2. Whole numbers are special fractions with a denominator of 1. So, 2 is the fraction $\frac{2}{1}$.

Write down the result: $\dfrac{8}{4} = \dfrac{2}{1}$

- Now key at least ten top-heavy fractions and convert them to mixed numbers. Keep the numbers sensible. For example, don't use 37 or 17.

- Write down your results.

- Look at your results. Can you see a way of converting a top-heavy fraction to a mixed number without using a calculator?

- Test your idea. Then use your calculator to check it.

Converting mixed numbers

Key the mixed number $2\frac{3}{4}$ into your calculator. $\boxed{2}$ $\boxed{a^{b/c}}$ $\boxed{3}$ $\boxed{a^{b/c}}$ $\boxed{4}$

The display will look like this. $2\lrcorner3\lrcorner4$

Now press the shift (or $\boxed{INV}$) key and then press the fraction key $\boxed{a^{b/c}}$

The display will change to: $11\lrcorner4$

This represents the top-heavy fraction $\frac{11}{4}$.

Write down the result. $2\frac{3}{4} = \frac{11}{4}$

- Now key at least ten more mixed numbers and convert them to top-heavy fractions. Keep your numbers sensible. For example, don't use $8\frac{16}{19}$ or $17\frac{11}{32}$.

- Write down your results.

- Look at your results. Can you see a way of converting a mixed number to a top-heavy fraction without using a calculator?

- Test your idea. Then use your calculator to check it.

EXERCISE 2E

Change each of these top-heavy fractions into a mixed number.

1 $\frac{7}{3}$	**2** $\frac{8}{3}$	**3** $\frac{9}{4}$	**4** $\frac{10}{7}$	**5** $\frac{12}{5}$	**6** $\frac{7}{5}$
7 $\frac{13}{5}$	**8** $\frac{15}{4}$	**9** $\frac{10}{3}$	**10** $\frac{15}{7}$	**11** $\frac{17}{6}$	**12** $\frac{18}{5}$
13 $\frac{19}{4}$	**14** $\frac{22}{7}$	**15** $\frac{14}{11}$	**16** $\frac{12}{11}$	**17** $\frac{28}{5}$	**18** $\frac{19}{7}$
19 $\frac{40}{7}$	**20** $\frac{42}{5}$	**21** $\frac{21}{10}$	**22** $\frac{5}{2}$	**23** $\frac{5}{3}$	**24** $\frac{25}{8}$
25 $\frac{23}{10}$	**26** $\frac{23}{11}$	**27** $\frac{38}{5}$	**28** $\frac{38}{7}$	**29** $\frac{40}{8}$	**30** $\frac{12}{6}$

Change each of these mixed numbers into a top-heavy fraction.

31 $3\frac{1}{3}$	**32** $5\frac{5}{6}$	**33** $1\frac{4}{5}$	**34** $5\frac{2}{7}$	**35** $4\frac{1}{10}$	**36** $5\frac{2}{3}$
37 $2\frac{1}{2}$	**38** $3\frac{1}{4}$	**39** $7\frac{1}{6}$	**40** $3\frac{5}{8}$	**41** $6\frac{1}{3}$	**42** $9\frac{8}{9}$
43 $11\frac{4}{5}$	**44** $3\frac{1}{5}$	**45** $4\frac{3}{8}$	**46** $3\frac{1}{9}$	**47** $5\frac{1}{5}$	**48** $2\frac{3}{4}$
49 $4\frac{2}{7}$	**50** $8\frac{1}{6}$	**51** $2\frac{8}{9}$	**52** $6\frac{1}{6}$	**53** $12\frac{1}{5}$	**54** $1\frac{5}{8}$
55 $7\frac{1}{10}$	**56** $8\frac{1}{9}$	**57** $7\frac{5}{8}$	**58** $10\frac{1}{2}$	**59** $1\frac{1}{16}$	**60** $4\frac{3}{4}$

Adding fractions with the same denominator

In this section you will learn how to:

● add and subtract two fractions with the same denominator, then simplify the result

Key words

lowest terms
mixed number
proper fraction
top-heavy
  fraction

When you add two fractions with the same denominator, you get one of the following:

● a **proper fraction** that cannot be cancelled, for example:

$$\frac{1}{5} + \frac{2}{5} = \frac{3}{5}$$

● a proper fraction that can be cancelled, for example:

$$\frac{1}{8} + \frac{3}{8} = \frac{4}{8} = \frac{1}{2}$$

● a **top-heavy fraction** that cannot be cancelled, so it is written at once as a **mixed number**, for example:

$$\frac{7}{8} + \frac{1}{4} = \frac{7}{8} + \frac{2}{8} = \frac{9}{8} = 1\frac{1}{8}$$

● a top-heavy fraction that can be cancelled before it is written as a mixed number, for example:

$$\frac{5}{8} + \frac{7}{8} = \frac{12}{8} = \frac{3}{2} = 1\frac{1}{2}$$

Note You must *always* cancel the fractions in answers to their **lowest terms**.

EXERCISE 2F

1 Copy and complete each of these additions.

a $\dfrac{5}{8} + \dfrac{1}{8}$ b $\dfrac{3}{10} + \dfrac{1}{10}$ c $\dfrac{2}{9} + \dfrac{4}{9}$ d $\dfrac{1}{4} + \dfrac{1}{2}$

e $\dfrac{3}{10} + \dfrac{3}{10}$ f $\dfrac{5}{12} + \dfrac{1}{12}$ g $\dfrac{3}{16} + \dfrac{5}{16}$ h $\dfrac{7}{16} + \dfrac{3}{16}$

2 Copy and complete each of these additions. Use equivalent fractions to make the denominators the same.

a $\dfrac{1}{2} + \dfrac{7}{10}$ b $\dfrac{1}{2} + \dfrac{5}{8}$ c $\dfrac{3}{4} + \dfrac{3}{8}$ d $\dfrac{3}{4} + \dfrac{7}{8}$

e $\dfrac{1}{2} + \dfrac{7}{8}$ f $\dfrac{1}{3} + \dfrac{5}{6}$ g $\dfrac{5}{6} + \dfrac{2}{3}$ h $\dfrac{3}{4} + \dfrac{1}{2}$

3 Copy and complete each of these additions.

a $\dfrac{3}{8} + \dfrac{7}{8}$ **b** $\dfrac{3}{4} + \dfrac{3}{4}$ **c** $\dfrac{2}{5} + \dfrac{3}{5}$ **d** $\dfrac{7}{10} + \dfrac{9}{10}$

e $\dfrac{5}{8} + \dfrac{5}{8}$ **f** $\dfrac{7}{16} + \dfrac{15}{16}$ **g** $\dfrac{5}{12} + \dfrac{11}{12}$ **h** $\dfrac{11}{16} + \dfrac{7}{16}$

i $1\dfrac{1}{2} + \dfrac{1}{4}$ **j** $2\dfrac{3}{4} + \dfrac{1}{2}$ **k** $3\dfrac{1}{2} + 2\dfrac{3}{4}$ **l** $2\dfrac{1}{8} + 1\dfrac{1}{2}$

4 Copy and complete each of these subtractions.

a $\dfrac{7}{8} - \dfrac{3}{8}$ **b** $\dfrac{7}{10} - \dfrac{1}{10}$ **c** $\dfrac{3}{4} - \dfrac{1}{2}$ **d** $\dfrac{5}{8} - \dfrac{1}{4}$

e $\dfrac{1}{2} - \dfrac{1}{4}$ **f** $\dfrac{7}{8} - \dfrac{1}{2}$ **g** $\dfrac{9}{10} - \dfrac{1}{2}$ **h** $\dfrac{11}{16} - \dfrac{3}{8}$

i $1 - \dfrac{3}{4}$ **j** $2 - \dfrac{1}{3}$ **k** $3\dfrac{3}{4} - 1\dfrac{1}{2}$ **l** $4\dfrac{5}{8} - 2\dfrac{1}{2}$

2.7 Problems in words

In this section you will learn how to:
● solve problems that have been put into words

Some of the questions you are going to meet in your GCSE exams will involve the use of fractions in real-life situations, which are described in words. You will have to decide what to do with the fractions given, then write down the calculation you need to do and work it out.

EXAMPLE 4

In a box of chocolates, quarter are truffles, half are orange creams and the rest are mints. What fraction are mints?

Truffles and orange creams together are $\dfrac{1}{4} + \dfrac{1}{2} = \dfrac{3}{4}$ of the box.

Take the whole box as 1. So, mints are $1 - \dfrac{3}{4} = \dfrac{1}{4}$ of the box.

EXERCISE 2G

1 At a recent First Division football match, $\frac{7}{8}$ of the crowd were home supporters. What fraction of the crowd were not home supporters?

2 After Emma had taken a slice of cake, $\frac{3}{4}$ of the cake was left. Ayesha then had $\frac{1}{2}$ of what was left.

   a What fraction of the cake did Emma eat?

   b What fraction of the cake did Ayesha have?

   c Who had more cake?

3 Three friends share two pizzas. Each pizza is cut into six equal slices. What fraction of a pizza did each friend get?

4 In a box of old CDs from a jumble sale, $\frac{1}{4}$ of them were rock music, $\frac{3}{8}$ of them were pop music and the rest were classical. What fraction of the CDs were classical?

5 In a car park, $\frac{1}{5}$ of the cars were British makes. Half of the rest were Japanese makes. What fraction of the cars were Japanese makes?

6 A fruit drink consists of $\frac{1}{2}$ orange juice, $\frac{1}{8}$ lemon juice and the rest is pineapple juice. What fraction of the drink is pineapple juice?

7 In a hockey team, $\frac{2}{11}$ of the team are French, $\frac{2}{11}$ are Italian, $\frac{3}{11}$ are Scottish and the rest are English. What fraction of the team is English?

8 In a packet of biscuits, $\frac{1}{6}$ are digestives, $\frac{2}{3}$ are bourbons and the rest are jammy dodgers. What fraction are jammy dodgers?

9 Jide pays $\frac{1}{4}$ of his wages in tax and $\frac{1}{8}$ of his wages in National Insurance. What fraction of his wages does he take home?

2.8 # Finding a fraction of a quantity

In this section you will learn how to:
- find a fraction of a given quantity

To do this, you simply multiply the quantity by the fraction.

EXAMPLE 5

Find $\frac{3}{4}$ of £196.

First, find $\frac{1}{4}$ by dividing by 4. Then find $\frac{3}{4}$ by multiplying your answer by 3:

$$196 \div 4 = 49 \qquad \text{then} \qquad 49 \times 3 = 147$$

The answer is £147.

Of course, you can use your calculator to do this problem by either:

- pressing the sequence: **1 9 6 ÷ 4 × 3 =**
- or using the key: **3 aᵇ/c 4 × 1 9 6 =**

EXERCISE 2H

1 Calculate each of these.

a $\frac{3}{5} \times 30$ **b** $\frac{2}{7} \times 35$ **c** $\frac{3}{8} \times 48$ **d** $\frac{7}{10} \times 40$

e $\frac{5}{6} \times 18$ **f** $24 \times \frac{3}{4}$ **g** $60 \times \frac{4}{5}$ **h** $72 \times \frac{5}{8}$

2 Calculate each of these quantities.

a $\frac{3}{4}$ of £2400   **b** $\frac{2}{5}$ of 320 grams   **c** $\frac{5}{8}$ of 256 kilograms

d $\frac{2}{3}$ of £174   **e** $\frac{5}{6}$ of 78 litres   **f** $\frac{3}{4}$ of 120 minutes

g $\frac{4}{5}$ of 365 days   **h** $\frac{7}{8}$ of 24 hours   **i** $\frac{3}{4}$ of 1 day

j $\frac{5}{9}$ of 4266 miles

3 In each case, find out which is the larger number.

a $\frac{2}{5}$ of 60 or $\frac{5}{8}$ of 40   **b** $\frac{3}{4}$ of 280 or $\frac{7}{10}$ of 290

c $\frac{2}{3}$ of 78 or $\frac{4}{5}$ of 70   **d** $\frac{5}{6}$ of 72 or $\frac{11}{12}$ of 60

e $\frac{4}{9}$ of 126 or $\frac{3}{5}$ of 95   **f** $\frac{3}{4}$ of 340 or $\frac{2}{3}$ of 381

4 A director was entitled to $\frac{2}{15}$ of his firm's profits. The firm made a profit of £45 600 in one year. What was the director's share of this profit?

5 A woman left $\frac{3}{8}$ of her estate to her favourite charity. What amount is this if her estate totalled £84 000?

6 There were 36 800 people at Hillsborough to see Sheffield Wednesday play Manchester United. Of this crowd, $\frac{3}{8}$ were female. How many male spectators were at the ground?

7 Two-thirds of a person's weight is water. Paul weighed 78 kg. How much of his body weight was water?

8 **a** Information from the first census in Singapore suggests that then $\frac{2}{25}$ of the population were Indian. The total population was 10 700. How many people were Indian?

b By 1990 the population of Singapore had grown to 3 002 800. Only $\frac{1}{16}$ of this population were Indian. How many Indians were living in Singapore in 1990?

 9 Mark normally earns £500 a week. One week he is given a bonus of $\frac{1}{10}$ of his wage.

a Find $\frac{1}{10}$ of £500.

b How much does he earn altogether for this week?

 10 The contents of a standard box of cereals weigh 720 g. A new larger box holds $\frac{1}{4}$ more than the standard box.

a Find $\frac{1}{4}$ of 720 g.

b How much do the contents of the new box of cereals weigh?

 11 The price of a new TV costing £360 is reduced by $\frac{1}{3}$ in a sale.

a Find $\frac{1}{3}$ of £360.

b How much does the TV cost in the sale?

 12 The price of a car in a showroom is given as £8000. Find the price of the car if a discount of $\frac{1}{5}$ of the price is allowed.

2.9 Multiplying fractions

In this section you will learn how to:
- multiply a fraction by a fraction

What is $\frac{1}{2}$ of $\frac{1}{4}$?

The diagram shows the answer is $\frac{1}{8}$.

In mathematics, you always write $\frac{1}{2}$ of $\frac{1}{4}$ as $\frac{1}{2} \times \frac{1}{4}$

So you know that $\frac{1}{2} \times \frac{1}{4} = \frac{1}{8}$

To multiply fractions, you multiply the numerators together and you multiply the denominators together.

EXAMPLE 6

Work out $\frac{1}{4}$ of $\frac{2}{5}$.

$$\frac{1}{4} \times \frac{2}{5} = \frac{1 \times 2}{4 \times 5} = \frac{2}{20} = \frac{1}{10}$$

EXERCISE 2I

Work out each of these multiplications.

1. $\frac{1}{2} \times \frac{1}{3}$ 2. $\frac{1}{4} \times \frac{1}{5}$ 3. $\frac{1}{3} \times \frac{2}{3}$ 4. $\frac{1}{4} \times \frac{2}{3}$

5. $\frac{1}{3} \times \frac{3}{4}$ 6. $\frac{2}{3} \times \frac{3}{5}$ 7. $\frac{3}{4} \times \frac{2}{3}$ 8. $\frac{5}{6} \times \frac{3}{5}$

9. $\frac{2}{7} \times \frac{3}{4}$ 10. $\frac{5}{6} \times \frac{7}{8}$ 11. $\frac{4}{5} \times \frac{2}{3}$ 12. $\frac{3}{4} \times \frac{7}{8}$

2.10 One quantity as a fraction of another

In this section you will learn how to:

- express one quantity as a fraction of another

You may often need to give one amount as a fraction of another amount.

EXAMPLE 7

Write £5 as a fraction of £20.

As a fraction this is written $\frac{5}{20}$. This cancels to $\frac{1}{4}$.

EXERCISE 2J

1 In each of the following, write the first quantity as a fraction of the second.

a 2 cm, 6 cm

b 4 kg, 20 kg

c £8, £20

d 5 hours, 24 hours

e 12 days, 30 days

f 50p, £3

g 4 days, 2 weeks

h 40 minutes, 2 hours

2 In a form of 30 pupils, 18 are boys. What fraction of the form consists of boys?

3 During March, it rained on 12 days. For what fraction of the month did it rain?

4 Reka wins £120 in a competition and puts £50 into her bank account. What fraction of her winnings does she keep to spend?

2.11 Reciprocals and rational numbers

In this section you will learn how to:

- recognise rational numbers, reciprocals, terminating decimals and recurring decimals
- convert terminal decimals to fractions
- convert fractions to recurring decimals
- find reciprocals of numbers or fractions

Key words

rational number

reciprocal

recurring decimal

terminating decimal

Rational decimal numbers

A fraction, also known as a **rational number**, can be expressed as a decimal that is either a **terminating decimal** or a **recurring decimal**.

A terminating decimal contains a finite number of digits (decimal places). For example, changing $\frac{3}{16}$ into a decimal gives 0.1875 exactly.

A recurring decimal contains a digit or a block of digits that repeats. For example, changing $\frac{5}{9}$ into a decimal gives 0.5555…, while changing $\frac{14}{27}$ into a decimal gives 0.518 518 5… with the recurring block 518

You can indicate recurring digits by placing a dot over the first and last digits in the recurring block; for example, 0.5555… becomes $0.\dot{5}$, 0.518 518 5… becomes $0.\dot{5}1\dot{8}$ and 0.583 33 becomes $0.58\dot{3}$

Converting terminal decimals into fractions

To convert a terminating decimal to a fraction, take the decimal number as the numerator. Then the denominator is 10, 100 or 1000, depending on the number of decimal places. Because a terminating decimal has a specific number of decimal places, you can use place value to work out exactly where the numerator and the denominator end. For example:

- $0.7 = \dfrac{7}{10}$

- $0.045 = \dfrac{45}{1000} = \dfrac{9}{200}$

- $2.34 = \dfrac{234}{100} = \dfrac{117}{50} = 2\dfrac{17}{50}$

- $0.625 = \dfrac{625}{1000} = \dfrac{5}{8}$

Converting fractions into recurring decimals

A fraction that does not convert to a terminating decimal will give a recurring decimal. You may already know that $\frac{1}{3} = 0.333… = 0.\dot{3}$ This means that the 3s go on for ever and the decimal never ends.

To convert the fraction, you can usually use a calculator to divide the numerator by the denominator. Note that calculators round off the last digit so it may not always be a true recurring decimal in the display. Use a calculator to check the following recurring decimals.

$$\frac{2}{11} = 0.181\,818… = 0.\dot{1}\dot{8}$$

$$\frac{4}{15} = 0.2666… = 0.2\dot{6}$$

$$\frac{8}{13} = 0.615\,384\,615\,384\,6… = 0.\dot{6}15\,38\dot{4}$$

Finding reciprocals of numbers or fractions

You can find the **reciprocal** of a number by dividing that number into 1. So the reciprocal of 2 is $1 ÷ 2 = \frac{1}{2}$ or 0.5

Reciprocals of fractions are quite easy to find as you just have to turn the fraction upside down. For example, the reciprocal of $\frac{2}{3}$ is $\frac{3}{2}$

EXERCISE 2K

1 Write each of these fractions as a decimal. Give them as terminating decimals or recurring decimals, as appropriate.

a $\dfrac{1}{2}$ **b** $\dfrac{1}{3}$ **c** $\dfrac{1}{4}$ **d** $\dfrac{1}{5}$ **e** $\dfrac{1}{6}$

f $\dfrac{1}{7}$ **g** $\dfrac{1}{8}$ **h** $\dfrac{1}{9}$ **i** $\dfrac{1}{10}$ **j** $\dfrac{1}{13}$

2 There are several patterns to be found in recurring decimals. For example:

$$\frac{1}{7} = 0.142\,857\,142\,857\,142\,857\,142\,857\ldots$$

$$\frac{2}{7} = 0.285\,714\,285\,714\,285\,714\,285\,714\ldots$$

$$\frac{3}{7} = 0.428\,571\,428\,571\,428\,571\,428\,571\ldots$$

and so on.

a Write down the decimals for each of the following to 24 decimal places.

i $\dfrac{4}{7}$ **ii** $\dfrac{5}{7}$ **iii** $\dfrac{6}{7}$

b What do you notice?

3 Work out the ninths, $\dfrac{1}{9}$, $\dfrac{2}{9}$, $\dfrac{3}{9}$, and so on up to $\dfrac{8}{9}$, as recurring decimals.

Describe any patterns that you notice.

4 Work out the elevenths, $\dfrac{1}{11}$, $\dfrac{2}{11}$, $\dfrac{3}{11}$, and so on up to $\dfrac{10}{11}$, as recurring decimals.

Describe any patterns that you notice.

5 Write each of these fractions as a decimal. Use your results to write the list in order of size, smallest first.

$\dfrac{4}{9}$ $\qquad$ $\dfrac{5}{11}$ $\qquad$ $\dfrac{3}{7}$ $\qquad$ $\dfrac{9}{22}$ $\qquad$ $\dfrac{16}{37}$ $\qquad$ $\dfrac{6}{13}$

6 Write the following list of fractions in order of size, smallest first.

$\dfrac{19}{60}$ $\qquad$ $\dfrac{7}{24}$ $\qquad$ $\dfrac{3}{10}$ $\qquad$ $\dfrac{2}{5}$ $\qquad$ $\dfrac{5}{12}$

7 Convert each of these terminating decimals to a fraction.

    a 0.125   **b** 0.34   **c** 0.725   **d** 0.3125

    e 0.89   **f** 0.05   **g** 2.35   **h** 0.218 75

8 Use a calculator to work out the reciprocal of each of the following.

    a 12   **b** 16   **c** 20   **d** 25   **e** 50

9 Write down the reciprocal of each of the following fractions.

    a $\dfrac{3}{4}$ **b** $\dfrac{5}{6}$ **c** $\dfrac{2}{5}$

    d $\dfrac{7}{10}$ **e** $\dfrac{11}{20}$ **f** $\dfrac{4}{15}$

10 Write the fractions and their reciprocals in question **9** as decimals. Write them as terminating decimals or recurring decimals, as appropriate.

Is it always true that a fraction that gives a terminating decimal has a reciprocal that gives a recurring decimal?

11 Multiply each of the fractions in question **9** by its reciprocal. What result do you get every time?

1 **a** What fraction of the shape below is shaded?

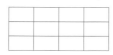

Give your answer as a fraction in its simplest form.

b Copy out and shade $\frac{3}{4}$ of the shape below.

2 Put the following fractions into order, smallest first.

$\frac{3}{4}$ $\frac{1}{2}$ $\frac{2}{5}$ $\frac{1}{3}$

3 Work out.

$\frac{7}{10} - \frac{2}{5}$

4 Work out $\frac{3}{5}$ of 185.

Edexcel, Question 4a, Paper 8B Foundation, January 2003

5 Alison travels by car to her meetings. Alison's company pays her 32p for each mile she travels.

One day Alison writes down the distance readings from her car.

Start of the day: 2430 miles

End of the day: 2658 miles

a Work out how much the company pays Alison for her day's travel.

The next day Alison travelled a total of 145 miles.

She travelled $\frac{2}{5}$ of this distance in the morning.

b How many miles did she travel during the rest of the day?

Edexcel, Question 9, Paper 2 Foundation, June 2005

6 Calculate the following, giving your answers as fractions in their simplest forms.

a $\frac{3}{8} + \frac{1}{8}$

b $\frac{9}{10} - \frac{1}{2}$

7 A fruit punch was made using $\frac{1}{2}$ lemonade, $\frac{1}{5}$ orange juice with the rest lemon juice. What fraction of the drink is lemon juice?

8 The land area of a farm is 385 acres. One-fifth of the land is used to grow barley. How many acres is this?

9 **a** Work out

   i $\frac{3}{5}$ of 175

   ii $\frac{3}{4} \times \frac{2}{3}$

b What fraction is 13 weeks out of a year of 52 weeks?

c What is $1 - \frac{2}{5}$?

10 Two-fifths of the price of a book goes to the bookshop. A book cost £12. How much goes to the bookshop?

11 When a cross is carved from a piece of wood, $\frac{4}{5}$ of the wood is cut away. The original block weighs 215 grams. What weight of wood is cut off?

12 Find $\frac{3}{5}$ of 45 kg.

13 Here are two fractions $\frac{3}{5}$ and $\frac{2}{3}$.

Explain which is the larger fraction.

You may copy and use the grids to help with your explanation.

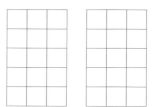

Edexcel, Question 19, Paper 1 Foundation, June 2003

14 **a** Work out $30 \times \frac{2}{3}$

b Work out the value of $\frac{14}{15} \times \frac{3}{4}$

Give your answer as a fraction in its simplest form.

15 Change the following fractions to decimals.

a $\frac{1}{5}$

b $\frac{1}{3}$

16 Packets of Wheetix used to contain 550 grams of cereal. New packets contain one-fifth more. How much does a new packet contain?

17 Change the following fractions to decimals.

a $\frac{1}{7}$

b $\frac{5}{13}$

WORKED EXAM QUESTION

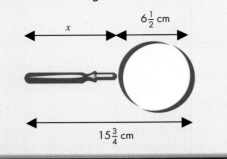

This is a drawing of a magnifying glass.
Calculate the length marked x.

$6\frac{1}{2}$ cm

x

$15\frac{3}{4}$ cm

Solution

$15\frac{3}{4} - 6\frac{1}{2}$ — First identify the problem as a subtraction.

$= 15 - 6 + \frac{3}{4} - \frac{1}{2}$ — Split the problem into whole numbers and fractions.

$= 9 + \frac{1}{4}$ — Work out each part.

$= 9\frac{1}{4}$ — Final answer

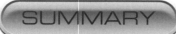

GRADE YOURSELF

G Able to state the fraction of a shape shaded

G Able to shade in a fraction of a shape

G Can add and subtract simple fractions

G Know how to recognise equivalent fractions

G Able to cancel a fraction (when possible)

G Able to put simple fractions into order of size

G Able to change top-heavy fractions into mixed numbers

G Able to find a fraction of an integer

F Able to change mixed numbers into top-heavy fractions

F Able to add more difficult fractions

F Able to solve fraction problems expressed in words

F Able to compare two fractions of quantities

E Can multiply a fraction by a fraction

E Can add and subtract mixed numbers

D Know how to write a quantity as a fraction of another quantity

C Can work out a reciprocal

C Know how to work out and recognise terminating and recurring decimals

What you should know now

- How to recognise and draw fractions of shapes
- How to add, subtract, multiply and cancel simple fractions without using a calculator
- How to work out equivalent fractions
- How to convert a top-heavy fraction to a mixed number (and the other way)
- How to calculate a fraction of a quantity
- How to solve simple practical problems using fractions
- How to work out reciprocals and decimals from fractions

Negative numbers

This chapter will show you ...

- how negative numbers are used in real life
- what is meant by a negative number
- how to use inequalities with negative numbers
- how to do arithmetic with negative numbers

Visual overview

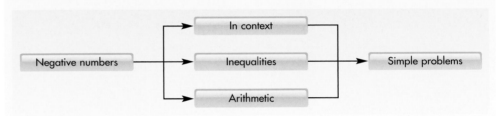

What you should already know

- What a negative number means
- How to put numbers in order

Quick check

Put the numbers in the following lists into order, smallest first.

1	8, 2, 5, 9, 1, 0, 4
2	14, 19, 11, 10, 17
3	51, 92, 24, 0, 32
4	87, 136, 12, 288, 56
5	5, 87, $\frac{1}{2}$, 100, 0, 50

In this section you will learn how:

- negative numbers can represent depths

Key word

negative number

ACTIVITY

Seaport colliery

Top of winding gear 80 ft above ground

Ground	400 ft
South drift	310 ft
225 ft	Closed gate
150 ft	Collapsed tunnel
Zero level	0 ft
−50 ft	North gate
A seam	−325 ft
B seam	−425 ft
−475 ft	Dead Man's seam
C seam	−550 ft
−600 ft	D seam
Bottom gate	−700 ft

Sea level

This is a section through Seaport Colliery.

The height above sea (zero) level for each tunnel is shown. Note that some of the heights are given as **negative numbers**.

The ground is 400 ft above sea level.

1 What is the difference in height between the following levels?

 a South drift and C seam

 b The ground and A seam

 c The closed gate and the collapsed tunnel

 d Zero level and Dead Man's seam

 e Ground level and the bottom gate

 f Collapsed tunnel and B seam

 g North gate and Dead Man's seam

 h Zero level and the south drift

 i Zero level and the bottom gate

 j South drift and the bottom gate

2 How high above sea level is the top of the winding gear?

3 How high above the bottom gate is the top of the winding gear?

4 There are two pairs of tunnels that are 75 ft apart. Which two pairs are they?

5 How much cable does the engineman let out to get the cage from the south drift to D seam?

6 There are two pairs of tunnels that are 125 ft apart. Which two pairs are they?

7 Which two tunnels are 200 ft apart?

Caves and mountains

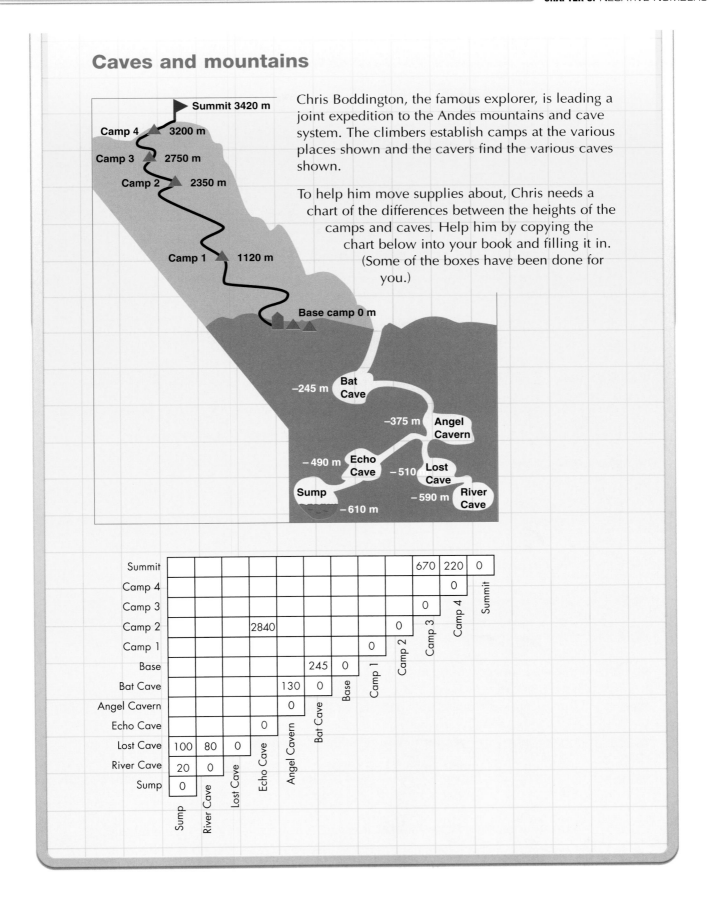

Chris Boddington, the famous explorer, is leading a joint expedition to the Andes mountains and cave system. The climbers establish camps at the various places shown and the cavers find the various caves shown.

To help him move supplies about, Chris needs a chart of the differences between the heights of the camps and caves. Help him by copying the chart below into your book and filling it in. (Some of the boxes have been done for you.)

Summit 3420 m
Camp 4   3200 m
Camp 3   2750 m
Camp 2   2350 m
Camp 1   1120 m
Base camp 0 m

−245 m Bat Cave
−375 m Angel Cavern
−490 m Echo Cave
−510 Lost Cave
−590 m River Cave
−610 m Sump

	Sump	River Cave	Lost Cave	Echo Cave	Angel Cavern	Bat Cave	Base	Camp 1	Camp 2	Camp 3	Camp 4	Summit
Summit										670	220	0
Camp 4											0	
Camp 3										0		
Camp 2			2840						0			
Camp 1								0				
Base					245	0						
Bat Cave				130	0							
Angel Cavern				0								
Echo Cave			0									
Lost Cave	100	80	0									
River Cave	20	0										
Sump	0											

3.2 Everyday use of negative numbers

In this section you will learn about:

- using positive and negative numbers in everyday life

Key words
after
before
below
loss
negative
  number
profit

You meet **negative numbers** often in winter when the temperature falls **below** freezing (0 °C). Negative numbers are less than 0.

You also meet negative numbers on graphs, and you may already have plotted coordinates with negative numbers.

There are many other situations where negative numbers are used. Here are three examples.

- When +15 m means 15 metres above sea level, then –15 m means 15 metres **below** sea level.

- When +2 h means 2 hours **after** midday, then –2 h means 2 hours **before** midday.

- When +£60 means a **profit** of £60, then –£60 means a **loss** of £60.

EXERCISE 3A

Copy and complete each of the following.

1 If +£5 means a profit of five pounds, then …… means a loss of five pounds.

2 If +£9 means a profit of £9, then a loss of £9 is …… .

3 If –£4 means a loss of four pounds, then +£4 means a …… of four pounds.

4 If +200 m means 200 metres above sea level, then …… means 200 metres below sea level.

5 If +50 m means fifty metres above sea level, then fifty metres below sea level is written …… .

6 If –100 m means one hundred metres below sea level, then +100 m means one hundred metres …… sea level.

7 If +3 h means three hours after midday, then …… means three hours before midday.

8 If +5 h means 5 hours after midday, then …… means 5 hours before midday.

9 If –6 h means six hours before midday, then +6 h means six hours …… midday.

10 If +2 °C means two degrees above freezing point, then …… means two degrees below freezing point.

11 If +8 °C means 8 °C above freezing point, then …… means 8 °C below freezing point.

12 If –5 °C means five degrees below freezing point, then +5 °C means five degrees …… freezing point.

13 If +70 km means 70 kilometres north of the equator, then …… means 70 kilometres south of the equator.

14 If +200 km means 200 kilometres north of the equator, then 200 kilometres south of the equator is written …… .

15 If –50 km means fifty kilometres south of the equator, then +50 km means fifty kilometres …… of the equator.

16 If 10 minutes before midnight is represented by –10 minutes, then five minutes after midnight is represented by …… .

17 If a car moving forwards at 10 mph is represented by +10 mph, then a car moving backwards at 5 mph is represented by …… .

18 In an office building, the third floor above ground level is represented by +3. So, the second floor below ground level is represented by …… .

3.3 The number line

In this section you will learn how to:
- use a number line to represent negative numbers
- use inequalities with negative numbers

Key words
greater than
inequality
less than
more than
negative
number line
positive

Look at the **number line**.

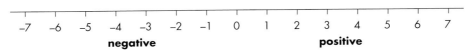

Notice that the **negative** numbers are to the left of 0, and the **positive** numbers are to the right of 0.

Numbers to the right of any number on the number line are always bigger than that number.

Numbers to the left of any number on the number line are always smaller than that number.

So, for example, you can see from a number line that:

2 is *smaller* than 5 because 2 is to the *left* of 5.

You can write this as 2 < 5.

−3 is *smaller* than 2 because −3 is to the *left* of 2.

You can write this as −3 < 2.

7 is *bigger* than 3 because 7 is to the *right* of 3.

You can write this as 7 > 3.

−1 is *bigger* than −4 because −1 is to the *right* of −4.

You can write this as −1 > −4.

Reminder　The **inequality** signs:

< means 'is **less than**'

> means 'is **greater than**' or 'is **more than**'

EXERCISE 3B

1 Copy and complete each of the following by putting a suitable number in the box.

a　☐ is smaller than 3　　　b　☐ is smaller than 1　　　c　☐ is smaller than −3

d　☐ is smaller than −7　　e　−5 is smaller than ☐　　f　−1 is smaller than ☐

g　3 is smaller than ☐　　　h　−2 is smaller than ☐　　i　☐ is smaller than 0

j　−4 is smaller than ☐　　k　☐ is smaller than −8　　l　−7 is smaller than ☐

2 Copy and complete each of the following by putting a suitable number in the box.

a　☐ is bigger than −3　　　b　☐ is bigger than 1　　　c　☐ is bigger than −2

d　☐ is bigger than −1　　　e　−1 is bigger than ☐　　f　−8 is bigger than ☐

g　1 is bigger than ☐　　　　h　−5 is bigger than ☐　　i　☐ is bigger than −5

j　2 is bigger than ☐　　　　k　☐ is bigger than −4　　l　−2 is bigger than ☐

3 Copy each of these and put the correct phrase in each space.

a　−1 ...... 3　　　　　b　3 ...... 2　　　　　c　−4 ...... −1

d　−5 ...... −4　　　　e　1 ...... −6　　　　f　−3 0

g　−2 ...... −1　　　　h　2 ...... −3　　　　i　5 ...... −6

j　3 ...... 4　　　　　k　−7 ...... −5　　　　l　−2 ...... −4

4

$$-1 \quad -\frac{3}{4} \quad -\frac{1}{2} \quad -\frac{1}{4} \quad 0 \quad \frac{1}{4} \quad \frac{1}{2} \quad \frac{3}{4} \quad 1$$

Copy each of these and put the correct phrase in each space.

a $\frac{1}{4}$ ...... $\frac{3}{4}$

b $-\frac{1}{2}$ 0

c $-\frac{3}{4}$ ...... $\frac{3}{4}$

d $\frac{1}{4}$ ...... $-\frac{1}{2}$

e -1 ...... $\frac{3}{4}$

f $\frac{1}{2}$ 1

5 In each case below, copy the statement and put the correct symbol, either < or >, in the box.

a 3 ☐ 5

b −2 ☐ −5

c −4 ☐ 3

d 5 ☐ 9

e −3 ☐ 2

f 4 ☐ −3

g −1 ☐ 0

h 6 ☐ −4

i 2 ☐ −3

j 0 ☐ −2

k −5 ☐ −4

l 1 ☐ 3

m −6 ☐ −7

n 2 ☐ −3

o −1 ☐ 1

p 4 ☐ 0

6 Copy these number lines and fill in the missing numbers.

a

−5   −2   0   1   3   5

b

−20   −10   0   5   15

c

−8   −4   0   2   6

d

−30   −10   0   10   20

e

−9   −6   0   3   6   12

f

−8   0   8   16

g

−2   −1   0   1   2

h

−100   −40   0   20   60

i

−100   0   50   200

Arithmetic with negative numbers

In this section you will learn how to:

- add and subtract positive and negative numbers to both positive and negative numbers

Key words

add

subtract

Adding and subtracting positive numbers

These two operations can be illustrated on a thermometer scale.

- **Adding** a positive number moves the marker *up* the thermometer scale. For example,

  $-2 + 6 = 4$

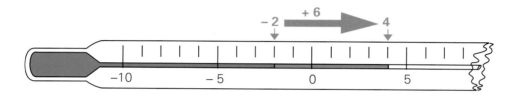

- **Subtracting** a positive number moves the marker *down* the thermometer scale. For example,

  $3 - 5 = -2$

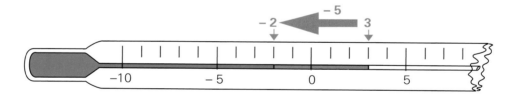

EXAMPLE 1

The temperature at midnight was 2 °C but then it fell by 5 degrees. What was the new temperature?

To put it simply, the problem is $2 - 5$, which is equal to -3. So, the new temperature is -3°C.

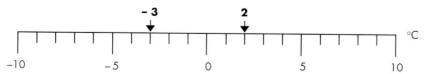

EXAMPLE 2

The temperature drops five degrees from −4 °C. What does it drop to?

To put it simply, the problem is −4 − 5, which is equal to −9. So, the new temperature is −9 °C.

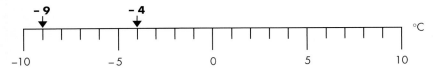

EXERCISE 3C

1 Use a thermometer scale to find the answer to each of the following.

a 2 °C − 4 °C =   **b** 4 °C − 7 °C =   **c** 3 °C − 5 °C =   **d** 1 °C − 4 °C =

e 6 °C − 8 °C =   **f** 5 °C − 8 °C =   **g** −2 + 5 =   **h** −1 + 4 =

i −4 + 3 =   **j** −6 + 5 =   **k** −3 + 5 =   **l** −5 + 2 =

m −1 − 3 =   **n** −2 − 4 =   **o** −5 − 1 =   **p** 3 − 4 =

q 2 − 7 =   **r** 1 − 5 =   **s** −3 + 7 =   **t** 5 − 6 =

u −2 − 3 =   **v** 2 − 6 =   **w** −8 + 3 =   **x** 4 − 9 =

2 Answer each of the following *without* the help of a thermometer scale.

a 5 − 9 =   **b** 3 − 7 =   **c** −2 − 8 =   **d** −5 + 7 =

e −1 + 9 =   **f** 4 − 9 =   **g** −10 + 12 =   **h** −15 + 20 =

i 23 − 30 =   **j** 30 − 42 =   **k** −12 + 25 =   **l** −30 + 55 =

m −10 − 22 =   **n** −13 − 17 =   **o** 45 − 50 =   **p** 17 − 25 =

q 18 − 30 =   **r** −25 + 35 =   **s** −23 − 13 =   **t** 31 − 45 =

u −24 + 65 =   **v** −19 + 31 =   **w** 25 − 65 =   **x** 199 − 300 =

3 Work out each of the following.

a 8 + 3 − 5 =   **b** −2 + 3 − 6 =   **c** −1 + 3 + 4 =

d −2 − 3 + 4 =   **e** −1 + 1 − 2 =   **f** −4 + 5 − 7 =

g −3 + 4 − 7 =   **h** 1 + 3 − 6 =   **i** 8 − 7 + 2 =

j −5 − 7 + 12 =   **k** −4 + 5 − 8 =   **l** −4 + 6 − 8 =

m 103 − 102 + 7 =   **n** −1 + 4 − 2 =   **o** −6 + 9 − 12 =

p −3 − 3 − 3 =   **q** −3 + 4 − 6 =   **r** −102 + 45 − 23 =

s 8 − 10 − 5 =   **t** 9 − 12 + 2 =   **u** 99 − 100 − 46 =

Adding and subtracting negative numbers

To *subtract a negative number* …

… treat the − − as a +

For example: $4 - (-2) = 4 + 2 = 6$

To *add a negative number* …

… treat the + − as a −

For example: $3 + (-5) = 3 - 5 = -2$

Using your calculator

Calculations involving negative numbers can be done on a calculator by using the **±** **(** **)** keys or the **(−)** key.

EXAMPLE 3

Work out −3 + 7.

Press **3** **±** **+** **7** **=**

The answer should be 4.

EXAMPLE 4

Work out −6 − (−2).

Press **(−)** **6** **−** **(−)** **2** **=**

The answer should be −4.

EXERCISE 3D

1 Answer each of the following. Check your answers on a calculator.

a $2 - (-4) =$	**b** $4 - (-3) =$	**c** $3 - (-5) =$	**d** $5 - (-1) =$
e $6 - (-2) =$	**f** $8 - (-2) =$	**g** $-1 - (-3) =$	**h** $-4 - (-1) =$
i $-2 - (-3) =$	**j** $-5 - (-7) =$	**k** $-3 - (-2) =$	**l** $-8 - (-1) =$
m $4 + (-2) =$	**n** $2 + (-5) =$	**o** $3 + (-2) =$	**p** $1 + (-6) =$
q $5 + (-2) =$	**r** $4 + (-8) =$	**s** $-2 + (-1) =$	**t** $-6 + (-2) =$
u $-7 + (-3) =$	**v** $-2 + (-7) =$	**w** $-1 + (-3) =$	**x** $-7 + (-2) =$

F

2 Write down the answer to each of the following, then check your answers on a calculator.

a −3 − 5 =   **b** −2 − 8 =   **c** −5 − 6 =   **d** 6 − 9 =

e 5 − 3 =   **f** 3 − 8 =   **g** −4 + 5 =   **h** −3 + 7 =

i −2 + 9 =   **j** −6 + −2 =   **k** −1 + −4 =   **l** −8 + −3 =

m 5 − −6 =   **n** 3 − −3 =   **o** 6 − −2 =   **p** 3 − −5 =

q −5 − −3 =   **r** −2 − −1 =   **s** −4 − 5 =   **t** 2 − 7 =

u −3 + 8 =   **v** −4 + − 5 =   **w** 1 − −7 =   **x** −5 − −5 =

3 The temperature at midnight was 4 °C. Find the temperature if it *fell* by:

a 1 degree   **b** 4 degrees   **c** 7 degrees   **d** 9 degrees   **e** 15 degrees

4 What is the *difference* between the following temperatures?

a 4 °C and −6 °C   **b** −2 °C and −9 °C   **c** −3 °C and 6 °C

5 Rewrite the following list, putting the numbers in order of size, lowest first.

1   −5   3   −6   −9   8   −1   2

6 Write down the answers to each of the following, then check your answers on a calculator.

a 2 − 5 =   **b** 7 − 11 =   **c** 4 − 6 =   **d** 8 − 15 =

e 9 − 23 =   **f** −2 − 4 =   **g** −5 − 7 =   **h** −1 − 9 =

i −4 + 8 =   **j** −9 + 5 =   **k** 9 − −5 =   **l** 8 − −3 =

m −8 − −4 =   **n** −3 − −2 =   **o** −7 + −3 =   **p** −9 + 4 =

q −6 + 3 =   **r** −1 + 6 =   **s** −9 − −5 =   **t** 9 − 17 =

7 Find what you have to *add to* 5 to get:

a 7   **b** 2   **c** 0   **d** −2   **e** −5   **f** −15

8 Find what you have to *subtract from* 4 to get:

a 2   **b** 0   **c** 5   **d** 9   **e** 15   **f** −4

9 Find what you have to *add to* −5 to get:

a 8   **b** −3   **c** 0   **d** −1   **e** 6   **f** −7

10 Find what you have to *subtract from* −3 to get:

a 7   **b** 2   **c** −1   **d** −7   **e** −10   **f** 1

11 Write down *ten* different addition sums that give the answer 1.

12 Write down *ten* different subtraction calculations that give the answer 1. There must be *one negative number* in each calculation.

13 Use a calculator to work out each of these.

a $-7 + -3 - -5 =$ **b** $6 + 7 - 7 =$ **c** $-3 + -4 - -7 =$

d $-1 - 3 - -6 =$ **e** $8 - -7 + -2 =$ **f** $-5 - 7 - -12 =$

g $-4 + 5 - 7 =$ **h** $-4 + -6 - -8 =$ **i** $103 - -102 - -7 =$

j $-1 + 4 - -2 =$ **k** $6 - -9 - 12 =$ **l** $-3 - -3 - -3 =$

m $-45 + -56 - -34 =$ **n** $-3 + 4 - -6 =$ **o** $102 + -45 - 32 =$

14 Give the outputs of each of these function machines.

a $-4, -3, -2, -1, 0 \rightarrow \boxed{+3} \rightarrow ?, ?, ?, ?, ?$

b $-4, -3, -2, -1, 0 \rightarrow \boxed{-2} \rightarrow ?, ?, ?, ?, ?$

c $-4, -3, -2, -1, 0 \rightarrow \boxed{+1} \rightarrow ?, ?, ?, ?, ?$

d $-4, -3, -2, -1, 0 \rightarrow \boxed{-4} \rightarrow ?, ?, ?, ?, ?$

e $-4, -3, -2, -1, 0 \rightarrow \boxed{-5} \rightarrow ?, ?, ?, ?, ?$

f $-4, -3, -2, -1, 0 \rightarrow \boxed{+7} \rightarrow ?, ?, ?, ?, ?$

g $-10, -9, -8, -7, -6 \rightarrow \boxed{-2} \rightarrow ?, ?, ?, ?, ?$

h $-10, -9, -8, -7, -6 \rightarrow \boxed{-6} \rightarrow ?, ?, ?, ?, ?$

i $-5, -4, -3, -2, -1, 0 \rightarrow \boxed{+3} \rightarrow ?, ?, ?, ?, ?, ? \rightarrow \boxed{-2} \rightarrow ?, ?, ?, ?, ?, ?$

j $-5, -4, -3, -2, -1, 0 \rightarrow \boxed{-7} \rightarrow ?, ?, ?, ?, ?, ? \rightarrow \boxed{-2} \rightarrow ?, ?, ?, ?, ?, ?$

k $-5, -4, -3, -2, -1, 0 \rightarrow \boxed{+3} \rightarrow ?, ?, ?, ?, ?, ? \rightarrow \boxed{+2} \rightarrow ?, ?, ?, ?, ?, ?$

l $-3, -2, -1, 0, 1, 2, 3 \rightarrow \boxed{-5} \rightarrow ?, ?, ?, ?, ?, ? \rightarrow \boxed{+3} \rightarrow ?, ?, ?, ?, ?, ?$

m $-3, -2, -1, 0, 1, 2, 3 \rightarrow \boxed{-7} \rightarrow ?, ?, ?, ?, ?, ?, ? \rightarrow \boxed{+9} \rightarrow ?, ?, ?, ?, ?, ?$

n $-3, -2, -1, 0, 1, 2, 3 \rightarrow \boxed{+6} \rightarrow ?, ?, ?, ?, ?, ?, ? \rightarrow \boxed{-8} \rightarrow ?, ?, ?, ?, ?, ?$

15 What numbers are missing from the boxes to make the number sentences true?

a $2 + -6 = \square$ **b** $4 + \square = 7$ **c** $-4 + \square = 0$ **d** $5 + \square = -1$

e $3 + 4 = \square$ **f** $\square - -5 = 7$ **g** $\square - 5 = 2$ **h** $6 + \square = 0$

i $\square - -5 = -2$ **j** $2 + -2 = \square$ **k** $\square - 2 = -2$ **l** $-2 + -4 = \square$

m $2 + 3 + \square = -2$ **n** $-2 + -3 + -4 = \square$ **o** $\square - 5 = -1$ **p** $\square - 8 = -8$

q $-4 + 2 + \square = 3$ **r** $-5 + 5 = \square$ **s** $7 - -3 = \square$ **t** $\square - -5 = 0$

u $3 - \square = 0$ **v** $-3 - \square = 0$ **w** $-6 + -3 = \square$ **x** $\square - 3 - -2 = -1$

y $\square - 1 = -4$ **z** $7 - \square = 10$

16 You have the following cards.

-9 **-8** **-4** **0** **+1** **+3** **+5**

a Which card should you choose to make the answer to the following sum as large as possible? What is the answer?

+6 $+$ ■ $= \ldots\ldots$

b Which card should you choose to make the answer to part **a** as small as possible? What is the answer?

c Which card should you choose to make the answer to the following subtraction as large as possible? What is the answer?

+6 $-$ ■ $= \ldots\ldots$

d Which card should you choose to make the answer to part **c** as small as possible? What is the answer?

17 You have the following cards.

-9 **-7** **-5** **-4** **0** **+1** **+2** **+4** **+7**

a Which cards should you choose to make the answer to the following calculation as large as possible? What is the answer?

+5 $+$ ■ $-$ ■ $= \ldots\ldots$

b Which cards should you choose to make the answer to part **a** as small as possible? What is the answer?

c Which cards should you choose to make the answer to the following number sentence zero? Give all possible answers.

■ $+$ ■ $= 0$

Negative magic squares

Make your own magic square with negative numbers. You need nine small square cards and two pens or pencils of different colours.

This is perhaps the best known magic square.

8	3	4
1	5	9
6	7	2

But magic squares can be made from many different sets of numbers, as shown by this second square.

This square is now used to show you how to make a magic square with negative numbers. But the method works with any magic square. So, if you can find one of your own, use it!

8	13	6
7	9	11
12	5	10

- Arrange the nine cards in a square and write on them the numbers of the magic square. Picture **a** below.

- Rearrange the cards in order, lowest number first, to form another square. Picture **b** below.

- Keeping the cards in order, turn them over so that the blank side of each card is face up. Picture **c** below.

a

8	13	6
7	9	11
12	5	10

b

5	6	7
8	9	10
11	12	13

c

- Now use a different coloured pen to avoid confusion.

- Choose any number (say 4) for the top left-hand corner of the square. Picture **d** below.

- Choose another number (say 3) and subtract it from each number in the first row to get the next number. Picture **e** below.

- Now choose a third number (say 2) and subtract it from each number in the top row to make the second row, and then again from each number in the second row. Picture **f** below.

d

4		

e

4	1	–2

f

4	1	–2
2	–1	–4
0	–3	–6

- Turn the cards over. Picture **g**.

- Rearrange the cards into the original magic square. Picture **h**.

- Turn them over again. Picture **i**.

g

5	6	7
8	9	10
11	12	13

h

8	13	6
7	9	11
12	5	10

i

2	−6	1
−2	−1	0
−3	4	−4

You should have a **magic square of negative numbers**.

Try it on any square. It works even with squares bigger than 3 × 3. Try it on this 4 × 4 square.

2	13	9	14
16	7	11	4
15	8	12	3
5	10	6	17

EXERCISE 3E

Copy and complete each of these magic squares. In each case, write down the 'magic number'.

1

−1		
−5	−4	−3
		−7

2

	−4	3
		−2
	4	−1

3

−6	−5	−4
		−10

4

	2	
−4		
−7	6	−8

5

		−9
−3	−6	−9

6

		−1
	−7	
−13		−12

7

−4		
−8		−6
−9		

8

2	1	−3
	0	

9

−2		
	−5	
−7		−8

10

−8			−14
−8	−9		
		−4	−5
1	−10	−12	−5

11

−7		2	−16
	−8		
−11	−3	0	−2
		−13	−1

1 The temperature in a school yard was measured at 9am each morning for one week.

Day	Monday	Tuesday	Wednesday	Thursday	Friday
9am temperature	−1	−3	−2	1	2

a Which day was the coldest at 9am?

b Which day was the warmest at 9am?

 2 The table shows the temperature in each of 6 cities on 1st January 2003.

a Write down the name of the city which had the *lowest* temperature.

b Work out the difference in temperature between Copenhagen and Cairo.

On 2nd January 2003, the temperature in Moscow had increased by 4 °C.

c Work out the new temperature in Moscow.

City	Temperature
Cairo	15 °C
Copenhagen	−1 °C
Helsinki	−9 °C
Manchester	3 °C
Moscow	−14 °C
Sydney	20 °C

Edexcel, Question 4, Paper 8A Foundation, March 2003

3 Write out and complete the following to make a correct statement.

a $3 - \boxed{} = -5$ **b** $\boxed{} + 4 = -5$ **c** $1 - \boxed{} = 8$

 4 The table shows the temperature on the surface of each of five planets.

a Work out the difference in temperature between Mars and Jupiter.

b Work out the difference in temperature between Venus and Mars.

c Which planet has a temperature 30 °C higher than the temperature on Saturn?

The temperature on Pluto is 20 °C lower than the temperature on Uranus.

d Work out the temperature on Pluto.

Planet	Temperature
Venus	480 °C
Mars	−60 °C
Jupiter	−150 °C
Saturn	−180 °C
Uranus	−210 °C

Edexcel, Question 8, Paper 2 Foundation, June 2005

 5 Write these numbers in order of size. Start with the smallest number.

i 75, 56, 37, 9, 59 **ii** 5, −6, −10, 2, −4 **iii** $\frac{1}{2}, \frac{2}{3}, \frac{2}{5}, \frac{3}{4}$

Edexcel, Question 9, Paper 1 Foundation, June 2003

 6 The temperatures of the first few days of January were recorded as

1 °C, −1 °C, 0 °C and −2 °C

a Write down the four temperatures, in order, with the lowest first.

b What is the difference between the coldest and the warmest of these four days?

 7 You have the following cards.

 $\boxed{+3}$ $\boxed{+8}$ $\boxed{-4}$ $\boxed{-7}$

a i What card should you choose to make the answer to the following sum as large as possible?

$\boxed{+1}$ + $\boxed{}$ = ...

ii What is the answer to the sum in **i**?

iii What card would you have chosen to make the sum as small as possible?

b i What card should you choose to make the answer to the following subtraction as large as possible?

ii What is the answer to the subtraction sum in **i**?

iii What card would you have chosen to make the subtraction as small as possible?

8 Nitrogen gas makes up most of the air we breathe.

Nitrogen freezes under –210 °C and is a gas above –196 °C. In between it is liquid.

Write down a possible temperature where nitrogen is

i a liquid

ii a gas

iii frozen.

9 The most common rocket fuel is liquid hydrogen and liquid oxygen. These two gases are kept in storage, as a liquid, at the following temperatures:

Liquid hydrogen   –253 °C

Liquid oxygen   –183 °C

a i Which of the two gases is kept at the coldest temperature?

ii What is the difference between the two storage temperatures?

b Scientists are experimenting with liquid methane as its liquid storage temperature is only –162 °C. How much warmer is the stored liquid methane than the

i stored liquid oxygen?

ii stored liquid hydrogen?

WORKED EXAM QUESTION

The number $2\frac{1}{2}$ is halfway between 1 and 4.

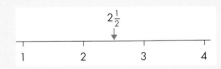

What number is halfway between:

a –8 and –1   b $\frac{1}{4}$ and $1\frac{1}{4}$?

Solution

a The number halfway between –8 and –1 is $-4\frac{1}{2}$.

> The hint in the question is to sketch the numbers on a number line.
>
>
>
> Just by counting from each end you can find the middle value.

b The number halfway between $\frac{1}{4}$ and $1\frac{1}{4}$ is $\frac{3}{4}$.

> Sketch the number line and mark on the quarters.
>
>
>
> Count from each end to identify the middle value.

SUMMARY

G Use negative numbers in context

G Use negative numbers with inequalities

F Add positive and negative numbers to positive and negative numbers

F Subtract positive and negative numbers from positive and negative numbers

E Solve problems involving simple negative numbers

What you should know now

- How to order positive and negative numbers
- How to add and subtract positive and negative numbers
- How to use negative numbers in practical situations
- How to use a calculator when working with negative numbers

More about number

This chapter will show you ...

- the meaning of multiples
- the meaning of factors
- the meaning of prime numbers
- how to work out squares, square roots and powers
- how to break a number down into its prime factors
- how to work out the lowest common multiple of two numbers
- how to work out the highest common factor of two numbers

Visual overview

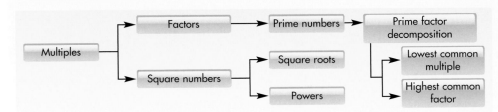

What you should already know

- Times tables up to 10×10

Quick check

Write down the answers to the following.

1	**a** 2×3	**b** 4×3	**c** 5×3
	d 6×3	**e** 7×3	**f** 8×3
2	**a** 2×4	**b** 4×4	**c** 5×4
	d 6×4	**e** 7×4	**f** 8×4
3	**a** 2×5	**b** 9×5	**c** 5×5
	d 6×5	**e** 7×5	**f** 8×5
4	**a** 2×6	**b** 9×6	**c** 8×8
	d 6×6	**e** 7×9	**f** 8×6
5	**a** 2×7	**b** 9×7	**c** 8×9
	d 6×7	**e** 7×7	**f** 8×7

Multiples of whole numbers

In this section you will learn how to:
- find multiples of whole numbers
- recognise multiples of numbers

Key words

multiple
times table

When you multiply any whole number by another whole number, the answer is called a **multiple** of either of those numbers.

For example, $5 \times 7 = 35$, which means that 35 is a multiple of 5 and it is also a multiple of 7. Here are some other multiples of 5 and 7:

multiples of 5 are   5   10   15   20   25   30   35   …

multiples of 7 are   7   14   21   28   35   42   …

Multiples are also called **times tables**.

Recognising multiples

You can recognise the multiples of 2, 3, 5 and 9 in the following ways.

- Multiples of 2 always end in an even number or 0. For example:

  12   34   96   1938   370

- Multiples of 3 are always made up of digits that add up to a multiple of 3. For example:

  15   because $1 + 5 = 6$ which is $2 \times \mathbf{3}$

  72   because $7 + 2 = 9$ which is $3 \times \mathbf{3}$

  201   because $2 + 0 + 1 = 3$ which is $1 \times \mathbf{3}$

- Multiples of 5 always end in 5 or 0. For example:

  35   60   155   300

- Multiples of 9 are always made up of digits that add up to a multiple of 9. For example:

  63   because $6 + 3 = 9$ which is $1 \times \mathbf{9}$

  738   because $7 + 3 + 8 = 18$ which is $2 \times \mathbf{9}$

You can find out whether numbers are multiples of 4, 6, 7 and 8 by using your calculator. For example, to find out whether 341 is a multiple of 7, you have to see whether 341 gives a whole number when it is divided by 7. You therefore key

3 4 1 ÷ 7 =

The answer is 48.714 286, which is a decimal number, not a whole number. So, 341 is *not* a multiple of 7.

EXERCISE 4A

 1 Write out the first five multiples of:

a 3   **b** 7   **c** 9   **d** 11   **e** 16

Remember: the first multiple is the number itself.

 2 From the numbers below, write down those that are:

a multiples of 2   **b** multiples of 3

c multiples of 5   **d** multiples of 9

111	254	255	108	73
68	162	711	615	98
37	812	102	75	270

HINTS AND TIPS

Remember the rules on page 68

 3 Use your calculator to see which of the numbers below are:

a multiples of 4   **b** multiples of 7

c multipies of 6

72	135	102	161	197
132	78	91	216	514
312	168	75	144	294

HINTS AND TIPS

There is no point testing odd numbers for multiplies of even numbers such as 4 and 6

 4 Find the biggest number smaller than 100 that is:

a a multiple of 2   **b** a multiple of 3   **c** a multiple of 4

d a multiple of 5   **e** a multiple of 7   **f** a multiple of 6

5 Find the smallest number that is bigger than 1000 that is:

a a multiple of 6   **b** a multiple of 8   **c** a multiple of 9

Grid locked

You need eight copies of this 10 × 10 grid.

1	2	3	4	5	6	7	8	9	10
11	12	13	14	15	16	17	18	19	20
21	22	23	24	25	26	27	28	29	30
31	32	33	34	35	36	37	38	39	40
41	42	43	44	45	46	47	48	49	50
51	52	53	54	55	56	57	58	59	60
61	62	63	64	65	66	67	68	69	70
71	72	73	74	75	76	77	78	79	80
81	82	83	84	85	86	87	88	89	90
91	92	93	94	95	96	97	98	99	100

Take one of the grids and shade in all the multiples of 2. You should find that they make a neat pattern.

Do the same thing for the multiples of 3, 4, … up to 9, using a fresh 10 × 10 grid for each number.

Next, draw a grid which is 9 squares wide and write the numbers from 1 to 100 in the grid, like this:

1	2	3	4	5	6	7	8	9
10	11	12	13	14	15	16	17	18
19	20	21	22	23	24			27

Make seven more copies of this grid. Then shade in the multiples of 2, 3, … up to 9, using a fresh grid for each number.

Write out the numbers from 1 to 100 on grids of different widths and shade in the multiples of 2, 3, … up to 9, as before.

Describe the patterns that you get.

4.2 Factors of whole numbers

In this section you will learn how to:
- identify the factors of a number

Key word
factor

A **factor** of a whole number is any whole number that divides into it exactly. So:

the factors of 20 are   1   2   4   5   10   20

the factors of 12 are   1   2   3   4   6   12

This is where it helps to know your times tables!

Factor facts

Remember these facts:

- 1 is always a factor and so is the number itself.

- When you have found one factor, there is always another factor that goes with it – unless the factor is multiplied by itself to give the number. For example, look at the number 20:

    $1 \times 20 = 20$ so 1 and 20 are both factors of 20

    $2 \times 10 = 20$ so 2 and 10 are both factors of 20

    $4 \times 5 = 20$ so 4 and 5 are both factors of 20

You may need to use your calculator to find the factors of large numbers.

EXAMPLE 1

Find the factors of 32.

Look for the pairs of numbers that make 32 when multiplied together. These are:

$1 \times 32 = 32$ $2 \times 16 = 32$ $4 \times 8 = 32$

So, the factors of 32 are 1, 2, 4, 8, 16, 32.

EXAMPLE 2

Find the factors of 36.

Look for the pairs of numbers that make 36 when multiplied together. These are:

$1 \times 36 = 36$ $2 \times 18 = 36$ $3 \times 12 = 36$ $4 \times 9 = 36$ $6 \times 6 = 36$

6 is a repeated factor which is counted only once.

So, the factors of 36 are 1, 2, 3, 4, 6, 9, 12, 18, 36.

EXERCISE 4B

1 What are the factors of each of these numbers?

a	10	**b**	28
c	18	**d**	17
e	25	**f**	40
g	30	**h**	45
i	24	**j**	16

2 Use your calculator to find the factors of each of these numbers.

a	120	**b**	150
c	144	**d**	180
e	169	**f**	108
g	196	**h**	153
i	198	**j**	199

HINTS AND TIPS

Remember that once you find one factor this will give you another, unless it is a repeated factor such as 5×5.

---

3 What is the biggest factor that is less than 100 for each of these numbers?

a	110	**b**	201
c	145	**d**	117
e	130	**f**	240
g	160	**h**	210
i	162	**j**	250

4 Find the largest common factor for each of the following pairs of numbers. (Do not include 1.)

a	2 and 4	**b**	6 and 10
c	9 and 12	**d**	15 and 25
e	9 and 15	**f**	12 and 21
g	14 and 21	**h**	25 and 30
i	30 and 50	**j**	55 and 77

HINTS AND TIPS

Look for the largest number that has both numbers in its times table.

Prime numbers

In this section you will learn how to:
- identify prime numbers

Key word

prime
    number

What are the factors of 2, 3, 5, 7, 11 and 13?

Notice that each of these numbers has only two factors: itself and 1. They are all examples of **prime numbers**.

So, a prime number is a whole number that has only two factors: itself and 1.

Note: 1 is *not* a prime number, since it has only one factor – itself.

The prime numbers up to 50 are:

    2, 3, 5, 7, 11, 13, 17, 19, 23, 29, 31, 37, 41, 43, 47

It will be useful to recognise all these as prime numbers.

ACTIVITY

Prime search

You need a 10 × 10 grid.

Cross out 1.

Leave 2 and cross out the rest of the multiples of 2.

Leave 3 and cross out the rest of the multiples of 3. Some of them will already have been crossed out.

Leave 5 and cross out the rest of the multiples of 5. Some of them will already have been crossed out.

Leave 7 and cross out the rest of the multiples of 7. All but three of them will already have been crossed out.

The numbers left are prime numbers.

The activity is known as the Sieve of Eratosthenes. (Eratosthenes, a Greek scholar, lived from about 275 BC to 194 BC.)

1	2	3	4	5	6	7	8	9	10
11	12	13	14	15	16	17	18	19	20
21	22	23	24	25	26	27	28	29	30
31	32	33	34	35	36	37	38	39	40
41	42	43	44	45	46	47	48	49	50
51	52	53	54	55	56	57	58	59	60
61	62	63	64	65	66	67	68	69	70
71	72	73	74	75	76	77	78	79	80
81	82	83	84	85	86	87	88	89	90
91	92	93	94	95	96	97	98	99	100

Square numbers

In this section you will learn how to:
- identify square numbers
- use a calculator to find the square of a number

Key words

square
square
   numbers

What is the next number in this sequence?

1, 4, 9, 16, 25, …

Writing each number in terms of its factors gives:

1 × 1, 2 × 2, 3 × 3, 4 × 4, 5 × 5, …

These factors can be represented by **square** patterns of dots:

From these patterns, you can see that the next pair of factors must be 6 × 6 = 36, therefore 36 is the next number in the sequence.

Because they form square patterns, the numbers 1, 4, 9, 16, 25, 36, … are called **square numbers**.

When you multiply any number by itself, the answer is called the *square of the number* or *the number squared*. This is because the answer is a square number. For example:

the square of 5 (or 5 squared) is 5 × 5 = 25

the square of 6 (or 6 squared) is 6 × 6 = 36

There is a short way to write the square of any number. For example:

5 squared (5 × 5) can be written as 5^2

13 squared (13 × 13) can be written as 13^2

So, the sequence of square numbers, 1, 4, 9, 16, 25, 36, …, can be written as:

1^2, 2^2, 3^2, 4^2, 5^2, 6^2, …

You are expected to know the square numbers up to 15 × 15 (= 225) for the GCSE exam.

EXERCISE 4C

 1 The square number pattern starts:

  1   4   9   16   25   …

Copy and continue the pattern above until you have written down the first 20 square numbers. You may use your calculator for this.

 2 Work out the answer to each of these number sentences.

  1 + 3 =

  1 + 3 + 5 =

  1 + 3 + 5 + 7 =

Look carefully at the pattern of the three number sentences. Then write down the next three number sentences in the pattern and work them out.

 3 Draw one counter.

Now add more counters to your picture to make the next square number.

a How many extra counters did you add?

Now add more counters to your picture to make the next square number.

b How many extra counters did you add?

c Without drawing, how many more counters will you need to make the next square number?

d Describe the pattern of counters you are adding.

4 Find the next three numbers in each of these number patterns. (They are all based on square numbers.) You may use your calculator.

	1	4	9	16	25	36	49	64	81
a	2	5	10	17	26	37	…	…	…
b	2	8	18	32	50	72	…	…	…
c	3	6	11	18	27	38	…	…	…
d	0	3	8	15	24	35	…	…	…
e	101	104	109	116	125	136	…	…	…

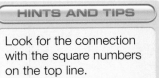

HINTS AND TIPS

Look for the connection with the square numbers on the top line.

5 Write down the answer to each of the following. You will need to use your calculator. Look for the x^2 key.

a 23^2 b 57^2 c 77^2 d 123^2 e 152^2

f 3.2^2 g 9.5^2 h 23.8^2 i $(-4)^2$ j $(-12)^2$

6 a Work out each of the following. You may use your calculator.

$3^2 + 4^2$ and 5^2
$5^2 + 12^2$ and 13^2
$7^2 + 24^2$ and 25^2
$9^2 + 40^2$ and 41^2
$11^2 + 60^2$ and 61^2

b Describe what you notice about your answers to part **a**.

EXERCISE 4D

The following exercise will give you some practice on multiplies, factors, square numbers and prime numbers.

1 Write out the first five multiples of:

a 6   b 13   c 8   d 20   e 18

Remember: the first multiple is the number itself.

2 Write out the first three numbers that are multiples of both of the numbers shown.

a 3 and 4   b 4 and 5   c 3 and 5   d 6 and 9   e 5 and 7

3 What are the factors of these numbers?

a 12   b 20   c 9   d 32   e 24

f 38   g 13   h 42   i 45   j 36

4 In question **3**, part **g**, there were only two factors. Why?

5 In question **3**, every number had an even number of factors except parts **c** and **j**. What sort of numbers are 9 and 36?

6 Write down the prime numbers up to 20.

7 Write down the square numbers up to 100.

8 If hot-dog sausages are sold in packs of 10 and hot-dog buns are sold in packs of 8, how many of each must you buy to have complete hot dogs with no extra sausages or buns?

9 Rover barks every 8 seconds and Spot barks every 12 seconds. If they both bark together, how many seconds will it be before they both bark together again?

10 A bell chimes every 6 seconds. Another bell chimes every 5 seconds. If they both chime together, how many seconds will it be before they both chime together again?

11 Fred runs round a running track in 4 minutes. Debbie runs round in 3 minutes. If they both start together on the line at the end of the finishing straight, when will they both be on the same line together again? How many laps will Debbie have run? How many laps will Fred have run?

12 From this box, choose one number that fits each of these descriptions.

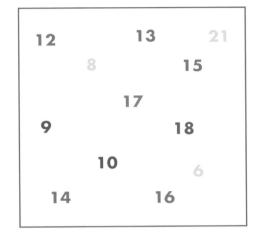

12   13   21
    8   15
        17
9   18
    10   6
14   16

   a a multiple of 3 and a multiple of 4

   b a square number and an odd number

   c a factor of 24 and a factor of 18

   d a prime number and a factor of 39

   e an odd factor of 30 and a multiple of 3

   f a number with 4 factors and a multiple of 2 and 7

   g a number with 5 factors exactly

   h a multiple of 5 and a factor of 20

   i an even number and a factor of 36 and a multiple of 9

   j a prime number that is one more than a square number

   k written in order, the four factors of this number make a number pattern in which each number is twice the one before

   l an odd number that is a multiple of 7.

13 Copy these number sentences and write out the *next four* sentences in the pattern.

$$1 = 1$$
$$1 + 3 = 4$$
$$1 + 3 + 5 = 9$$
$$1 + 3 + 5 + 7 = 16$$

14 The following numbers are described as triangular numbers:

1, 3, 6, 10, 15

   a Investigate why they are called triangular numbers.

   b Write down the next five triangular numbers.

4.5 Square roots

In this section you will learn how to:
- find a square root of a square number
- use a calculator to find the square roots of any number

Key word

square root

The **square root** of a given number is a number that, when multiplied by itself, produces the given number.

For example, the square root of 9 is 3, since $3 \times 3 = 9$.

Numbers also have a negative square root, since -3×-3 also equals 9.

A square root is represented by the symbol $\sqrt{}$. For example, $\sqrt{16} = 4$.

EXERCISE 4E

1 Write down the positive square root of each of these numbers.

a 4	**b** 25	**c** 49	**d** 1	**e** 81
f 100	**g** 64	**h** 9	**i** 36	**j** 16
k 121	**l** 144	**m** 400	**n** 900	**o** 169

2 Write down both possible values of each of these square roots.

a $\sqrt{25}$	**b** $\sqrt{36}$	**c** $\sqrt{100}$	**d** $\sqrt{49}$	**e** $\sqrt{64}$
f $\sqrt{16}$	**g** $\sqrt{9}$	**h** $\sqrt{81}$	**i** $\sqrt{1}$	**j** $\sqrt{144}$

3 Write down the value of each of these. You need only give positive square roots. You will need to use your calculator for some of them. Look for the [√x] key.

a 9^2	**b** $\sqrt{1600}$	**c** 10^2	**d** $\sqrt{196}$	**e** 6^2
f $\sqrt{225}$	**g** 7^2	**h** $\sqrt{144}$	**i** 5^2	**j** $\sqrt{441}$
k 11^2	**l** $\sqrt{256}$	**m** 8^2	**n** $\sqrt{289}$	**o** 21^2

4 Write down the positive value of each of the following. You will need to use your calculator.

a $\sqrt{576}$	**b** $\sqrt{961}$	**c** $\sqrt{2025}$	**d** $\sqrt{1600}$	**e** $\sqrt{4489}$
f $\sqrt{10\ 201}$	**g** $\sqrt{12.96}$	**h** $\sqrt{42.25}$	**i** $\sqrt{193.21}$	**j** $\sqrt{492.84}$

Powers

In this section you will learn how to:

- use powers

Key words

cube
indices
power
square

Powers are a convenient way of writing repetitive multiplications. (Powers are also called **indices** – singular, index.)

The power that you will use most often is 2, which has the special name **square**. The only other power with a special name is 3, which is called **cube**.

You are expected to know the cubes of numbers, $1^3 = 1$, $2^3 = 8$, $3^3 = 27$, $4^3 = 64$, $5^3 = 125$ and $10^3 = 1000$, for the GCSE exam.

EXAMPLE 3

a What is the value of:

   i   7 squared   ii   5 cubed?

b Write each of these numbers out in full.

   i 4^6 ii 6^4 iii 7^3 iv 12^2

c Write the following numbers in index form.

   i $3 \times 3 \times 3 \times 3 \times 3 \times 3 \times 3 \times 3$

   ii $13 \times 13 \times 13 \times 13 \times 13$

   iii $7 \times 7 \times 7 \times 7$

   iv $5 \times 5 \times 5 \times 5 \times 5 \times 5 \times 5$

a The value of 7 squared is $7^2 = 7 \times 7 = 49$

   The value of 5 cubed is $5^3 = 5 \times 5 \times 5 = 125$

b i $4^6 = 4 \times 4 \times 4 \times 4 \times 4 \times 4$

   ii $6^4 = 6 \times 6 \times 6 \times 6$

   iii $7^3 = 7 \times 7 \times 7$

   iv $12^2 = 12 \times 12$

c i $3 \times 3 \times 3 \times 3 \times 3 \times 3 \times 3 \times 3 = 3^8$

   ii $13 \times 13 \times 13 \times 13 \times 13 = 13^5$

   iii $7 \times 7 \times 7 \times 7 = 7^4$

   iv $5 \times 5 \times 5 \times 5 \times 5 \times 5 \times 5 = 5^7$

Working out powers on your calculator

How would you work out the value of 5^7 on a calculator?

You could key it in as $5 \times 5 \times 5 \times 5 \times 5 \times 5 \times 5 =$. But as you key it in, you may miss a number or press a wrong key. If your calculator has one, you could use the power key, $\boxed{x^y}$ or $\boxed{y^x}$.

$$5^7 = \boxed{5}\ \boxed{x^y}\ \boxed{7}\ \boxed{=}\ 78\,125$$

Make sure you know where to find the power key on your calculator. It may be an INV or SHIFT function.

Try using your calculator to work out 3^4, 7^8, 23^4 and 72^3.

Check that you get 81, 5 764 801, 279 841 and 373 248.

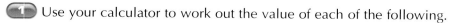

EXERCISE 4F

1 Use your calculator to work out the value of each of the following.

    a 3^3 **b** 5^3 **c** 6^3 **d** 12^3 **e** 2^4

    f 4^4 **g** 5^4 **h** 2^5 **i** 3^7 **j** 2^{10}

2 Work out the values of the following powers of 10.

    a 10^2 **b** 10^3 **c** 10^4 **d** 10^5 **e** 10^6

    f Describe what you notice about your answers.

    g Now write down the value of each of these.

        i 10^8 **ii** 10^{10} **iii** 10^{15}

3 Rewrite each of these, using power notation. Do not work them out yet.

    a $2 \times 2 \times 2 \times 2$ **b** $3 \times 3 \times 3 \times 3 \times 3$

    c 7×7 **d** $5 \times 5 \times 5$

    e $10 \times 10 \times 10 \times 10 \times 10 \times 10 \times 10$ **f** $6 \times 6 \times 6 \times 6$

    g $4 \times 4 \times 4 \times 4$ **h** $1 \times 1 \times 1 \times 1 \times 1 \times 1 \times 1$

    i $0.5 \times 0.5 \times 0.5 \times 0.5$ **j** $100 \times 100 \times 100$

> **HINTS AND TIPS**
>
> When working out a power, make sure you multiply the number by itself and not by the power. A very common error is to write, for example, $2^3 = 6$ instead of $2^3 = 2 \times 2 \times 2 = 8$.

4 Write these power terms out in full. Do not work them out yet.

    a 3^4 **b** 9^3 **c** 6^2 **d** 10^5 **e** 2^{10}

    f 8^6 **g** 0.1^3 **h** 2.5^2 **i** 0.7^3 **j** 1000^2

5 Using the power key on your calculator (or another method), work out the values of the power terms in question **3**.

6 Using the power key on your calculator (or another method), work out the values of the power terms in question **4**.

7 Write the answer to question **3**, part **j** as a power of 10.

8 Write the answer to question **4**, part **j** as a power of 10.

> **HINTS AND TIPS**
>
> Use the answer you found for question **2f** to help you.

9 Copy this pattern of powers of 2 and continue it for another five terms.

2^2 2^3 2^4 …   …   …   …   …

4   8   16   …   …   …   …   …

10 Copy the pattern of powers of 10 and fill in the previous five and the next five terms.

…   …   …   …   … 10^2 10^3 …   …   …   …   …

…   …   …   …   …   100   1000   …   …   …   …   …

4.7 Multiplying and dividing by powers of 10

In this section you will learn how to:
- multiply and divide by powers of 10

The last question in the above exercise uses powers of 10, which you have already seen are special.

When you write a million in figures, how many zeros does it have? What is a million as a power of 10? This table shows some of the pattern of the powers of 10.

Number	0.001	0.01	0.1	1	10	100	1000	10 000	100 000
Powers	10^{-3}	10^{-2}	10^{-1}	10^0	10^1	10^2	10^3	10^4	10^5

What pattern is there in the top row?

What pattern is there in the powers in the bottom row?

The easiest number to multiply by is zero, because any number multiplied by zero is zero.

The next easiest number to multiply by is 1, because any number multiplied by 1 stays the same.

After that it is a matter of opinion, but it is generally accepted that multiplying by 10 is simple. Try these on your calculator.

a 7×10 **b** 7.34×10 **c** 43×10

d 0.678×10 **e** 0.007×10 **f** 34.5×10

Can you see the rule for multiplying by 10? You may have learnt that when you multiply a number by 10, you add a zero to the number. This is only true when you start with a whole number. It is not true for a decimal. The rule is:

- Every time you multiply a number by 10, move the digits in the number one place to the left.

Check to make sure that this happened in examples **a** to **f** above.

It is almost as easy to multiply by 100. Try these on your calculator.

a 7×100 **b** 7.34×100 **c** 43×100

d 0.678×100 **e** 0.007×100 **f** 34.5×100

This time you should find that the digits move two places to the left.

You can write 100, 1000, 10 000 as powers of 10. For example:

$$100 = 10 \times 10 = 10^2$$
$$1000 = 10 \times 10 \times 10 = 10^3$$
$$10\,000 = 10 \times 10 \times 10 \times 10 = 10^4$$

You should know the connection between the number of zeros and the power of 10. Try these on your calculator. Look for the connection between the calculation and the answer.

a 12.3×10 **b** 3.45×1000 **c** 3.45×10^3

d $0.075 \times 10\,000$ **e** 2.045×10^2 **f** 6.78×1000

g 25.67×10^4 **h** 34.21×100 **i** $0.032\,4 \times 10^4$

Can you find a similar connection for division by multiples of 10? Try these on your calculator. Look for the connection between the calculation and the answer.

a $12.3 \div 10$ **b** $3.45 \div 1000$ **c** $3.45 \div 10^3$

d $0.075 \div 100$ **e** $2.045 \div 10^2$ **f** $6.78 \div 1000$

g $25.67 \div 10^4$ **h** $34.21 \div 100$ **i** $0.032\,4 \div 10^4$

You can use this principle to multiply multiples of 10 – 100 and so on. You use this method in estimation. You should have the skill to do this mentally so that you can check that your answers to calculations are about right. (Approximation of calculations is covered on page 190.)

Use a calculator to work out these multiplications.

a $200 \times 300 =$ **b** $100 \times 40 =$ **c** $2000 \times 3000 =$

d $200 \times 50 =$ **e** $200 \times 5000 =$ **f** $300 \times 40 =$

Can you see a way of doing them without using a calculator or pencil and paper? Dividing is almost as simple. Use a calculator to do these divisions.

a $400 \div 20 =$ **b** $200 \div 50 =$ **c** $1000 \div 200 =$

d $300 \div 30 =$ **e** $250 \div 50 =$ **f** $30\,000 \div 600 =$

Once again, there is an easy way of doing these 'in your head'. Look at these examples.

$300 \times 4000 = 1\,200\,000$ $5000 \div 200 = 25$ $200 \times 50 = 10\,000$

$60 \times 5000 = 300\,000$ $400 \div 20 = 20$ $30\,000 \div 600 = 500$

In 200×3000, for example, you multiply the non-zero digits ($2 \times 3 = 6$) and then write the total number of zeros in both numbers at the end, to give $600\,000$.

$$200 \times 3000 = 2 \times 100 \times 3 \times 1000 = 6 \times 100\,000 = 600\,000$$

For division, you divide the non-zero digits and then cancel the zeros. For example:

$$400\,000 \div 80 = \frac{400\,000}{80} = \frac{^5\cancel{400\,000}}{_1\cancel{80}} = 5000$$

Standard form on a calculator

Sometimes calculators display small and large numbers in this format

$$\boxed{1.7^{-03}} \qquad \boxed{5.3^{12}}$$

This is known as standard form and means 1.7×10^{-3} and 5.3×10^{12}.

This means the first display represents $1.7 \times 10^{-3} = 0.0017$ and the second display represents $5.3 \times 10^{12} = 5\,300\,000\,000\,000$.

EXAMPLE 4

On a calculator, calculate $3.7 \times 10^5 \times 2.8 \times 10^7$, giving your answer as the normal number represented by the display.

Using a scientific calculator, key in

The calculator shows a display similar to

$$\boxed{1.036^{13}}$$

Which as a normal number is $10\,360\,000\,000\,000$

EXERCISE 4G

1 Write down the value of each product.

a 3.1×10 **b** 3.1×100 **c** 3.1×1000 **d** $3.1 \times 10\,000$

2 Write down the value of each product.

a 6.5×10 **b** 6.5×10^2 **c** 6.5×10^3 **d** 6.5×10^4

3 In questions **1** and **2** there is a connection between the multipliers. What is the connection? (It isn't that the first number is the same.)

D

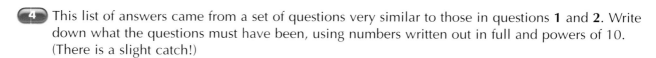

D

4 This list of answers came from a set of questions very similar to those in questions **1** and **2**. Write down what the questions must have been, using numbers written out in full and powers of 10. (There is a slight catch!)

a 73 **b** 730 **c** 7300 **d** 730 000

5 Write down the value of each of the following.

a 3.1 ÷ 10 **b** 3.1 ÷ 100 **c** 3.1 ÷ 1000 **d** 3.1 ÷ 10 000

6 Write down the value of each of the following.

a 6.5 ÷ 10 **b** $6.5 ÷ 10^2$ **c** $6.5 ÷ 10^3$ **d** $6.5 ÷ 10^4$

7 In questions **5** and **6** there is a connection between the divisors. What is it?

8 This list of answers came from a set of questions very similar to those in questions **5** and **6**. Write down what the questions must have been, using numbers written out in full and powers of 10. (There is a slight catch!)

a 0.73 **b** 0.073 **c** 0.0073 **d** 0.000 073

9 Without using a calculator, write down the answers to these.

a 2.5 × 100 **b** 3.45 × 10 **c** 4.67 × 1000

d 34.6 × 10 **e** 20.789 × 10 **f** 56.78 × 1000

g $0.897 × 10^5$ **h** 0.865 × 1000 **i** $100.5 × 10^2$

j $0.999 × 10^6$ **k** $234.56 × 10^2$ **l** $98.7654 × 10^3$

10 Without using a calculator, write down the answers to these.

a 2.5 ÷ 100 **b** 3.45 ÷ 10

c 4.67 ÷ 1000 **d** 34.6 ÷ 10

e 20.789 ÷ 100 **f** 56.78 ÷ 1000

g $2.46 ÷ 10^2$ **h** 0.865 ÷ 1000 **i** $100.5 ÷ 10^2$

j $0.999 ÷ 10^6$ **k** $203.67 ÷ 10^1$ **l** 76.43 ÷ 10

> **HINTS AND TIPS**
>
> Even though you are really moving digits left or right, you may think of it as if the decimal point moves right or left.

11 Without using a calculator, write down the answers to these.

a 200 × 300 **b** 30 × 4000 **c** 50 × 200

d 100 × 2000 **e** 20 × 1400 **f** 30 × 30

g $(20)^2$ **h** $(20)^3$ **i** $(400)^2$

12 Without using a calculator, write down the answers to these.

a $3000 \div 150$ **b** $400 \div 200$ **c** $5000 \div 5000$

d $4000 \div 250$ **e** $300 \div 2$ **f** $6000 \div 500$

g $30\,000 \div 2000$ **h** $2000 \times 40 \div 2000$ **i** $200 \times 20 \div 800$

j $200 \times 6000 \div 30\,000$ **k** $20 \times 80 \times 600 \div 3000$

13 **i**   Write down what each of these calculator display means in the form $a \times 10n$.
ii   Work out the value of each display as an ordinary number.

a $\boxed{2.3^{07}}$ **b** $\boxed{3.4^{-02}}$ **c** $\boxed{6.3^{10}}$

d $\boxed{1.6^{-03}}$ **e** $\boxed{5.5^{-04}}$ **f** $\boxed{1.2^{14}}$

14 Using a scientific calculator, evaluate each of the following.

Write down the ordinary number represented by the calculator display.

a $6.8 \times 10^4 \times 7.5 \times 10^5$ **b** $9.6 \times 10^5 \times 8.5 \times 10^6$

c $6.4 \times 10^{12} \div 1.2 \times 10$ **d** $2.2^5 \times 10^{15} \div 1.5 \times 10^9$

4.8 Prime factors

In this section you will learn how to:
- identify prime factors
- identify the lowest common multiple (LCM) of two numbers
- identify the highest common factor (HCF) of two numbers

Key words
prime factor
prime factor tree
lowest common multiple
highest common factor

Start with a number, such as 110, and find two numbers that, when multiplied together, give that number, for example, 2×55. Are they both prime? No, 55 isn't. So take 55 and repeat the operation, to get 5×11. Are these both prime? Yes. So:

$110 = 2 \times 5 \times 11$

The **prime factors** of 110 are 2, 5 and 11.

This method is not very logical and you need to know your times tables well to use it. There are, however, two methods that you can use to make sure you do not miss any of the prime factors.

EXAMPLE 5

Find the prime factors of 24.

Divide 24 by any prime number that goes into it. (2 is an obvious choice.)

Now divide the answer (12) by a prime number. As 12 is even, again 2 is the obvious choice.

Repeat this process until you finally have a prime number as the answer.

So, written as a product of its prime factors, $24 = 2 \times 2 \times 2 \times 3$.

A quicker and neater way to write this answer is to use index notation, expressing the answer in powers. (Powers are dealt with on pages 79–81.)

In index notation, as a product of its prime factors, $24 = 2^3 \times 3$.

```
2 | 24
2 | 12
3 |  6
   |  2
```

EXAMPLE 6

Find the prime factors of 96.

As a product of prime factors, 96 is $2 \times 2 \times 2 \times 2 \times 2 \times 3 = 2^5 \times 3$.

```
2 | 96
2 | 48
2 | 24
2 | 12
2 |  6
   |  3
```

The method shown below is called a **prime factor tree**.

You start by splitting the number into a product of two factors. Then you split these factors, and carry on splitting, until you reach prime numbers.

EXAMPLE 7

Find the prime factors of 76.

Stop splitting the factors here because 2, 2 and 19 are all prime numbers.

So, as a product of prime factors, 76 is $2 \times 2 \times 19 = 2^2 \times 19$.

EXAMPLE 8

Find the prime factors of 420.

You can work it upside down, to make an upright tree.

So, as a product of prime factors:

$$420 = 2 \times 5 \times 2 \times 3 \times 7 = 2^2 \times 3 \times 5 \times 7$$

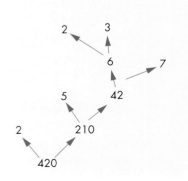

EXERCISE 4H

1 Copy and complete these prime factor trees.

a

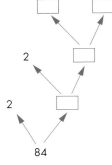

84 = 2 × 2 ... × ...

b

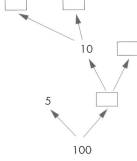

100 = 5 × 2 ... × ...

c

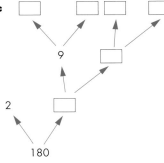

180 = 2 × ... × ... × ... × ...

d

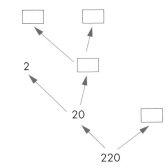

220 = 2 × ... × ... × ...

e

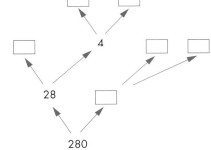

280 = ... × ... × ... × ... × ...

f

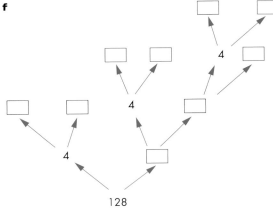

128 = ... × ... × ... × ... × ... × ... × ...

g

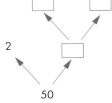

50 = ... × ... × ...

h

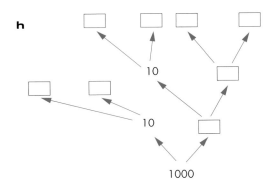

1000 = ... × ... × ... × ... × ... × ...

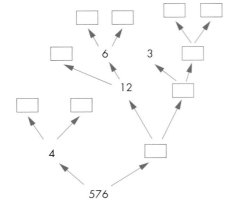

i

576 = ... × ... × ... × ... × ... × ... × ... × ...

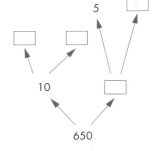

j

650 = ... × ... × ... × ...

2 Using index notation, for example:

$$100 = 2 \times 2 \times 5 \times 5 = 2^2 \times 5^2$$

and $$540 = 2 \times 2 \times 3 \times 3 \times 3 \times 5 = 2^2 \times 3^3 \times 5$$

rewrite your answers to question **1**, parts **a** to **j**.

3 Write the numbers from 1 to 50 as products of their prime factors. Use index notation. For example:

$1 = 1 \qquad 2 = 2 \qquad 3 = 3 \qquad 4 = 2^2 \qquad 5 = 5 \qquad 6 = 2 \times 3 \qquad ...$

> **HINTS AND TIPS**
>
> Use your previous answers to help you. For example, $9 = 3^2$ so as $18 = 2 \times 9$, $18 = 2 \times 3^2$.

4 **a** What is special about the numbers 2, 4, 8, 16, 32, ...?

b What are the next two terms in this series?

c What are the next three terms in the series 3, 9, 27, ...?

d Continue the series 4, 16, 64, ..., for three more terms.

e Rewrite all the series in parts **a**, **b**, **c** and **d** in index notation. For example, the first series is:

$$2^2, 2^3, 2^4, 2^5, 2^6, 2^7, ...$$

Lowest common multiple

The **lowest common multiple** (or *least common multiple*, usually called the LCM) of two numbers is the smallest number that appears in the times tables of both numbers.

For example, the LCM of 3 and 5 is 15, the LCM of 2 and 7 is 14 and the LCM of 6 and 9 is 18.

There are two ways of working out the LCM.

EXAMPLE 9

Find the LCM of 18 and 24.

Write out the 18 times table: 18, 36, 54, (72), 90, 108, …

Write out the 24 times table: 24, 48, (72), 96, 120, …

Numbers that appear in both tables are *common multiples*. You can see that 72 is the smallest (lowest) number that appears in both tables, so it is the lowest common multiple.

EXAMPLE 10

Find the LCM of 42 and 63.

Write 42 in prime factor form: $42 = 2 \times 3 \times 7$

Write 63 in prime factor form: $63 = 3^2 \times 7$

Write down the smallest number, in prime factor form, that includes all the prime factors of both 42 and 63.

$2 \times 3^2 \times 7$ (This includes $2 \times 3 \times 7$ and $3^2 \times 7$.)

Then work it out:

$2 \times 3^2 \times 7 = 2 \times 9 \times 7 = 18 \times 7 = 126$

Highest common factor

The **highest common factor** (usually called the HCF) of two numbers is the biggest number that divides exactly into both of them.

For example, the HCF of 24 and 18 is 6, the HCF of 45 and 36 is 9 and the HCF of 15 and 22 is 1.

There are two ways of working out the HCF.

EXAMPLE 11

Find the HCF of 28 and 16.

Write out the factors of 28:   {1, 2, (4), 7, 14, 28}

Write out the factors of 16:   {1, 2, (4), 8, 16}

Numbers that appear in both sets of factors are *common factors*. You can see that 4 is the biggest (highest) number that appears in both lists, so it is the highest common factor.

EXAMPLE 12

Find the HCF of 48 and 120.

Write 48 in prime factor form: $48 = 2^4 \times 3$

Write 120 in prime factor form: $120 = 2^3 \times 3 \times 5$

Write down, in prime factor form, the biggest number that is in the prime factors of 48 and 120.

$2^3 \times 3$ (This is in both $2^4 \times 3$ and $2^3 \times 3 \times 5$.)

Then work it out.

$2^3 \times 3 = 8 \times 3 = 24$

EXERCISE 4I

1 Find the LCM of the numbers in each pair.

a 4 and 5   b 7 and 8   c 2 and 3   d 4 and 7

e 2 and 5   f 3 and 5   g 3 and 8   h 5 and 6

2 What connection is there between the LCMs and the pairs of numbers in question **1**?

3 Find the LCM of the numbers in each pair.

a 4 and 8   b 6 and 9   c 4 and 6   d 10 and 15

4 Does the connection you found in question **2** still work for the numbers in question **3**? If not, can you explain why not?

5 Find the LCM of these pairs of numbers.

a 24 and 56   b 21 and 35   c 12 and 28   d 28 and 42

e 12 and 32   f 18 and 27   g 15 and 25   h 16 and 36

6 Find the HCF of these pairs of numbers.

a 24 and 56   b 21 and 35   c 12 and 28   d 28 and 42

e 12 and 32   f 18 and 27   g 15 and 25   h 16 and 36

i 42 and 27   j 48 and 64   k 25 and 35   l 36 and 54

7 In prime factor form $1250 = 2 \times 5^4$ and $525 = 3 \times 5^2 \times 7$.

a Which of these are common multiples of 1250 and 525?

i $2 \times 3 \times 5^3 \times 7$ ii $2^3 \times 3 \times 5^4 \times 7^2$ iii $2 \times 3 \times 5^4 \times 7$ iv $2 \times 3 \times 5 \times 7$

b Which of these are common factors of 1250 and 525?

i 2×3 ii 2×5 iii 5^2 iv $2 \times 3 \times 5 \times 7$

Rules for multiplying and dividing powers

In this section you will learn how to:

- use rules for multiplying and dividing powers

When you multiply numbers that are written as powers of the same variable or number, something unexpected happens. For example:

$$a^2 \times a^3 = (a \times a) \times (a \times a \times a) = a^5$$

$$3^3 \times 3^5 = (3 \times 3 \times 3) \times (3 \times 3 \times 3 \times 3 \times 3) = 3^8$$

Can you see the rule? You can find these products just by *adding* the powers. For example:

$$a^3 \times a^4 = a^{3+4} = a^7 \qquad 2^3 \times 2^4 \times 2^5 = 2^{12}$$

A similar rule applies when you divide powers of the same variable or number. For example:

$$a^5 \div a^2 = (a \times a \times a \times a \times a) \div (a \times a) = a \times a \times a = a^3$$

$$7^6 \div 7 = (7 \times 7 \times 7 \times 7 \times 7 \times 7) \div (7) = 7 \times 7 \times 7 \times 7 \times 7 = 7^5$$

Can you see the rule? You can do these divisions just by *subtracting* the powers. For example:

$$a^4 \div a^3 = a^{4-3} = a^1 = a \qquad b^7 \div b^4 = b^3$$

EXERCISE 4J

1 Write these as single powers of 5.

  a $5^2 \times 5^2$ **b** $5^4 \times 5^6$ **c** $5^2 \times 5^3$ **d** 5×5^2 **e** $5^6 \times 5^9$

  f 5×5^8 **g** $5^2 \times 5^4$ **h** $5^6 \times 5^3$ **i** $5^2 \times 5^6$

2 Write these as single powers of 6.

  a $6^5 \div 6^2$ **b** $6^7 \div 6^2$ **c** $6^3 \div 6^2$ **d** $6^4 \div 6^4$ **e** $6^5 \div 6^4$

  f $6^5 \div 6^2$ **g** $6^4 \div 6^2$ **h** $6^4 \div 6^3$ **i** $6^5 \div 6^3$

3 Simplify these (write them as single powers of x).

  a $x^2 \times x^6$ **b** $x^5 \times x^4$ **c** $x^6 \times x^2$ **d** $x^3 \times x^2$ **e** $x^6 \times x^6$

  f $x^5 \times x^8$ **g** $x^7 \times x^4$ **h** $x^2 \times x^8$ **i** $x^{12} \times x^4$

4 Simplify these (write them as single powers of x).

  a $x^7 \div x^3$ **b** $x^8 \div x^3$ **c** $x^4 \div x$ **d** $x^6 \div x^3$ **e** $x^{10} \div x^4$

  f $x^6 \div x$ **g** $x^8 \div x^6$ **h** $x^8 \div x^2$ **i** $x^{12} \div x^3$

1 **a** Write down the largest multiple of 3 smaller than 100.

b Write down the smallest multiple of 6 larger than 100.

 2 Look at the numbers in this cloud.

4   8   15   16   21   25
32   36   45   49   50   54
64   66   75   80   81   90

Write down all the square numbers that are inside the cloud.

 3 **a** Write down the largest factor of 360, smaller than 100.

b Write down the smallest factor of 315 larger than 100.

 4 Using only the numbers in the cloud, write down

i all the multiples of 6,

ii all the square numbers,

iii all the factors of 12,

iv all the cube numbers.

8   12   27
4   6
16   5   3

Edexcel, Question 11, Paper 1 Foundation, June 2003

 5 **a** Copy and complete the missing numbers in the following pattern:

	Last digit
$4^1 = 4 = 4$	4
$4^2 = 4 \times 4 = 16$	6
$4^3 = 4 \times 4 \times 4 = 64$	
$4^4 = 4 \times 4 \times 4 \times 4 = 256$	
$4^5 = \rule{2cm}{0.4pt} = \rule{1cm}{0.4pt}$	

b What will the last digit of 4^{17} be?

 6 **a** Write down the first five multiples of 6.

 b Write down the factors of 12.

c Write down a square number between 20 and 30.

d Write down two prime numbers between 20 and 30.

7 Here are six number cards.

 4   5   8   9   10   11

a Which of the numbers are multiples of 4?

b Which of the numbers are factors of 10?

c Which of the numbers are prime numbers?

d Which numbers are square numbers?

e Which number is a cube number?

f Use the numbers to complete the magic square below so that every row, every column and both diagonals add up to 21.

		6
3	7	

 8 **a** Find the value of

3.7^2

The table shows some numbers.

51	52	53	54	55	56	57	58	59

Two of the numbers are prime numbers.

b Which two numbers are these?

 9 Write down the value of

a 2^3

b $\sqrt{64}$

 10 John set up two computer virus checkers on his computer on January 1st.

Checker A would check every 8 days.

Checker B would check every 10 days.

After how many days will both checkers be checking on the same day again?

 11 Mary set up her Christmas Tree with two sets of twinkling lights.

Set A would twinkle every 3 seconds.

Set B would twinkle every 4 seconds.

How many times in a minute will both sets be twinkling at the same time?

 12 Write down the answers to

a 4000×20

b $4000 \div 20$

c $\dfrac{120\,000}{200 \times 300}$

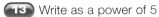

13 Write as a power of 5

  a $5^4 \times 5^2$

  b $5^9 \div 5^6$

    Edexcel, Question 15a, Paper 3 Intermediate, June 2005

14 **a** Write down 44 as the product of its prime numbers.

  b Find the lowest common multiple (LCM) of 44 and 66.

15 Find the Highest Common Factor of 108 and 252.

WORKED EXAM QUESTION

a Write 36 as a product of prime factors.

b Find the lowest common multiple (LCM) of 36 and 45.

c Find the highest common factor (HCF) of 45 and 60.

Solution

a $2^2 \times 3^2$

b 36, 72, 108, 144, ⓘ80, ...
45, 90, 135, ⓘ80, ...
So the LCM of 36 and 45 is 180.

c Factors of 45 = {3, 5, 9, ⑮, 45}
Factors of 60 = {1, 2, 3, 4, 5, 6, 10, 12, ⑮, 20, 30, 60}
So the HCF of 45 and 60 is 15.

> Split 36 into products until there are only prime numbers. $36 = 4 \times 9 = 2 \times 2 \times 9 = 2 \times 2 \times 3 \times 3$ Write the answer in index form.

> Write out the multiples of 36 and 45 until there is a common multiple then pick out the smallest (lowest), value in both (common) lists (multiples).

> Write out the factors of 48 and 60, then pick out the largest (highest) value in both (common) lists (factors).

GRADE YOURSELF

G Able to recognise multiples of the first ten whole numbers

G Able to find factors of numbers less than 100

G Able to recognise the square numbers up to 100

F Able to write down the square of any number up to $15 \times 15 = 225$

F Able to write down the cubes of 1, 2, 3, 4, 5 and 10

F Know how to find the square root of any number using a calculator

E Can calculate simple powers of whole numbers

E Able to recognise two-digit prime numbers

D Can multiply and divide by powers of 10

D Can multiply together numbers that are multiples of 10

C Can work out the prime factor form of numbers

C Can work out the LCM and HCF of two numbers

C Can simplify multiplications and divisions of powers

What you should know now

- What multiples are
- How to find the factors of any whole number
- What a prime number is
- What square numbers are
- What square roots are
- How to find powers of numbers
- How to write numbers in prime factor form
- How to find the LCM and HCF of any pair of numbers

Perimeter and area

This chapter will show you ...

- how to work out the perimeters and the areas of some common 2-D shapes
- the types of problem you will be able to solve with knowledge of area
- how to recognise compound formulae for length, area and volume

Visual overview

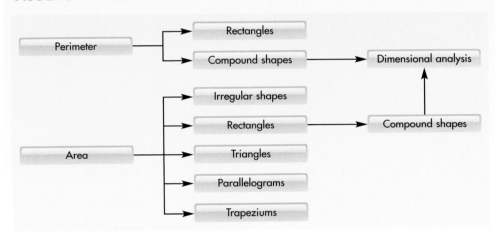

What you should already know

- The common units of length are millimetre (mm), centimetre (cm), metre (m) and kilometre (km).
- Area is the amount of space inside a shape. The common units of area are the square millimetre (mm^2), the square centimetre (cm^2), the square metre (m^2) and the square kilometre (km^2).

Quick check

This rectangle has sides of length 8 cm and 2 cm.

a What is the total length of all four sides?

b How many centimetre squares are there in the rectangle?

8 cm

2 cm

Perimeter

In this section you will learn how to:

- find the perimeter of a rectangle and compound shapes

Key words

compound
   shape
perimeter
rectangle

The **perimeter** of a rectangle is the sum of the lengths of all its sides.

ACTIVITY

Round about

On a piece of 1-cm squared paper draw this **rectangle**.

Measure its perimeter. You should get:

   3 cm + 2 cm + 3 cm + 2 cm = 10 cm

Draw a different rectangle that also has a perimeter of 10 cm.

See how many different rectangles you can draw that each have a perimeter of 10 cm.

There are only three different rectangles that each have a perimeter of 12 cm and whole numbers of centimetres for their length and breadth. Can you draw all three?

Can you draw a rectangle that has a perimeter of 7 cm?

If not, why not? If you can, what is so strange about it?

Try drawing a rectangle that has a perimeter of 13 cm.

EXAMPLE 1

Find the perimeter of this rectangle.

7 cm

3 cm

Perimeter = 7 + 3 + 7 + 3 = 20 cm

A **compound shape** is any 2-D shape that is made up of other simple shapes such as rectangles and triangles.

EXAMPLE 2

Find the perimeter of this compound shape.

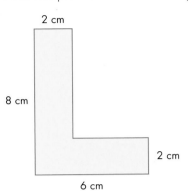

2 cm

8 cm

6 cm

2 cm

The lengths of the two missing sides are 6 cm and 4 cm.

So, the perimeter = 2 + 6 + 4 + 2 + 6 + 8 = 28 cm

EXERCISE 5A

Calculate the perimeter of each of the following shapes. Draw them first on squared paper if it helps you.

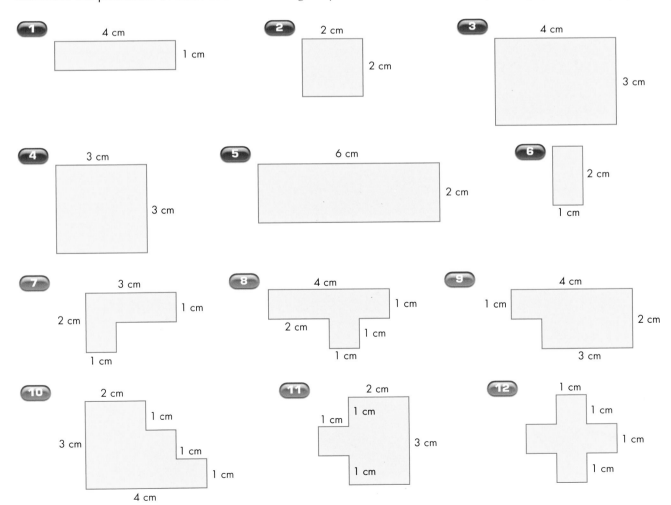

1 4 cm 1 cm

2 2 cm 2 cm

3 4 cm 3 cm

4 3 cm 3 cm

5 6 cm 2 cm

6 2 cm 1 cm

7 3 cm 1 cm 2 cm 1 cm

8 4 cm 1 cm 2 cm 1 cm 1 cm

9 4 cm 1 cm 2 cm 3 cm

10 2 cm 1 cm 3 cm 1 cm 1 cm 4 cm

11 2 cm 1 cm 1 cm 3 cm 1 cm

12 1 cm 1 cm 1 cm 1 cm

In this section you will learn how to:

- estimate the area of an irregular 2-D shape by counting squares

ACTIVITY

A different area

Take a piece of 1-cm squared paper. Draw on it a rectangle of 2 cm by 6 cm.

Check that it has a perimeter of 16 cm.

Count the number of squares inside the rectangle. This should come to 12.

This means that the **area** of this shape is 12 square centimetres.

Draw a different rectangle that has an area of 12 square centimetres but a perimeter that is smaller than 16 cm.

Draw another different rectangle that also has an area of 12 square centimetres, but a perimeter that is larger than 16 cm.

Using whole squares only, how many rectangles can you draw that have *different* perimeters but the *same* area of 16 square centimetres?

To find the area of an irregular shape, you can put a square grid over the shape and **estimate** the number of complete squares that are covered.

The most efficient way to do this is:

- First, count all the whole squares.

- Second, put together parts of squares to make whole and almost whole squares.

- Finally, add together the two results.

EXAMPLE 3

Below is a map of a lake. Each square represents 1 km². Estimate the area of the lake.

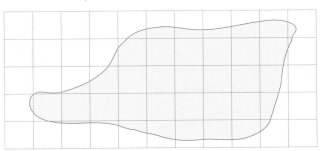

First, count all the whole squares. You should count 16.

Next, put together the parts of squares around the edge of the lake.

This should make up about ten squares.

Finally, add together the 16 and the 10 to get an area of 26 km².

Note: This is only an *estimate*. Someone else may get a slightly different answer. However, provided the answer is close to 26, it is acceptable.

EXERCISE 5B

1 These shapes were drawn on centimetre-squared paper. By counting squares, estimate the area of each of them, giving your answers in square centimetres.

a

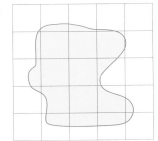

b

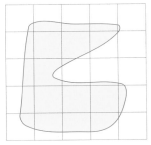

c

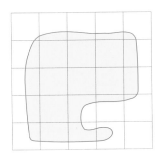

d

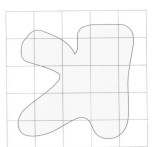

2 On a piece of 1-cm squared paper, draw round each of your hands to find its area. Do both hands have the same area?

3 Draw some shapes of your own on squared paper. First, guess the area of each shape. Then count up the squares and see how close your estimate was.

5.3 Area of a rectangle

In this section you will learn how to:
- find the area of a rectangle
- use the formula for the area of a rectangle

Key words

area
length
width

Look at these rectangles and their areas.

Area 6 cm²   Area 9 cm²   Area 15 cm²

Notice that the area of each rectangle is given by its length multiplied by its width.

So, the formula to find the area of a rectangle is:

area = length × width

As an algebraic formula, this is written as:

$A = lw$

EXAMPLE 4

Calculate the area of this rectangle.

Area of rectangle = length × width
= 11 cm × 4 cm
= 44 cm²

11 cm

4 cm

EXERCISE 5C

Calculate the area and the perimeter for each of the rectangles 1 to 8.

7 cm

5 cm

 2
11 cm

3 cm

3
15 cm

3 cm

   4
10 cm

7 cm

   5
8 cm

7 cm

   6
5 cm

2 cm

F

7 8.2 cm

6.5 cm

8 11.8 cm

7.2 cm

 9 Copy and complete the table on the right for rectangles **a** to **h**.

	Length	Width	Perimeter	Area
a	7 cm	3 cm		
b	5 cm	4 cm		
c	4 cm		12 cm	
d	5 cm		16 cm	
e	6 mm			18 mm^2
f	7 mm			28 mm^2
g		2 m	14 m	
h		5 m		35 m^2

10 A rectangular field is 150 m long and 45 m wide.

a What length of fencing is needed to go all the way round the field?

b What is the area of the field?

11 A rugby pitch is 160 m long and 70 m wide.

a Before a game, the players have to run all the way round the pitch twice to help them loosen up. What is the distance that they have to run?

b The groundsman waters the pitch at the rate of 100 m^2 per minute. How long will it take him to water the whole pitch?

12 How much will it cost to buy enough carpet for a rectangular room 12 m by 5 m, if the carpet costs £13.99 per square metre?

 13 What is the perimeter of a square with an area of 100 cm^2?

 14 a The two squares on the right have the same area. Calculate the areas of square A and square B. Copy and complete: 1 cm^2 = ... mm^2

1 cm

A 1 cm

10 mm

B 10 mm

b Change the following into square millimetres.

i 3 cm^2 **ii** 5 cm^2 **iii** 6.3 cm^2

15 a The two squares on the right have the same area. Calculate the areas of square A and square B. Copy and complete: 1 m^2 = ... cm^2

1 m

A 1 m

100 cm

B 100 cm

b Change the following into square centimetres.

i 2 m^2 **ii** 4 m^2 **iii** 5.6 m^2

Area of a compound shape

In this section you will learn how to:

- find the area of a compound shape by splitting it into rectangles

Key words

area

compound shape

Some 2-D shapes are made up of two or more rectangles or triangles.

These **compound shapes** can be split into simpler shapes, which makes it easy to calculate the **areas** of these shapes.

EXAMPLE 5

Find the area of the shape on the right.

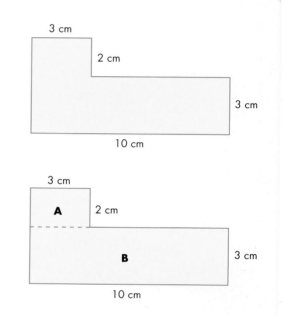

First, split the shape into two rectangles, A and B.

Then, calculate the area of each one.

area of A = 2 × 3 = 6 cm^2

area of B = 10 × 3 = 30 cm^2

The area of the shape is given by:

area of A + area of B = 6 + 30 = 36 cm^2

EXERCISE 5D

Calculate the area of each of the compound shapes below as follows.

- First, split it into rectangles.

- Then, calculate the area of each rectangle.

- Finally, add together the areas of the rectangles.

HINTS AND TIPS

Be careful to work out the length and width of each separate rectangle. You will usually have to add or subtract lengths to find some of these.

1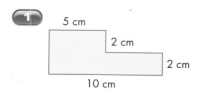

2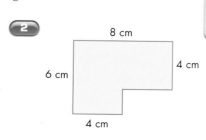

D

3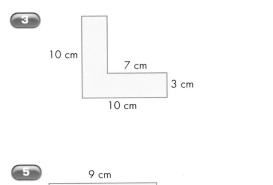

10 cm

7 cm

3 cm

10 cm

4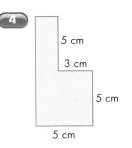

5 cm

3 cm

5 cm

5 cm

5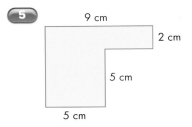

9 cm

2 cm

5 cm

5 cm

6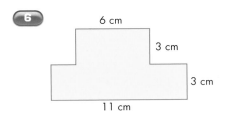

6 cm

3 cm

3 cm

11 cm

7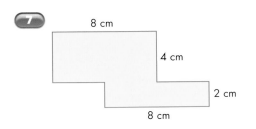

8 cm

4 cm

2 cm

8 cm

8

3 cm

9 cm

2 cm

5 cm

 9 A square lawn of side 5 m has a rectangular path, 1 m wide, running all the way round the outside of it. What is the area of the path?

5.5 Area of a triangle

In this section you will learn how to:
- find the area of a triangle
- use the formula for the area of a triangle

Key words
area
base
height
perpendicular
  height
triangle

Area of a right-angled triangle

It is easy to see that the **area** of a right-angled **triangle** is half the area of the rectangle with the same **base** and **height**. Hence:

area = $\frac{1}{2}$ × base × height

As an algebraic formula, this is written as:

$A = \frac{1}{2}bh$

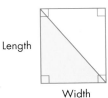

Length

Width

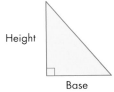

Height

Base

EXAMPLE 6

Find the area of this right-angled triangle.

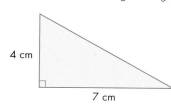

$$\text{Area} = \frac{1}{2} \times 7 \text{ cm} \times 4 \text{ cm}$$
$$= \frac{1}{2} \times 28 \text{ cm}^2$$
$$= 14 \text{ cm}^2$$

EXERCISE 5E

1 Write down the area and the perimeter of each triangle.

a
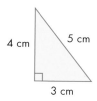
4 cm   5 cm   3 cm

b
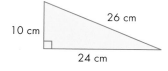
10 cm   26 cm   24 cm

c
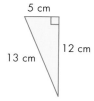
5 cm   12 cm   13 cm

2 Find the area of the shaded triangle RST.

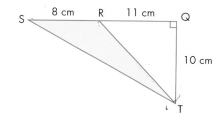
S   8 cm   R   11 cm   Q   10 cm   T

HINTS AND TIPS

Find the area of triangle QST and subtract the area of triangle QRT.

3 A tree is in the middle of a garden.
Around the tree there is a square region where nothing will be planted. The dimensions of the garden are shown in the diagram.

How much area can be planted?

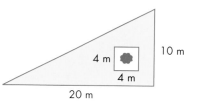
4 m   10 m   4 m   20 m

4 Find the area of the shaded part of each triangle.

a
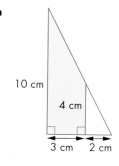
10 cm   4 cm   3 cm   2 cm

b
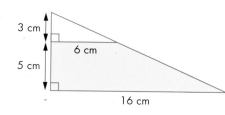
3 cm   6 cm   5 cm   16 cm

c
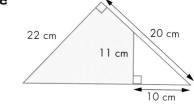
22 cm   20 cm   11 cm   10 cm

Area of any triangle

A rectangle can be drawn around any triangle with dimensions base × vertical height.

This triangle can be split into two smaller rectangles of which each is halved to show part of the larger triangle as shown.

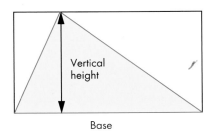
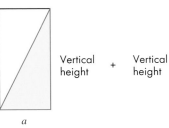
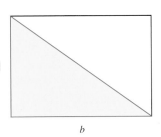

Area of triangle $= \frac{1}{2} \times a \times$ vertical height $+$ $\frac{1}{2} \times b \times$ vertical height

$= \frac{1}{2} \times (a + b) \times$ vertical height

In algebraic form, this is written as $A = \frac{1}{2}bh$

EXAMPLE 7

Calculate the area of this triangle.

Area $= \frac{1}{2} \times 9$ cm $\times 4$ cm

$= \frac{1}{2} \times 36$ cm^2

$= 18$ cm^2

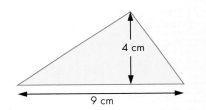

EXAMPLE 8

Calculate the area of the shape shown below.

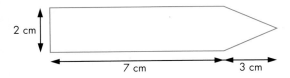

This is a compound shape that can be split into a rectangle (R) and a triangle (T).

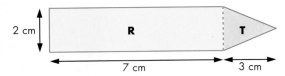

Area of the shape $=$ area of R + area of T

$= 7 \times 2 + \frac{1}{2} \times 2 \times 3$

$= 14 + 3$

$= 17$ cm^2

EXERCISE 5F

1 Calculate the area of each of these triangles.

a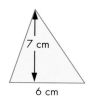
7 cm
6 cm

b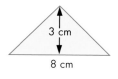
3 cm
8 cm

c
7 cm
4 cm

d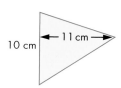
10 cm
11 cm

e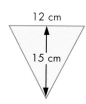
12 cm
15 cm

f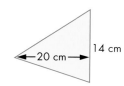
20 cm
14 cm

2 Copy and complete the following table for triangles **a** to **f**.

	Base	Perpendicular height	Area
a	8 cm	7 cm	
b		9 cm	36 cm²
c		5 cm	10 cm²
d	4 cm		6 cm²
e	6 cm		21 cm²
f	8 cm	11 cm	

3 Find the area of each of these shapes.

a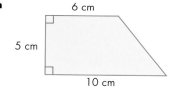
6 cm
5 cm
10 cm

b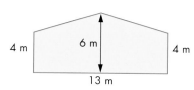
4 m
6 m
4 m
13 m

HINTS AND TIPS

Refer to Example 8 on how to find the area of a compound shape.

c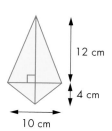
12 cm
4 cm
10 cm

4 Find the area of each shaded shape.

a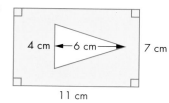
4 cm
6 cm
7 cm
11 cm

b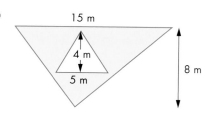
15 m
4 m
5 m
8 m

HINTS AND TIPS

Find the area of the outer shape and subtract the area of the inner shape.

5 Write down the dimensions of two different-sized triangles that have the same area of 50 cm².

In this section you will learn how to:
● find the area of a parallelogram
● use the formula for the area of a parallelogram

Key words
parallelogram
area
base
height
vertices

A **parallelogram** can be changed into a rectangle by moving a triangle.

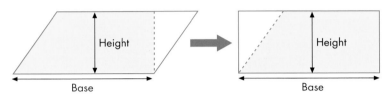

This shows that the **area** of the parallelogram is the area of a rectangle with the same **base** and **height**. The formula is:

area of a parallelogram = base × height

As an algebraic formula, this is written as:

$A = bh$

EXAMPLE 9

Find the area of this parallelogram.

Area = 8 cm × 6 cm
     = 48 cm^2

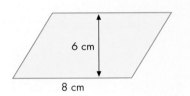

ACTIVITY

Pick's theorem

This quadrilateral has an area of $16\frac{1}{2}$ square units.

The perimeter of the quadrilateral passes through nine dots. Thirteen dots are contained within the perimeter of the quadrilateral.

Draw some quadrilaterals of different shapes and sizes on dotty paper. Make sure the **vertices** are all on dots on the paper. Investigate the connection between the area and the total number of dots inside and the total number of dots on the perimeter of the shape.

Then, from your findings, write down Pick's theorem.

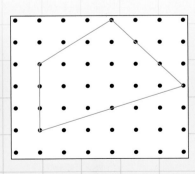

D

Calculate the area of each parallelogram below.

1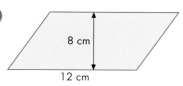
8 cm
12 cm

2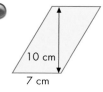
10 cm
7 cm

3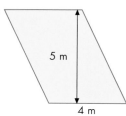
5 m
4 m

4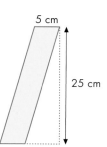
5 cm
25 cm

5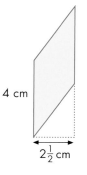
4 cm
$2\frac{1}{2}$ cm

6
14 m
8 m

5.7 Area of a trapezium

In this section you will learn how to:
- find the area of a trapezium
- use the formula for the area of a trapezium

Key words
area
height
trapezium

The **area** of a **trapezium** is calculated by finding the average of the lengths of its parallel sides and multiplying this by the perpendicular **height** between them.

The area of a trapezium is given by this formula:

$$A = \tfrac{1}{2}(a + b)h$$

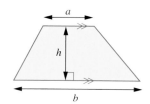

EXAMPLE 10

Find the area of the trapezium ABCD.

Area $= \tfrac{1}{2}(4 + 7) \times 3$

$= \tfrac{1}{2} \times 11 \times 3$

$= 16.5 \text{ cm}^2$

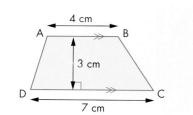

EXERCISE 5H

1 Copy and complete the following table for each trapezium.

	Parallel side 1	Parallel side 2	Perpendicular height	Area
a	8 cm	4 cm	5 cm	
b	10 cm	12 cm	7 cm	
c	7 cm	5 cm	4 cm	
d	5 cm	9 cm	6 cm	
e	3 cm	13 cm	5 cm	
f	4 cm	10 cm		42 cm^2
g	7 cm	8 cm		22.5 cm^2

2 Calculate the perimeter and the area of each trapezium.

a
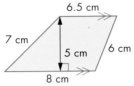

b

c
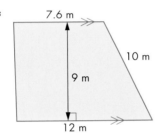

3 A trapezium has an area of 25 cm^2. Its vertical height is 5 cm. Write down five different possible pairs of lengths for the two parallel sides.

4 Which of the following shapes has the largest area?

a
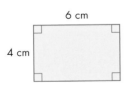

b
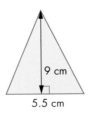

c
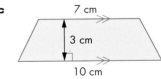

5 Which of the following shapes has the smallest area?

a
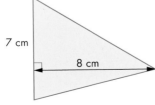

b
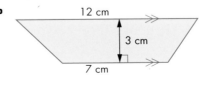

c
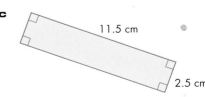

In this section you will learn how to:
- recognise whether a formula represents a length, an area or a volume

Dimensions of length

When we have an unknown **length** or distance in a problem, we represent it by a single letter, followed by the unit in which it is measured. For example, t centimetres, x miles and y kilometres

---

EXAMPLE 11

Find a formula the perimeters of these shapes.

a

b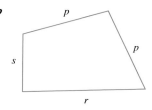

Shape **a** is a rectangle. Its perimeter is given by the formula

$P = x + y + x + y = 2x + 2y$

Shape **b** is irregular quadrilateral. Its perimeter is given by the formula

$P = p + p + r + s = 2p + r + s$

In the example, each letter is a length and has the **dimension** or measure of length, i.e. centimetre, metre, kilometre, etc. The numbers or coefficients written before the letters are *not* lengths and therefore have *no* dimensions. So, for example, $2x$, $5y$ or $\frac{1}{2}p$ have the same dimension as x, y or p respectively.

When just lengths are involved in a formula, the formula is said to have one dimension or 1-D, which is sometimes represented by the symbol [L].

EXERCISE 5I

Find a formula for the perimeter of each of these shapes. Each letter represents a length.

 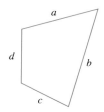

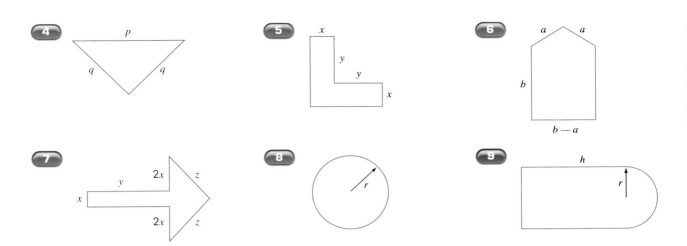

Dimensions of area

EXAMPLE 12

Look at these four examples of formulae for calculating area.

$A = lb$ gives the area of a rectangle
$A = x^2$ gives the area of a square
$A = 2ab + 2ac + 2bc$ gives the surface area of a cuboid
$A = \pi r^2$ gives the area of a circle

These formulae have one thing in common. They all consist of terms that are the product of two lengths. You can recognise this by counting the number of letters in each term of the formula. The first formula has two (l and b). The second has two (x and x). The third has three terms, each of two letters (a and b, a and c, b and c). The fourth also has only two letters (r and r) because π is a number (3.14159…) which has no dimension.

We can recognise formulae for **area** because they only have terms that consist of two letters – that is, two lengths multiplied together. Numbers are not defined as lengths, since they have no dimensions. These formulae therefore have two dimensions or 2-D, which is sometimes represented by the symbol [L^2].

This confirms the units in which area is usually measured. For example, square metres (m × m or m^2) and square centimetres (cm × cm or cm^2)

EXERCISE 5J

Find a formula for the area of each of these shapes. Each letter represents a length.

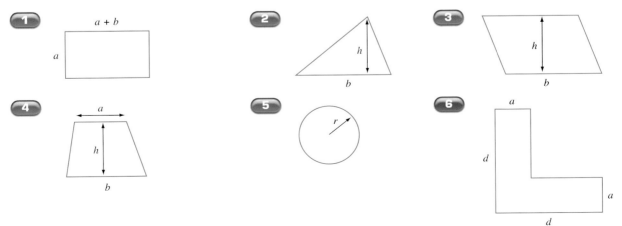

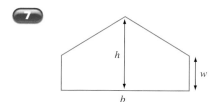

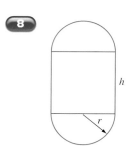

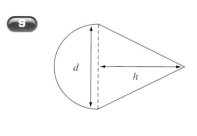

Dimensions of volume

EXAMPLE 13

Look at these three examples of formulae for calculating volume.

$V = lbh$ gives the volume of a cuboid
$V = x^3$ gives the volume of a cube
$V = \pi r^2 h + \pi r^3$ gives the volume of a cylinder with hemispherical ends

Again, these formulae have one thing in common. They all consist of terms that are the product of three lengths. You can recognise this by counting the number of letters in each term of the formula. The first formula has three (l, b and h). The second has three (x, x and x). The third has two terms, each of three letters (r, r and h; r, r and r). Remember, π has no dimension.

We can recognise formulae for **volume** because they only have terms that consist of three letters – that is, three lengths multiplied together. They therefore have three dimensions or 3-D, which is sometimes represented by the symbol $[L^3]$. Once more, numbers are not defined as lengths, since they have no dimensions.

This confirms the units in which volume is usually measured. For example,

cubic metres (m × m × m or m^3)

cubic centimetres (cm × cm × cm or cm^3)

 EXERCISE 5K

Find a formula for the volume of each of these shapes. Each letter represents a length.

1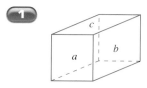

2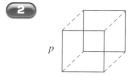

3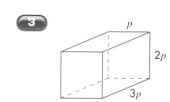

4

5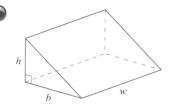

6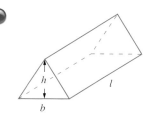

Recognising formulae

Scientists use dimensional analysis to check if complicated formulae are consistent. We are only concerned with length, areas or volume. It is possible to recognise if a formula is a length, area or volume by looking at the number of variables in each term.

Each term in a formula must have the correct number of dimensions. It is not possible to have a formula with a mixture of terms, some of which have, for example, one dimension and some two dimensions. When terms are found to be mixed, the formula is said to be *inconsistent* and is not possible.

We are only concerned with lengths, areas and volumes, so it is easy for us to test for consistency.

EXAMPLE 14

One of the these formulae represents a length (L), one represents an area (A), and one represents a volume (V). Which is which?

a $\pi r^2 + ab$ **b** $\dfrac{(ab^2 + a^2b)}{2}$ **c** $\pi(R + r)$

a This is an area because the first term has two letters (r and r) multiplied by a dimensionless number (π), and the second term also has two letters (a and b). $[L^2] + [L^2] = [L^2]$.

b This is a volume because each term is 3-D. $[L^3] + [L^3] = [L^3]$ is consistent.

c This is a length. There are two terms which are both single letters. So $[L] + [L] = [L]$.

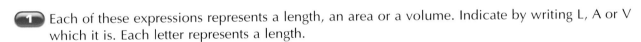

EXERCISE 5L

1 Each of these expressions represents a length, an area or a volume. Indicate by writing L, A or V which it is. Each letter represents a length.

a x^2 **b** $2y$ **c** πa **d** πab

e xyz **f** $3x^3$ **g** x^2y **h** $2xy$

i $4y$ **j** $3ab^2$ **k** $4xz$ **l** $5z$

m abc **n** $ab + bc$ **o** $abc + d^3$ **p** $2ab + 3bc$

q $a^2b + ab^2$ **r** $a^2 + b^2$ **s** πa^2 **t** $\dfrac{abc}{d}$

u $\dfrac{(ab + bc)}{d}$ **v** $\dfrac{ab}{2}$ **w** $(a + b)^2$ **x** $4a^2 + 2ab$

y $3abc + 2abd + 4bcd + 2acd$ **z** $4\pi r^3 + \pi r^2h$

2 One of these formulae is a length (L), 5 of them are areas (A), 4 of them are volumes (V) and the remaining 6 are mixtures which are impossible formulae (I). Indicate which are which by writing L, A, V or I.

a $a + b$ **b** $a^2 + b$ **c** $a^2 + b^2$ **d** $ab + c$

e $ab + c^2$ **f** $a^3 + bc$ **g** $a^3 + abc$ **h** $a^2 + abc$

i $3a^2 + bc$ **j** $4a^3b + 2ab^2$ **k** $3abc + 2x^2y$ **l** $3a(ab + bc)$

m $4a^2 + 3ab$ **n** $\pi a^2(a + b)$ **o** $\pi a^2 + 2r^2$ **p** $\pi r^2h + \pi rh$

1

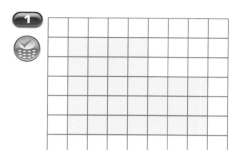

A shaded shape is shown on the grid of centimetre squares.

a Find the area of the shaded shape.

b Find the perimeter of the shaded shape.

Edexcel, Question 5, Paper 11B Foundation, January 2003

2 Here is a rectangle.

a Find the perimeter of the rectangle. State the units of your answer.

b Find the area of the rectangle. State the units of your answer.

3 A parallelogram is drawn on a centimetre square grid.

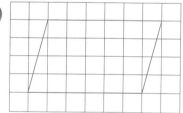

Calculate the area of the parallelogram.

4

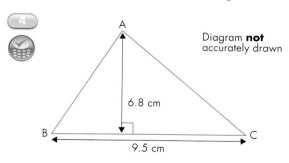

Diagram **not** accurately drawn

Work out the area of triangle ABC.

Edexcel, Question 7, Paper 11B Foundation, March 2004

5 This diagram shows a wall with a door in it.

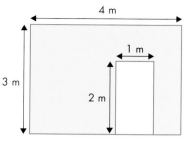

Diagram **not** accurately drawn

Work out the shaded area.

Edexcel, Question 23a, Paper 1 Foundation, June 2005

6 The diagram shows a trapezium ABCD.

AB = 8 cm, AD = 7 cm, DC = 12 cm

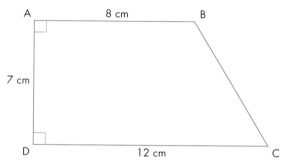

Find the area of the trapezium ABCD. Remember to state the units of your answer.

7 In this question, the letters x, y and z represent lengths. State whether each expression could represent a length, an area or a volume.

a xyz **b** $\pi(x + y + z)$

8 In this question, the letters x, y and z represent lengths. State whether each expression could represent a length, an area or a volume.

a $\pi x^2 y$ **b** $x + y + z$ **c** $x^2 + y^2$

WORKED EXAM QUESTIONS

1   A tile is shown below.

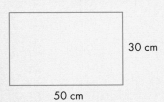

30 cm

50 cm

Find the area of the tile. Give your answer in square metres.

Solution

Area of tile = 50 × 30 = 1500 cm^2

10 000 cm^2 = 1 m^2

So: area = 1500 ÷ 10 000 = 0.15 m^2

2   The diagram shows a Tangram.

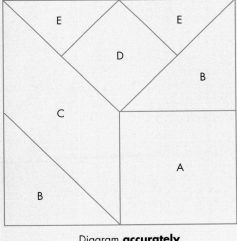

Diagram **accurately** drawn

The Tangram is a large square that is made up from

one square A,

two triangles B,

one parallelogram C,

another square D and

two small triangles E.

The total area of the Tangram is 64 cm^2.

Find the area of

a square A,

b triangle B,

c parallelogram C.

Edexcel, Question 4, Paper 3 Intermediate,
November 2004

Solution

a   Area of square A = 64 ÷ 4 = 16 cm^2 ———— Square A is $\frac{1}{4}$ of the large square

b   Area of triangle B = 16 ÷ 2 = 8 cm^2 ———— Triangle B is $\frac{1}{2}$ square A

c   Area of parallelogram C = 2 × 8 = 16 cm^2 ———— Parallelogram C is made from two triangles B

Mr Slater buys a new house.

He decides to put laminate flooring throughout the whole ground floor.

The laminate flooring he has chosen comes in packs which each cover 2 m².

Each room also needs an edging strip around the perimeter of the room.

The edging comes in packs which have a total length of 12 m.

The hall and bathroom are to have beech laminate flooring and the other rooms oak.

Mr Slater calculates the floor area of each room.

He also calculates the edging needed for every room (he includes the doorways to make sure he has enough).

Help him by completing the table to find the total floor area and the length of edging he needs.

Beech effect

Room	Floor area (m²)	Edging needed (m)
Hall		
Bathroom		
Total		

Oak effect

Room	Floor area (m²)	Edging needed (m)
Lounge		
Sitting room		
Kitchen/diner		
Conservatory		
Total		

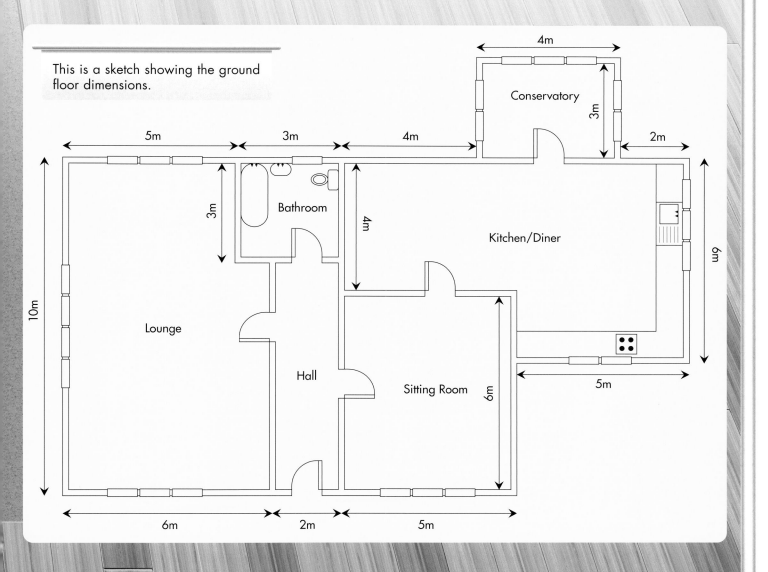

This is a sketch showing the ground floor dimensions.

Calculate for Mr Slater the total cost of the flooring and the edging.

Oak effect

	Number of packs	Price per pack	Total cost
Beech flooring		£32	
Beech edging		£18	
Oak flooring		£38	
Oak edging		£22	
		Total	

This total price must now have VAT added onto it.

VAT is at 17.5%.

What is the new total, once VAT has been added?

117

GRADE YOURSELF

G Can find the perimeter of a 2-D shape

G Can find the area of a 2-D shape by counting squares

F Can find the area of a rectangle using the formula $A = lw$

E Can find the area of a triangle using the formula $A = \frac{1}{2}bh$

D Can find the area of a parallelogram using the formula $A = bh$

D Can find the area of a trapezium using the formula $A = \frac{1}{2}(a + b)h$

D Can find the area of a compound shape

D Able to work out a formula for the perimeter, area or volume of simple shapes

C Able to work out a formula for the perimeter, area or volume of complex shapes

C Able to work out whether an expression or formula is dimensionally consistent and whether it represents a length, an area or a volume

What you should know now

- How to find the perimeter and area of 2-D shapes by counting squares
- How to find the area of a rectangle
- How to find the area of a triangle
- How to find the area of a parallelogram and a trapezium
- How to find the area of a compound shape

Statistical representation

This chapter will show you ...

- how to collect and organise data, and how to represent data on various types of diagram
- how to draw diagrams for data, including line graphs for time series and frequency diagrams
- how to draw diagrams for discrete data, including stem-and-leaf diagrams

Visual overview

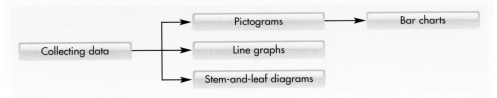

What you should already know

- How to use a tally for recording data
- How to read information from charts and tables

Quick check

Zoe works in a dress shop. She recorded the sizes of all the dresses sold during a week. The table shows the results.

Day	Size of dresses sold								
Monday	12	8	10	8	14	8	12	8	8
Tuesday	10	10	8	12	14	16	8	12	14	16
Wednesday	16	8	12	10					
Thursday	12	8	8	10	12	14	16	12	8
Friday	10	10	8	10	12	14	14	12	10	8
Saturday	10	8	8	12	10	12	8	10	

a Use a tallying method to make a table showing how many dresses of each size were sold in the week.

b Which dress size had the most sales?

In this section you will learn how to:

- collect and represent discrete and grouped data using tally charts and frequency tables

Key words

class
class interval
data collection sheet
experiment
frequency
frequency table
grouped data
grouped frequency table
observation
sample
tally chart

Statistics is concerned with the collection and organisation of data, the representation of data on diagrams and the interpretation of data.

When you are collecting data for simple surveys, it is usual to use a **data collection sheet**, also called a **tally chart**. For example, data collection sheets are used to gather information on how people travel to work, how students spend their free time and the amount of time people spend watching TV.

It is easy to record the data by using tally marks, as shown in Example 1. Counting up the tally marks in each row of the chart gives the **frequency** of each category. By listing the frequencies in a column on the right-hand side of the chart, you can make a **frequency table** (see Example 1). Frequency tables are an important part of making statistical calculations, as you will see in Chapter 11.

Three methods are used to collect data.

- **Taking a sample** For example, to find out which 'soaps' students watch, you would need to take a sample from the whole school population by asking at random an equal number of boys and girls from each year group. In this case, a good sample size would be 50.

- **Observation** For example, to find how many vehicles a day use a certain road, you would need to count and record the number of vehicles passing a point at different times of the day.

- **Experiment** For example, to find out how often a six occurs when you throw a dice, you would need to throw the dice 50 times or more and record each score.

EXAMPLE 1

Sandra wanted to find out about the ways in which students travelled to school. She carried out a survey. Her frequency table looked like this:

Method of travel	Tally	Frequency
Walk	‖‖ ‖‖ ‖‖ ‖‖ ‖‖ ‖‖ |||	28
Car	‖‖ ‖‖ ||	12
Bus	‖‖ ‖‖ ‖‖ ‖‖ |||	23
Bicycle	‖‖	5
Taxi	||	2

By adding together all the frequencies, you can see that 70 students took part in the survey. The frequencies also show you that more students travelled to school on foot than by any other method of transport.

EXAMPLE 2

Andrew wanted to find out the most likely outcome when two coins are tossed. He carried out an experiment by tossing two coins 50 times. His frequency table looked like this.

Number of heads	Tally	Frequency
0	ⅢⅢ ⅢⅢ II	12
1	ⅢⅢ ⅢⅢ ⅢⅢ ⅢⅢ ⅢⅢ II	27
2	ⅢⅢ ⅢⅢ I	11

From Andrew's table, you can see that a single head appeared the highest number of times.

Grouped data

Many surveys produce a lot of data that covers a wide range of values. In these cases, it is sensible to put the data into groups before attempting to compile a frequency table. These groups of data are called **classes** or **class intervals**.

Once the data has been grouped into classes, a **grouped frequency table** can be completed. The method is shown in Example 3.

EXAMPLE 3

These marks are for 36 students in a Year 10 mathematics examination.

31	49	52	79	40	29	66	71	73	19	51	47
81	67	40	52	20	84	65	73	60	54	60	59
25	89	21	91	84	77	18	37	55	41	72	38

a Construct a frequency table, using classes of 1–20, 21–40 and so on.

b What was the most common mark interval?

a Draw the grid of the table shown below and put in the headings.

Next, list the classes, in order, in the column headed 'Marks'.

Using tally marks, indicate each student's score against the class to which it belongs. For example, 81, 84, 89 and 91 belong to the class 81–100, giving five tally marks, as shown below.

Finally, count the tally marks for each class and enter the result in the column headed 'Frequency'. The table is now complete.

Marks	Tally	Frequency
1–20	III	3
21–40	ⅢⅢ III	8
41–60	ⅢⅢ ⅢⅢ I	11
61–80	ⅢⅢ IIII	9
81–100	ⅢⅢ	5

b From the grouped frequency table, you can see that the highest number of students obtained a mark in the 41–60 interval.

1 Philip kept a record of the number of goals scored by Burnley Rangers in the last 20 matches. These are his results:

0 1 1 0 2 0 1 3 2 1

0 1 0 3 2 1 0 2 1 1

a Draw a frequency table for his data.

b Which score had the highest frequency?

c How many goals were scored in total for the 20 matches?

2 Monica was doing a geography project on the weather. As part of her work, she kept a record of the daily midday temperatures in June.

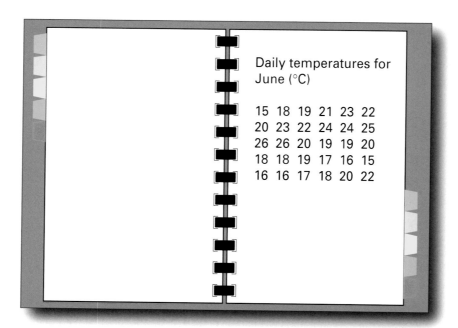

Daily temperatures for June (°C)

15 18 19 21 23 22
20 23 22 24 24 25
26 26 20 19 19 20
18 18 19 17 16 15
16 16 17 18 20 22

a Copy and complete the grouped frequency table for her data.

Temperature (°C)	Tally	Frequency
14–16		
17–19		
20–22		
23–25		
26–28		

b In which interval do the most temperatures lie?

c Describe what the weather was probably like throughout the month.

3 For the following surveys, decide whether the data should be collected by:

    i   sampling

    ii observation

    iii experiment.

HINTS AND TIPS

Look back to page 120 where each method of collecting data is discussed.

  a The number of people using a new superstore.

  b How people will vote in a forthcoming election.

  c The number of times a person scores double top in a game of darts.

  d Where people go for their summer holidays.

  e The frequency of a bus service on a particular route.

  f The number of times a drawing pin lands point up when dropped.

4 In a game of Hextuple, Mitesh used a six-sided dice. He decided to keep a record of his scores to see whether the dice was fair. His scores were:

    2 4 2 6 1 5 4 3 3 2 3 6 2 1 3

    5 4 3 4 2 1 6 5 1 6 4 1 2 3 4

  a Draw a frequency table for his data.

  b How many throws did Mitesh have during the game?

  c Do you think the dice was a fair one? Explain why.

5 The data shows the heights, in centimetres, of a sample of 32 Year 10 students.

    172 158 160 175 180 167 159 180

    167 166 178 184 179 156 165 166

    184 175 170 165 164 172 154 186

    167 172 170 181 157 165 152 164

  a Draw a grouped frequency table for the data, using class intervals 151–155, 156–160, …

  b In which interval do the most heights lie?

  c Does this agree with a survey of the students in your class?

6 Conduct some surveys of your own choice and draw frequency tables for your data.

ACTIVITY

Double dice

This is an activity for two or more players. Each player needs two six-sided dice.

Each player throws their two dice together 100 times. For each throw, add together the two scores to get a total score.

What is the lowest total score anyone can get? What is the highest total score?

Everyone keeps a record of their 100 throws in a frequency table.

Compare your frequency table with someone else's and comment on what you notice. For example: Which scores appear the most often? What about 'doubles'?

How might this information be useful in games that use two dice?

Repeat the activity in one or more of the following ways.

- For each throw, multiply the score on one dice by the score on the other.

- Use two four-sided dice (tetrahedral dice), adding or multiplying the scores.

- Use two different-sided dice, adding or multiplying the scores.

- Use three or more dice, adding and/or multiplying the scores.

6.2 Statistical diagrams

In this section you will learn how to:
- show collected data as pictograms

Key words
key
pictograms
symbol

Data collected from a survey can be presented in pictorial or diagrammatic form to help people to understand it more quickly. You see plenty of examples of this in newspapers and magazines and on TV, where every type of visual aid is used to communicate statistical information.

Pictograms

A **pictogram** is a frequency table in which frequency is represented by a repeated **symbol**. The symbol itself usually represents a number of items, as Example 5 shows. However, sometimes it is more sensible to let a symbol represent just a single unit, as in Example 4. The **key** tells you how many items are represented by a symbol.

EXAMPLE 4

The pictogram shows the number of telephone calls made by Mandy during a week.

Sunday	☎ ☎ ☎ ☎ ☎
Monday	☎ ☎ ☎
Tuesday	☎ ☎
Wednesday	☎ ☎ ☎ ☎
Thursday	☎ ☎ ☎
Friday	☎ ☎ ☎ ☎
Saturday	☎ ☎ ☎ ☎ ☎ ☎

Key ☎ represents 1 call

How many calls did Mandy make in the week?

From the pictogram, you can see that Mandy made a total of 27 telephone calls.

Although pictograms can have great visual impact (particularly as used in advertising) and are easy to understand, they have a serious drawback. Apart from a half, fractions of a symbol cannot usually be drawn accurately and so frequencies are often represented only approximately by symbols.

Example 5 highlights this difficulty.

EXAMPLE 5

The pictogram shows the number of Year 10 students who were late for school during a week.

Monday	👤 👤 👤 👤
Tuesday	👤 👤
Wednesday	👤 👤 👤
Thursday	👤 👤 👤
Friday	👤 👤 👤 👤 👤

Key 👤 represents 5 pupils

How many pupils were late on:

a   Monday

b   Thursday?

Precisely how many students were late on Monday and Thursday respectively?

If you assume that each 'limb' of the symbol represents one student and its 'body' also represents one student, then the answers are:

a   19 students were late on Monday.

b   13 on Thursday.

1 The frequency table shows the numbers of cars parked in a supermarket's car park at various times of the day. Draw a pictogram to illustrate the data. Use a key of 1 symbol = 5 cars.

Time	9 am	11 am	1 pm	3 pm	5 pm
Frequency	40	50	70	65	45

2 Mr Weeks, a milkman, kept a record of how many pints of milk he delivered to ten flats on a particular morning. Draw a pictogram for the data. Use a key of 1 symbol = 1 pint.

Flat 1	Flat 2	Flat 3	Flat 4	Flat 5	Flat 6	Flat 7	Flat 8	Flat 9	Flat 10
2	3	1	2	4	3	2	1	5	1

3 The pictogram, taken from a Suntours brochure, shows the average daily hours of sunshine for five months in Tenerife.

   a Write down the average daily hours of sunshine for each month.

   b Which month had the most sunshine?

   c Give a reason why pictograms are useful in holiday brochures.

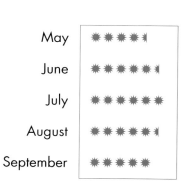

May	✳ ✳ ✳ ✳ ✳
June	✳ ✳ ✳ ✳ ✳ ✳
July	✳ ✳ ✳ ✳ ✳ ✳
August	✳ ✳ ✳ ✳ ✳ ✳
September	✳ ✳ ✳ ✳ ✳

Key ✳ represents 2 hours

4 The pictogram shows the amounts of money collected by six students after they had completed a sponsored walk for charity.

   a Who raised the most money?

   b How much money was raised altogether by the six pupils?

   c Robert also took part in the walk and raised £32. Why would it be difficult to include him on the pictogram?

Anthony	£ £ £ £ £
Ben	£ £ £ £ £ £
Emma	£ £ £ £ £
Leanne	£ £ £ £
Reena	£ £ £ £ £ £
Simon	£ £ £ £ £ £ £

Key £ represents £5

5 Draw pictograms of your own to show the following data.

   a The number of hours for which you watched TV every evening last week.

   b The magazines that students in your class read.

   c The favourite colours of students in your class.

In this section you will learn how to:

● draw bar charts to represent statistical data

Key words

axis
bar chart
class interval
dual bar
    chart

A **bar chart** consists of a series of bars or blocks of the *same* width, drawn either vertically or horizontally from an **axis**.

The heights or lengths of the bars always represent *frequencies*.

Sometimes, the bars are separated by narrow gaps of equal width, which makes the chart easier to read.

EXAMPLE 6

The grouped frequency table below shows the marks of 24 students in a test. Draw a bar chart for the data.

Marks	1–10	11–20	21–30	31–40	41–50
Frequency	2	3	5	8	6

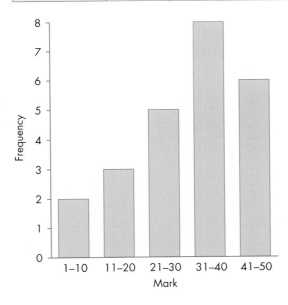

Note:

● Both axes are labelled.

● The **class intervals** are written under the middle of each bar.

● Bars are separated by equal spaces.

By using a **dual bar chart**, it is easy to compare two sets of related data, as Example 7 shows.

EXAMPLE 7

This dual bar chart shows the average daily maximum temperatures for England and Turkey over a five-month period.

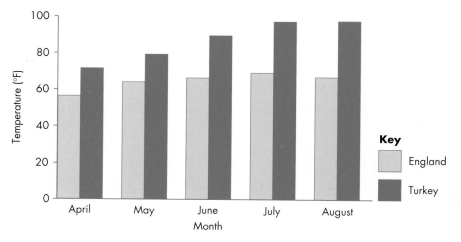

In which month was the difference between temperatures in England and Turkey the greatest?

The largest difference can be seen in August.

Note: You must always include a key to identify the two different sets of data.

1 For her survey on fitness, Maureen asked a sample of people, as they left a sports centre, which activity they had taken part in. She then drew a bar chart to show her data.

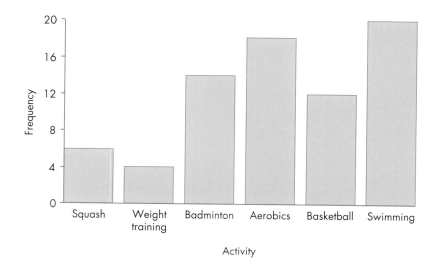

a Which was the most popular activity?

b How many people took part in Maureen's survey?

c Give a probable reason why fewer people took part in weight training than in any other activity.

d Is a sports centre a good place in which to do a survey on fitness? Explain why.

2 The frequency table below shows the levels achieved by 100 Year 9 students in their KS3 mathematics tests.

Level	3	4	5	6	7	8
Frequency	12	22	24	25	15	2

a Draw a suitable bar chart to illustrate the data.

b What fraction of the students achieved Level 6 or Level 7?

c State an advantage of drawing a bar chart rather than a pictogram for this data.

3 This table shows the number of points Richard and Derek were each awarded in eight rounds of a general knowledge quiz.

Round	1	2	3	4	5	6	7	8
Richard	7	8	7	6	8	6	9	4
Derek	6	7	6	9	6	8	5	6

a Draw a dual bar chart to illustrate the data.

b Comment on how well each of them did in the quiz.

4 Kay did a survey on the time it took students in her form to get to school on a particular morning. She wrote down their times to the nearest minute.

15 23 36 45 8 20 34 15 27 49

10 60 5 48 30 18 21 2 12 56

49 33 17 44 50 35 46 24 11 34

a Draw a grouped frequency table for Kay's data, using class intervals 1–10, 11–20, …

b Draw a bar chart to illustrate the data.

c Comment on how far from school the students live.

5 This table shows the number of accidents at a dangerous crossroads over a six-year period.

Year	2000	2001	2002	2003	2004	2005
No. of accidents	6	8	7	9	6	4

a Draw a pictogram for the data.

b Draw a bar chart for the data.

c Which diagram would you use if you were going to write to your local council to suggest that traffic lights should be installed at the crossroads? Explain why.

6 Conduct a survey to find the colours of cars that pass your school or your home.

a Draw pictograms and bar charts to illustrate your data.

b Compare your results with someone else's in your class and comment on anything you find about the colours of cars in your area.

7 Choose two daily newspapers (for example, the *Sun* and *The Times*) and take a fairly long article from each paper. Count the number of words in the first 50 sentences of each article.

a For each article, draw a grouped frequency table for the number of words in each of the first 50 sentences.

b Draw a dual bar chart for your data.

c Comment on your results.

6.4 Line graphs

In this section you will learn how to:
- draw a line graph to show trends in data

Key words
line graphs
trends

Line graphs are usually used in statistics to show how data changes over a period of time. One such use is to indicate **trends**, for example, whether the Earth's temperature is increasing as the concentration of carbon dioxide builds up in the atmosphere, or whether a firm's profit margin is falling year on year.

Line graphs are best drawn on graph paper.

EXAMPLE 8

This line graph shows the outside temperature at a weather station, taken at hourly intervals. Estimate the temperature at 3:30 pm.

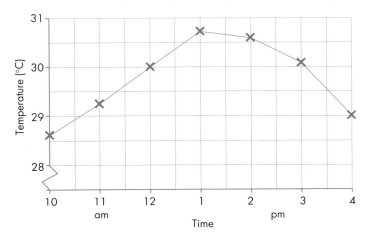

At 3.30 the temperature is approximately 29.5 °C.

Note: The temperature axis starts at 28 °C rather than 0 °C. This allows the use of a scale which makes it easy to plot the points and then to read the graph. The points are joined with lines so that the intermediate temperatures can be estimated for other times of the day.

EXAMPLE 9

This line graph shows the profit made each year by a company over a six-year period. Between which years did the company have the greatest increase in profits?

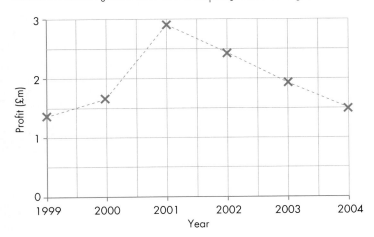

The greatest increase in profits was between 2000 and 2001.

For this graph, the values between the plotted points have no meaning because the profit of the company would have been calculated at the end of every year. In cases like this, the lines are often dashed. Although the trend appears to be that profits have fallen after 2001, it would not be sensible to predict what would happen after 2004.

EXERCISE 6D

1 This line graph shows the value of Spevadon shares on seven consecutive trading days.

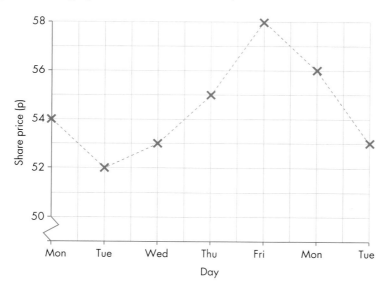

a On which day did the share price have its lowest value and what was that value?

b By how much did the share price rise from Wednesday to Thursday?

c Which day had the greatest rise in the share price from the previous day?

d Mr Hardy sold 500 shares on Friday. How much profit did he make if he originally bought the shares at 40p each?

2 The table shows the population of a town, rounded to the nearest thousand, after each census.

Year	1941	1951	1961	1971	1981	1991	2001
Population (1000s)	12	14	15	18	21	25	23

a Draw a line graph for the data.

b From your graph estimate the population in 1966.

c Between which two consecutive censuses did the population increase the most?

d Can you predict the population for 2011? Give a reason for your answer.

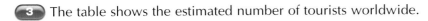

3 The table shows the estimated number of tourists worldwide.

Year	1965	1970	1975	1980	1985	1990	1995	2000
No. of tourists (millions)	60	100	150	220	280	290	320	340

a Draw a line graph for the data.

b From your graph estimate the number of tourists in 1977.

c Between which two consecutive years did world tourism increase the most?

d Explain the trend in world tourism. What reasons can you give to explain this trend?

4 The table shows the maximum and minimum daily temperatures for London over a week.

Day	Sunday	Monday	Tuesday	Wednesday	Thursday	Friday	Saturday
Maximum (°C)	12	14	16	15	16	14	10
Minimum (°C)	4	5	7	8	7	4	3

a Draw line graphs on the *same* axes to show the maximum and minimum temperatures.

b Find the smallest and greatest differences between the maximum and minimum temperatures.

ACTIVITY

Diagrams from the press

This is an activity for a group of two or more people. You will need a large selection of recent newspapers and magazines.

In a group, look through the newspapers and magazines.

Cut out any statistical diagrams and stick them on large sheets of coloured paper.

Underneath each diagram, explain what the diagram shows and how useful the diagram is in showing that information.

If any of the diagrams appears to be misleading, explain why.

You now have a lot of up-to-date statistics to display in your classroom.

In this section you will learn how to:

● draw and read information from an ordered stem-and-leaf diagram

Key words
discrete data
ordered data
raw data
unordered data

Raw data

If you were recording the ages of the first 20 people who line up at a bus stop in the morning, the **raw data** might look like this.

23, 13, 34, 44, 26, 12, 41, 31, 20, 18, 19, 31, 48, 32, 45, 14, 12, 27, 31, 19

This data is **unordered** and is difficult to read and analyse. When the data is **ordered**, it will look like this.

12, 12, 13, 14, 18, 19, 19, 20, 23, 26, 27, 31, 31, 31, 32, 34, 41, 44, 45, 48

This is easier to read and analyse.

Another method for displaying **discrete data** is a stem-and-leaf diagram. The tens digits will be the 'stem' and the units digits will be the 'leaves'.

Key 1 | 2 represents 12

1	2	2	3	4	8	9	9
2	0	3	6	7			
3	1	1	1	2	4		
4	1	4	5	8			

This is called an ordered stem-and-leaf diagram and gives a better idea of how the data is distributed.

A stem-and-leaf diagram should always have a key.

EXAMPLE 10

Put the following data into an ordered stem-and-leaf diagram.

45, 62, 58, 58, 61, 49, 61, 47, 52, 58, 48, 56, 65, 46, 54

a   What is the largest value?

b   What is the most common value?

c   What is the difference between the largest and smallest values?

First decide on the stem and the leaf.

In this case, the tens digit will be the stem and the units digit will be the leaf.

Key 4 | 5 represents 45

4	5	6	7	8	9
5	2	4	6	8	8	8
6	1	1	2	5	

a   The largest value is 65.

b   The most common value is 58 which occurs three times.

c   The difference between the largest and the smallest is $65 - 45 = 20$.

EXERCISE 6E

1   The following stem-and-leaf diagram shows the times taken for 15 students to complete a mathematical puzzle.

Key 1 | 7 represents 17 seconds

1	7	8	8	9		
2	2	2	2	5	6	9
3	3	4	5	5	8	

a   What is the shortest time to complete the puzzle?

b   What is the most common time to complete the puzzle?

c   What is the difference between the longest time and the shortest time to complete the puzzle?

2 This stem-and-leaf diagram shows the marks for the boys and girls in form 7E in a maths test.

Key Boys: 2 | 4 means 42 marks

Girls: 3 | 5 means 35 marks

HINTS AND TIPS

Read the boys' marks from right to left.

Boys						Girls					
6	4	2	3	3	3	5	7	9			
9	9	6	2	4	4	2	2	3	8	8	8
7	6	6	6	5	5	1	1	5			

a What was the highest mark for the boys?

b What was the highest mark for the girls?

c What was the most common mark for the boys?

d What was the most common mark for the girls?

e Overall, who did better in the test, the boys or the girls? Give a reason for your answer.

3 The heights of 15 sunflowers were measured.

43 cm, 39 cm, 41 cm, 29 cm, 36 cm,

34 cm, 43 cm, 48 cm, 38 cm, 35 cm,

41 cm, 38 cm, 43 cm, 28 cm, 48 cm

a Show the results in an ordered stem-and-leaf diagram, using this key:

Key 4 | 3 represents 43 cm

b What was the largest height measured?

c What was the most common height measured?

d What is the difference between the largest and smallest heights measured?

4 A student records the number of text messages she receives each day for two weeks.

12, 18, 21, 9, 17, 23, 8, 2, 20, 13, 17, 22, 9, 9

a Show the results in an ordered stem-and-leaf diagram, using this key:

Key 1 | 2 represents 12 messages

b What was the largest number of text messages received in a day?

c What is the most common number of text messages received in a day?

Map colouring

What is the smallest number of colours needed to colour this map so that areas of the same colour do not touch? The blue border is one colour.

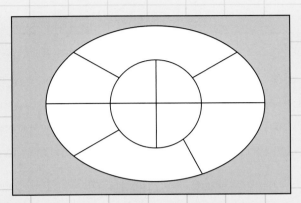

Missing £1

A father wants to share £17 between his three children so that one has $\frac{1}{2}$, one has $\frac{1}{3}$ and the other has $\frac{1}{9}$, but decides that this is not possible.

The youngest son, who is good at maths, had a clever idea. He borrowed £1 and added it to the £17 to get £18. He then split up the £18 as follows:

$\frac{1}{2}$ of £18 = £9

$\frac{1}{3}$ of £18 = £6

$\frac{1}{9}$ of £18 = £2

which add up to £17.

So, the son was able to give back the £1 he had borrowed. Can you explain this?

Going round in circles

Arrange all the other numbers from 1 to 9 so that each line of three numbers adds up to the same number.

Does the puzzle work if you put a different number in the middle circle?

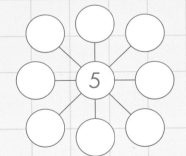

1 The pictogram shows the number of packets of crisps sold by a shop on each of Monday, Tuesday and Wednesday.

Monday	☺ ☺ ☺ ☺ ☺ ☺ (
Tuesday	☺ ☺ ☺ ☺ ☺
Wednesday	☺ ☺
Thursday	
Friday	

Key ☺ = 4 packets

a Write down the number of packets sold on Tuesday.

16 packets were sold on Thursday.

6 packets were sold on Friday.

b Using this information copy and complete the pictogram.

Edexcel, Question 1, Paper 11A Foundation, January 2003

2 The pictogram below shows the number of football matches attended by four members of a family in one season.

 represents four matches

Name		Number of matches
Joy	⚽ ⚽ ⚽	
Joe	⚽ ⚽	
John		20
James		28

a How many matches did Joy attend?

b Copy and complete the pictogram.

3 The bar chart shows the number of DVDs Beth, Terry and Abbas watched in one week.

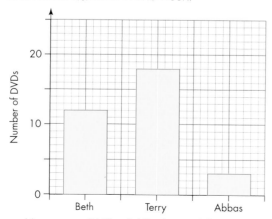

a How many DVDs did Beth watch?

b How many DVDs did Beth, Terry and Abbas watch altogether?

c How many more DVDs did Terry watch than Abbas?

4 The bar chart shows the number of packets of different flavoured crisps sold at a canteen one morning.

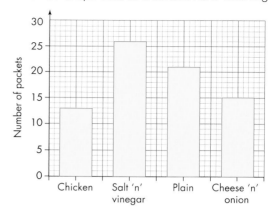

a How many packets of chicken-flavoured crisps were sold?

b Which was the most popular flavour?

c How many more packets of plain crisps than packets of cheese 'n' onion were sold?

d How many packets of crisps were sold altogether?

5 Martin asked his friends to choose, from a list, which Star Trek series they like best.

Their replies were:

Deep Space 9   Enterprise   Deep Space 9
Voyager   Deep Space 9   Voyager
Deep Space 9   Next Generation   Deep Space 9
Next Generation   Enterprise   Next Generation
Enterprise   Next Generation   Deep Space 9

a Copy and complete the tally and the frequency columns in the table below.

Star Trek series	Tally	Frequency
Deep Space 9		
Voyager		
Enterprise		
Next Generation		

b Draw a pictogram to show these results.

Use the symbol to represent two replies.

6 The table shows the average height in centimetres of boys and girls in a village school for six years.

a i The difference between the heights of the two sexes is calculated. Complete the last row to show these differences.

	2000	2001	2002	2003	2004	2005
Boys	112.7	112.2	113.1	113.5	113.0	113.5
Girls	111.4	111.0	111.2	111.5	111.8	112.1
Difference	1.3			2.0		1.4

ii Compare the heights of the boys with the heights of the girls. What do you notice?

b A bar chart to show the heights of the boys and girls is drawn.

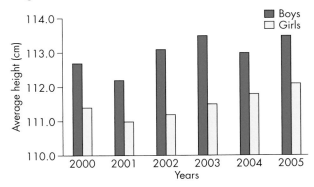

Explain why the bar chart is misleading.

7 A shop has a sale. The bar chart shows some information about the sale.

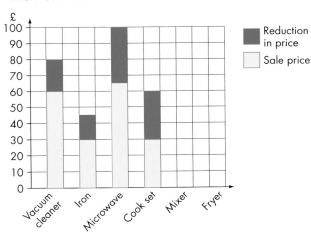

The normal price of a vacuum cleaner is £80.
The sale price of a vacuum cleaner is £60.

a Write the sale price of a vacuum clearner as a fraction of its normal price. Give your answer in its simplest form.

b Find the reduction in the price of the iron.

c Which two items have the same sale price?

Edexcel, Question 9, Paper 2 Foundation, June 2004

8 A coach company asks some of its passengers if their service has improved. Here are the results.

Reply	Percentage
Improved	35%
Same	24%
Not as good	29%
Don't know	12%

Copy and complete the bar chart to show these results.

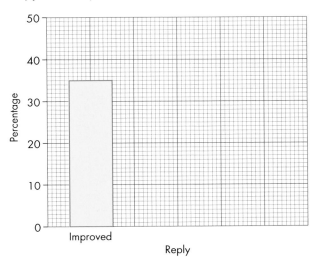

9 The diagram shows the number of babies born in hospital or at home on one weekend in five towns.

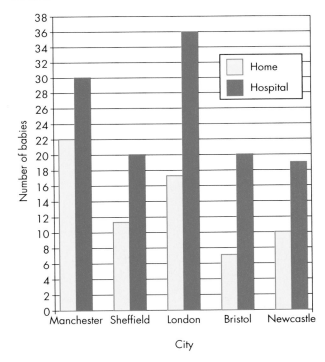

a Which two cities had the same number of babies born in hospital?

b Work out the difference between the number of babies born at home and in hospital for:

i Manchester

ii Newcastle

c Lisa says the number of babies born in hospital is double those born at home.

Give an example to show that Lisa is wrong.

Give a reason for your choice.

Anil counted the number of letters in each of 30 sentences in a newspaper. Anil showed his results in a stem and leaf diagram.

Key 4 | 1 stands for 41 letters

```
0 | 8  8  9
1 | 1  2  3  4  4  8  9
2 | 0  3  5  5  7  7  8
3 | 2  2  3  3  6  6  8  8
4 | 1  2  3  3  5
```

a Write down the number of sentences with 36 letters.

b Work out the range.

c Work out the median.

Edexcel, Question 7, Paper 4 Foundation, November 2004

 The graph shows the average annual water rates in a town.

a By how much did the average annual water rates increase from 2003 to 2005?

b Between which two years was there the largest annual increase in water rates?

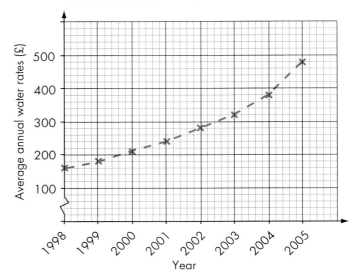

 The height of a sunflower is measured at the end of each week.

The graph shows the height of the sunflower. At the end of week 5 the height of the sunflower was 100 cm.

a At the end of week 6 the height of the sunflower was 106 cm. At the end of week 10 the height of the sunflower was 118 cm.

   i Copy the graph and plot these points on the graph.

   ii Complete the graph with straight lines.

b Use your graph to estimate the height of the sunflower in centimetres at the end of week 9.

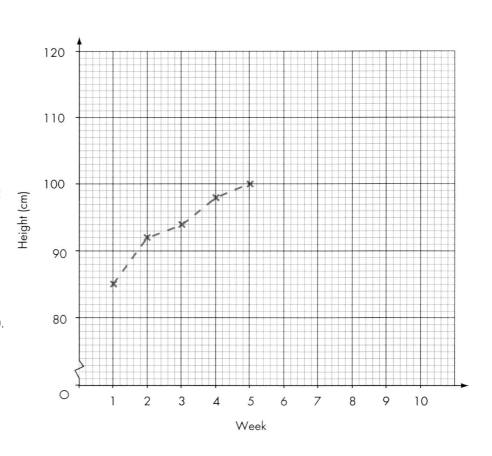

WORKED EXAM QUESTION

The number of cars stolen in 20 cities in one weekend is recorded.

8   20   1   10   6   22   4   3   17   3
13   14   9   16   23   17   10   19   22   19

Draw a stem-and-leaf diagram to represent these data and
complete the key.

Key | represents ....

0 ....

1 ....

2 ....

Solution

Key   1 | 5 represents 15

You can see from the basic diagram that the stem is the tens digits and the leaves are the units digits. Complete the key, using any value.

0 | 1   3   3   4   6   8   9

1 | 0   0   3   4   6   7   7   9   9

2 | 0   2   2   3

Now complete the stem-and-leaf diagram keeping the data in order.

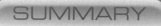
SUMMARY

Basic algebra

This chapter will show you ...

- how to use letters to represent numbers
- how to form simple algebraic expressions
- how to simplify such expressions by collecting like terms
- how to factorise expressions
- how to express simple rules in algebraic form
- how to substitute numbers into expressions and formulae
- how to expand the product of two linear brackets

Visual overview

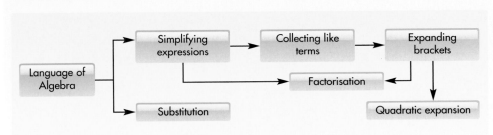

What you should already know

- The **BODMAS** rule, which gives the order in which you must do the operations of arithmetic when they occur together

Quick check

1 Write the answer to each expression.

  a $(5 - 1) \times 2$

  b $5 - (1 \times 2)$

2 Work out $(7 - 5) \times (5 + 4 - 2)$.

3 **a** Put brackets in the calculation to make the answer 40.

    $2 + 3 + 5 \times 4$

  b Put brackets in the calculation to make the answer 34.

    $2 + 3 + 5 \times 4$

In this section you will learn how to:
- use letters, numbers and mathematical symbols to write algebraic expressions and formulae

Algebra is based on the idea that if something works with numbers, it will work with letters. The main difference is that when you work only with numbers, the answer is also a number. When you work with letters, you get an **expression** as the answer.

Algebra follows the same rules as arithmetic, and uses the same **symbols** ($+$, $-$, $\times$ and $\div$). Below are seven important algebraic rules.

- Write '4 more than x' as $4 + x$ or $x + 4$.

- Write '6 less than p' or 'p minus 6' as $p - 6$.

- Write '4 times y' as $4 \times y$ or $y \times 4$ or $4y$. The last one of these is the neatest way to write it.

- Write 'b divided by 2' as $b \div 2$ or $\dfrac{b}{2}$.

- When a number and a letter or a letter and a letter appear together, there is a hidden multiplication sign between them. So, $7x$ means $7 \times x$ and ab means $a \times b$.

- Always write '$1 \times x$' as x.

- Write 't times t' as $t \times t$ or t^2.

EXAMPLE 1

What is the area of each of these rectangles?

a 4 cm by 6 cm   **b** 4 cm by w cm   **c** l cm by w cm

You have already met the rule for working out the area of a rectangle:

area = length $\times$ width

So, the area of rectangle **a** is $4 \times 6 = 24$ cm^2

The area of rectangle **b** is $4 \times w = 4w$ cm^2

The area of rectangle **c** is $l \times w = lw$ cm^2

Now, if A represents the area of rectangle **c**:

$$A = lw$$

This is an example of a rule expressed algebraically.

EXAMPLE 2

What is the perimeter of each of these rectangles?

a 6 cm by 4 cm   **b** 4 cm by w cm   **c** l cm by w cm

The rule for working out the perimeter of a rectangle is:

perimeter = twice the longer side + twice the shorter side

So, the perimeter of rectangle **a** is $2 \times 6 + 2 \times 4 = 20$ cm

The perimeter of rectangle **b** is $2 \times 4 + 2 \times w = 8 + 2w$ cm

The perimeter of rectangle **c** is $2 \times l + 2 \times w = 2l + 2w$ cm

Now, let P represent the perimeter of rectangle **c**, so:

$$P = 2l + 2w$$

which is another example of a rule expressed algebraically.

Expressions such as $A = lw$ and $P = 2l + 2w$ are called **formulae** (the plural of formula).

As the two examples above show, a formula states the connection between two or more quantities, each of which is represented by a different letter.

In a formula, the letters are replaced by numbers when a calculation has to be made. This is called *substitution* and is explained on page 159.

EXERCISE 7A

1 Write down the algebraic expression for:

a 2 more than x

b 6 less than x

c k more than x

d x minus t

e x added to 3

f d added to m

g y taken away from b

h p added to t added to w

i 8 multiplied by x

j h multiplied by j

k x divided by 4

l 2 divided by x

m y divided by t

n w multiplied by t

o a multiplied by a

p g multiplied by itself

2 Here are four squares.

a Work out the area and perimeter of each square.

i 1 by 1

ii x by x

iii 3 by 3

iv t by t

b Copy and complete these rules.

i The perimeter, P, of a square of side s centimetres is
$P = \ldots\ldots$

ii The area, A, of a square of side s centimetres is $A = \ldots\ldots$

3 Asha, Bernice and Charu are three sisters. Bernice is x years old. Asha is three years older than Bernice. Charu is four years younger than Bernice.

    a How old is Asha?

    b How old is Charu?

4 An approximation method of converting from degrees Celsius to degrees Fahrenheit is given by this rule:

    Multiply by 2 and add 30.

    Using C to stand for degrees Celsius and F to stand for degrees Fahrenheit, complete this formula.

    $F = \ldots\ldots$

5 Cows have four legs. Which of these formulae connects the number of legs (L) and the number of cows (C)?

    a $C = 4L$ **b** $L = C + 4$ **c** $L = 4C$ **d** $L + C = 4$

6 There are 3 feet in a yard. The rule $F = 3Y$ connects the number of feet (F) and the number of yards (Y). Write down rules, using the letters shown, to connect:

    a the number of centimetres (C) in metres (M)

    b the number of inches (N) in feet (F)

    c the number of wheels (W) on cars (C)

    d the number of heads (H) on people (P).

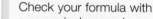

> **HINTS AND TIPS**
>
> Check your formula with a numerical example. In 4 yards there are 12 feet, so, if $F = 3Y$ is correct, then $12 = 3 \times 4$, which is true.

7 **a** Anne has three bags of marbles. Each bag contains n marbles. How many marbles does she have altogether?

    b Beryl gives her another three marbles. How many marbles does Anne have now?

    c Anne puts one of her new marbles in each bag. How many marbles are there now in each bag?

    d Anne takes two marbles out of each bag. How many marbles are there now in each bag?

8 Simon has n cubes.

    • Rob has twice as many cubes as Simon.

    • Tom has two more than Simon.

    • Vic has three fewer than Simon.

    • Wes has three more than Rob.

    How many cubes does each person have?

> **HINTS AND TIPS**
>
> Remember that you do not have to write down a multiplication sign between numbers and letters, or letters and letters.

a John has been drawing squares and writing down the area and the perimeter of each of them. He has drawn three squares. Finish his work by writing down the missing areas and perimeters.

 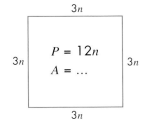

b Write down the area and the perimeter of this partly covered square.

 a I go shopping with £10 and spend £6. How much do I have left?

b I go shopping with £10 and spend £x. How much do I have left?

c I go shopping with £y and spend £x. How much do I have left?

d I go shopping with £$3x$ and spend £x. How much do I have left?

11 Give the total cost of:

   a 5 pens at 15p each

   b x pens at 15p each

   c 4 pens at Ap each

   d y pens at Ap each.

12 A boy went shopping with £A. He spent £B. How much has he got left?

13 Five ties cost £A. What is the cost of one tie?

14 My dad is 72 and I am T years old. How old shall we each be in x years' time?

15 I am twice as old as my son. I am T years old.

   a How old is my son?

   b How old will my son be in four years' time?

   c How old was I x years ago?

16 What is the total perimeter of each of these figures?

a
Square

b
Equilateral triangle

c
Regular hexagon

147

17 Write down the number of marbles each pupil ends up with.

Pupil	Action	Marbles
Andrea	Start with three bags each containing n marbles and give away one marble from each bag	
Bert	Start with three bags each containing n marbles and give away one marble from one bag	
Colin	Start with three bags each containing n marbles and give away two marbles from each bag	
Davina	Start with three bags each containing n marbles and give away n marbles from each bag	
Emma	Start with three bags each containing n marbles and give away n marbles from one bag	
Florinda	Start with three bags each containing n marbles and give away m marbles from each bag	

7.2 Simplifying expressions

In this section you will learn how to:
- simplify algebraic expressions by multiplying terms
- simplify algebraic expressions by collecting like terms

Key words
like terms
simplify

Simplifying an algebraic expression means making it neater and, usually, shorter by combining its terms where possible.

Multiplying expressions

When you multiply algebraic expressions, first you combine the numbers, then the letters.

EXAMPLE 3

Simplify:

a $2 \times t$ **b** $m \times t$ **c** $2t \times 5$ **d** $3y \times 2m$

The convention is to write the number first then the letters, but if there is no number just put the letters in alphabetical order.

a $2 \times t = 2t$ **b** $m \times t = mt$ **c** $2t \times 5 = 10t$ **d** $3y \times 2m = 6my$

In an examination you will not be penalised for writing $2ba$ instead of $2ab$, but you will be penalised if you write $ab2$ as this can be confused with powers, so *always* write the number first.

EXAMPLE 4

Simplify:

a $t \times t$ **b** $3t \times 2t$ **c** $3t^2 \times 4t$ **d** $2t^3 \times 4t^2$

Combine the same letters together using powers. The indices are added together.

a $t \times t = t^2$ (Remember: $t = t^1$)   **b** $3t \times 2t = 6t^2$

c $3t^2 \times 4t = 12t^3$ **d** $2t^3 \times 4t^2 = 8t^5$

EXERCISE 7B

Simplify the following expressions:

HINTS AND TIPS

Remember to multiply numbers and add indices.

1. $2 \times 3t$ 2. $3 \times 4y$ 3. $5y \times 3$

4. $2w \times 4$ 5. $3t \times t$ 6. $5b \times b$

7. $2w \times w$ 8. $5y \times 3y$ 9. $4p \times 2p$

10. $3t \times 2t$ 11. $4m \times 3m$ 12. $5t \times 3t$

13. $m \times 2t$ 14. $3y \times w$ 15. $5t \times q$ 16. $n \times 6m$

17. $3t \times 2q$ 18. $4f \times 3g$ 19. $5h \times 2k$ 20. $3p \times 7r$

21. $y^2 \times y$ 22. $t \times t^2$ 23. $3m \times m^2$ 24. $4t^2 \times t$

25. $3n \times 2n^2$ 26. $4r^2 \times 5r$ 27. $t^2 \times t^2$ 28. $h^3 \times h^2$

29. $3n^2 \times 4n^3$ 30. $5t^3 \times 2t^4$ 31. $3a^4 \times 2a^3$ 32. $k^5 \times 4k^2$

33. $-t^2 \times -t$ 34. $-2y \times -3y$ 35. $-4d^2 \times -3d$ 36. $-3p^4 \times -5p^2$

37. $3mp \times p$ 38. $2ty \times 3t$ 39. $3mn \times 2m$ 40. $4mp \times 2mp$

Collecting like terms

Collecting **like terms** generally involves two steps.

- Collect like terms into groups.

- Then combine the like terms in each group.

Like terms are those that are multiples of the same letter or of the same combination of letters. For example, a, $3a$, $9a$, $\frac{1}{4}a$ and $-5a$ are all like terms.

So are $2xy$, $7xy$ and $-5xy$, and so are $6x^2$, x^2 and $-3x^2$.

Only like terms can be added or subtracted to simplify an expression. For example,

$a + 3a + 9a - 5a$	simplifies to	$8a$
$2xy + 7xy - 5xy$	simplifies to	$4xy$

and

$6x^2 + x^2 - 3x^2$	simplifies to	$4x^2$

But an expression such as $4p + 8t + 5x - 9$ cannot be made simpler, because $4p$, $8t$, $5x$ and -9 are *unlike terms*, which *cannot* be combined.

EXAMPLE 5

Simplify $7x^2 + 3y - 6z + 2x^2 + 3z - y + w + 9$

Write out the expression:

$$7x^2 + 3y - 6z + 2x^2 + 3z - y + w + 9$$

Then collect like terms:

$$\boxed{7x^2 + 2x^2} \boxed{+3y - y} \boxed{-6z + 3z} \boxed{+ w} \boxed{+ 9}$$

Then combine them:

$$9x^2 \quad + \quad 2y \quad - \quad 3z \quad + w + 9$$

So, the expression in its simplest form is:

$$9x^2 + 2y - 3z + w + 9$$

EXERCISE 7C

1 Joseph is given £t, John has £3 more than Joseph, Joy has £$2t$.

a How much more money has Joy than Joseph?

b How much do the three of them have altogether?

2 Write down an expression for the perimeter of each of these shapes.

a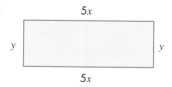

b

c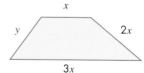

3 Write each of these expressions in a shorter form.

a $a + a + a + a + a$

b $c + c + c + c + c + c$

c $4e + 5e$

d $f + 2f + 3f$

e $g + g + g + g - g$

f $3i + 2i - i$

g $5j + j - 2j$

h $9q - 3q - 3q$

i $3r - 3r$

j $2w + 4w - 7w$

k $5x^2 + 6x^2 - 7x^2 + 2x^2$

l $8y^2 + 5y^2 - 7y^2 - y^2$

m $2z^2 - 2z^2 + 3z^2 - 3z^2$

> **HINTS AND TIPS**
>
> The term a has a coefficient of 1. i.e. $a = 1a$, but you do not need to write the 1.

4 Simplify each of the following expressions.

a $3x + 4x$ **b** $4y + 2y$

c $5t - 2t$ **d** $t - 4t$

e $-2x - 3x$ **f** $-k - 4k$

g $m^2 + 2m^2 - m^2$ **h** $2y^2 + 3y^2 - 5y^2$

i $-f^2 + 4f^2 - 2f^2$

5 Simplify each of the following expressions.

a $5x + 8 + 2x - 3$ **b** $7 - 2x - 1 + 7x$

c $4p + 2t + p - 2t$ **d** $8 + x + 4x - 2$

e $3 + 2t + p - t + 2 + 4p$ **f** $5w - 2k - 2w - 3k + 5w$

g $a + b + c + d - a - b - d$ **h** $9k - y - 5y - k + 10$

6 Write each of these in a shorter form. (Be careful – two of them will not simplify.)

a $c + d + d + d + c$ **b** $2d + 2e + 3d$

c $f + 3g + 4h$ **d** $3i + 2k - i + k$

e $4k + 5p - 2k + 4p$ **f** $3k + 2m + 5p$

g $4m - 5n + 3m - 2n$ **h** $n + 3p - 6p + 5n$

i $5u - 4v + u + v$ **j** $2v - 5w + 5w$

k $2w + 4y - 7y$ **l** $5x^2 + 6x^2 - 7y + 2y$

m $8y^2 + 5z - 7z - 9y^2$ **n** $2z^2 - 2x^2 + 3x^2 - 3z^2$

7 Find the perimeter of each of these shapes, giving it in its simplest form.

a
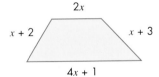

b
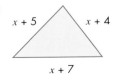

c
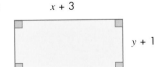

In this section you will learn how to:
- expand brackets such as $2(x - 3)$
- expand and simplify brackets

Key words
expand
expand and
simplify
multiply out
simplify

Expanding

In mathematics, the term '**expand**' usually means '**multiply out**'. For example, expressions such as $3(y + 2)$ and $4y^2(2y + 3)$ can be expanded by multiplying them out.

Remember that there is an invisible multiplication sign between the outside number and the opening bracket. So $3(y + 2)$ is really $3 \times (y + 2)$, and $4y^2(2y + 3)$ is really $4y^2 \times (2y + 3)$.

You expand by multiplying *everything inside* the brackets by what is outside the brackets.

EXAMPLE 6

Expand $3(y + 2)$.

$3(y + 2) = 3 \times (y + 2) = 3 \times y + 3 \times 2 = 3y + 6$

EXAMPLE 7

Expand $4y^2(2y + 3)$.

$4y^2(2y + 3) = 4y^2 \times (2y + 3) = 4y^2 \times 2y + 4y^2 \times 3 = 8y^3 + 12y^2$

Look at these next examples of expansion, which show clearly how each term inside the brackets has been multiplied by the term outside the brackets.

$2(m + 3) = 2m + 6$ $y(y^2 - 4x) = y^3 - 4xy$

$3(2t + 5) = 6t + 15$ $3x^2(4x + 5) = 12x^3 + 15x^2$

$m(p + 7) = mp + 7m$ $-3(2 + 3x) = -6 - 9x$

$x(x - 6) = x^2 - 6x$ $-2x(3 - 4x) = -6x + 8x^2$

$4t(t + 2) = 4t^2 + 8t$ $3t(2 + 5t - p) = 6t + 15t^2 - 3pt$

EXERCISE 7D

Expand these expressions.

1 $2(3 + m)$

2 $5(2 + l)$

3 $3(4 - y)$

4 $4(5 + 2k)$

5 $3(2 - 4f)$

6 $2(5 - 3w)$

7 $3(g + h)$

8 $5(2k + 3m)$

9 $4(3d - 2n)$

10 $t(t + 3)$

11 $m(m + 5)$

12 $k(k - 3)$

13 $g(3g + 2)$

14 $y(5y - 1)$

15 $p(5 - 3p)$

16 $3m(m + 4)$

17 $4t(t - 1)$

18 $2k(4 - k)$

19 $4g(2g + 5)$

20 $5h(3h - 2)$

21 $3t(5 - 4t)$

22 $3d(2d + 4e)$

23 $2y(3y + 4k)$

24 $5m(3m - 2p)$

25 $y(y^2 + 5)$

26 $h(h^3 + 7)$

27 $k(k^2 - 5)$

28 $3t(t^2 + 4)$

29 $4h(h^3 - 1)$

30 $5g(g^3 - 2)$

31 $4m(3m^2 + m)$

32 $5k(2k^3 + k^2)$

33 $3d(5d^2 - d^3)$

34 $3w(2w^2 + t)$

35 $5a(3a^2 - 2b)$

36 $3p(4p^3 - 5m)$

37 $m^2(5 + 4m)$

38 $t^3(t + 2t)$

39 $g^2(5t - 4g^2)$

40 $3t^2(5t + m)$

41 $4h^2(3h + 2g)$

42 $2m^2(4m + m^2)$

Expand and simplify

This usually means that you need to expand more than one set of brackets and **simplify** the resulting expressions.

You will often be asked to **expand and simplify** expressions.

EXAMPLE 8

Expand and simplify $3(4 + m) + 2(5 + 2m)$.

$$3(4 + m) + 2(5 + 2m) = 12 + 3m + 10 + 4m = 22 + 7m$$

EXAMPLE 9

Expand and simplify $3t(5t + 4) - 2t(3t - 5)$.

$$3t(5t + 4) - 2t(3t - 5) = 15t^2 + 12t - 6t^2 + 10t = 9t^2 + 22t$$

EXAMPLE 10

Expand and simplify $4a(2b - 3f) - 3b(a + 2f)$.

$$4a(2b - 3f) - 3b(a + 2f) = 8ab - 12af - 3ab - 6bf = 5ab - 12af - 6bf$$

---

1 Simplify these expressions.

a $4t + 3t$ **b** $5m + 4m$ **c** $2y + y$ **d** $3d + 2d + 4d$

e $5e - 2e$ **f** $7g - 5g$ **g** $4p - p$ **h** $3t - t$

i $2t^2 + 3t^2$ **j** $6y^2 - 2y^2$ **k** $3ab + 2ab$ **l** $7a^2d - 4a^2d$

2 Expand and simplify these expressions.

a $3(4 + t) + 2(5 + t)$ **b** $5(3 + 2k) + 3(2 + 3k)$

c $4(1 + 3m) + 2(3 + 2m)$ **d** $2(5 + 4y) + 3(2 + 3y)$

e $4(3 + 2f) + 2(5 - 3f)$ **f** $5(1 + 3g) + 3(3 - 4g)$

g $3(2 + 5t) + 4(1 - t)$ **h** $4(3 + 3w) + 2(5 - 4w)$

HINTS AND TIPS

Expand the expression before trying to collect like terms. If you try to expand and collect at the same time you will probably make a mistake.

3 Expand and simplify these expressions.

a $4(3 + 2h) - 2(5 + 3h)$ **b** $5(3g + 4) - 3(2g + 5)$

c $3(4y + 5) - 2(3y + 2)$ **d** $3(5t + 2) - 2(4t + 5)$

e $5(5k + 2) - 2(4k - 3)$ **f** $4(4e + 3) - 2(5e - 4)$

g $3(5m - 2) - 2(4m - 5)$ **h** $2(6t - 1) - 3(3t - 4)$

4 Expand and simplify these expressions.

a $m(4 + p) + p(3 + m)$ **b** $k(3 + 2h) + h(4 + 3k)$

c $t(2 + 3n) + n(3 + 4t)$ **d** $p(2q + 3) + q(4p + 7)$

e $3h(2 + 3j) + 2j(2h + 3)$ **f** $2y(3t + 4) + 3t(2 + 5y)$

g $4r(3 + 4p) + 3p(8 - r)$ **h** $5k(3m + 4) - 2m(3 - 2k)$

HINTS AND TIPS

Be careful with minus signs. They are causes of the most common errors students make in examinations. Remember $-2 \times -4 = 8$ but $-2 \times 5 = -10$. You will learn more about multiplying and dividing with negative numbers in Chapter 8.

5 Expand and simplify these expressions.

a $t(3t + 4) + 3t(3 + 2t)$ **b** $2y(3 + 4y) + y(5y - 1)$

c $4w(2w + 3) + 3w(2 - w)$ **d** $5p(3p + 4) - 2p(3 - 4p)$

e $3m(2m - 1) + 2m(5 - m)$ **f** $6d(4 - 2d) + d(3d - 2)$

g $4e(3e - 5) - 2e(e - 7)$ **h** $3k(2k + p) - 2k(3p - 4k)$

6 Expand and simplify these expressions.

a $4a(2b + 3c) + 3b(3a + 2c)$ **b** $3y(4w + 2t) + 2w(3y - 4t)$

c $2g(3h - k) + 5h(2g - 2k)$ **d** $3h(2t - p) + 4t(h - 3p)$

e $a(3b - 2c) - 2b(a - 3c)$ **f** $4p(3q - 2w) - 2w(p - q)$

g $5m(2n - 3p) - 2n(3p - 2m)$ **h** $2r(3r + r^2) - 3r^2(4 - 2r)$

Factorisation

In this section you will learn how to:

- 'reverse' the process of expanding brackets by taking out a common factor from each term in an expression

Key words

factor
factorisation

Factorisation is the opposite of expansion. It puts an expression back into the brackets it may have come from.

To factorise an expression, look for the common **factors** in every term of the expression. Follow through the examples below to see how this works.

EXAMPLE 11

Factorise each expression. **a** $6t + 9m$ **b** $6my + 4py$
                              c $8kp + 4k - 12km$ **d** $8kp + 4kt - 12km$

a The common factor is 3, so $6t + 9m = 3(2t + 3m)$

b The common factor is $2y$, so $6my + 4py = 2y(3m + 2p)$

c The common factor is $4k$, so $8kp + 4k - 12km = 4k(2p + 1 - 3m)$

d The common factor is $4k$, so $8kp + 4kt - 12km = 4k(2p + t - 3m)$

Notice that if you multiply out each answer you will get the expressions you started with.

This diagram may help you to see the difference and the connection between expansion and factorisation.

Note: When the whole term is the common factor, as in part **c**, then you are left with 1, not 0, inside the brackets.

Expanding

$$3(2t + 3m) = 6t + 9m$$

Factorising

Factorise the following expressions.

1 $6m + 12t$

2 $9t + 3p$

3 $8m + 12k$

4 $4r + 8t$

5 $mn + 3m$

6 $5g^2 + 3g$

7 $4w - 6t$

8 $8p - 6k$

9 $16h - 10k$

10 $2mp + 2mk$

11 $4bc + 2bk$

12 $6ab + 4ac$

13 $3y^2 + 2y$

14 $4t^2 - 3t$

15 $4d^2 - 2d$

16 $3m^2 - 3mp$

HINTS AND TIPS

First look for a common factor of the numbers and then look for common factors of the letters.

D

17 $6p^2 + 9pt$

18 $8pt + 6mp$

19 $8ab - 4bc$

20 $12a^2 - 8ab$

21 $9mt - 6pt$

22 $16at^2 + 12at$

23 $5b^2c - 10bc$

24 $8abc + 6bed$

25 $4a^2 + 6a + 8$

26 $6ab + 9bc + 3bd$

27 $5t^2 + 4t + at$

28 $6mt^2 - 3mt + 9m^2t$

29 $8ab^2 + 2ab - 4a^2b$

30 $10pt^2 + 15pt + 5p^2t$

Factorise the following expressions where possible. List those that cannot be factorised.

31 $7m - 6t$

32 $5m + 2mp$

33 $t^2 - 7t$

34 $8pt + 5ab$

35 $4m^2 - 6mp$

36 $a^2 + b$

37 $4a^2 - 5ab$

38 $3ab + 4cd$

39 $5ab - 3b^2c$

7.5 Quadratic expansion

In this section you will learn how to:

● expand the product of two linear expressions to obtain a quadratic expression

Key words

quadratic expansion

quadratic expression

A **quadratic expression** is one in which the highest power of any of its terms is 2. For example:

$$y^2 \qquad 3t^2 + 5t \qquad 5m^2 + 3m + 8$$

are quadratic expressions.

An expression such as $(3y + 2)(4y - 5)$ can be expanded to give a quadratic expression. Multiplying out pairs of brackets in this way is usually called **quadratic expansion**.

The rule for expanding expressions such as $(t + 5)(3t - 4)$ is similar to that for expanding single brackets: multiply everything in one pair of brackets by everything in the other pair of brackets.

Follow through the four examples below to see how brackets can be expanded. Notice how to split up the terms in the first pair of brackets and make each of these terms multiply everything in the second pair of brackets. Then simplify the outcome.

EXAMPLE 12

Expand $(x + 3)(x + 4)$.

$$(x + 3)(x + 4) = x(x + 4) + 3(x + 4)$$
$$= x^2 + 4x + 3x + 12$$
$$= x^2 + 7x + 12$$

EXAMPLE 13

Expand $(t + 5)(t - 2)$.

$$(t + 5)(t - 2) = t(t - 2) + 5(t - 2)$$
$$= t^2 - 2t + 5t - 10$$
$$= t^2 + 3t - 10$$

EXAMPLE 14

Expand $(m - 3)(m + 1)$.

$$(m - 3)(m + 1) = m(m + 1) - 3(m + 1)$$
$$= m^2 + m - 3m - 3$$
$$= m^2 - 2m - 3$$

EXAMPLE 15

Expand $(k - 3)^2$.

$$(k - 3)^2 = (k - 3)(k - 3) = k(k - 3) - 3(k - 3)$$
$$= k^2 - 3k - 3k + 9$$
$$= k^2 - 6k + 9$$

Warning: Be careful with the signs! This is the main reason that marks are lost in examination questions involving the expansion of brackets.

HINTS AND TIPS

You can also use FOIL. FOIL stands for First, Outer, Inner and Last terms.

$(t + 5)(t - 2)$

F gives t^2
O gives $-2t$
I gives $5t$
L gives -10

$= t^2 - 2t + 5t - 10$
$= t^2 + 3t - 10$

HINTS AND TIPS

You can also use the box method.

	k	-3
k	k^2	$-3k$
-3	$-3k$	$+9$

$= (k - 3)(k - 3)$
$= k^2 - 3k - 3k + 9$
$= k^2 - 6k + 9$

EXERCISE 7G

Expand the following expressions.

1 $(x + 3)(x + 2)$ **2** $(t + 4)(t + 3)$ **3** $(w + 1)(w + 3)$ **4** $(m + 5)(m + 1)$

5 $(k + 3)(k + 5)$ **6** $(a + 4)(a + 1)$ **7** $(x + 4)(x - 2)$ **8** $(t + 5)(t - 3)$

9 $(w + 3)(w - 1)$ **10** $(f + 2)(f - 3)$ **11** $(g + 1)(g - 4)$ **12** $(y + 4)(y - 3)$

13 $(x - 3)(x + 4)$ **14** $(p - 2)(p + 1)$ **15** $(k - 4)(k + 2)$

16 $(y - 2)(y + 5)$ **17** $(a - 1)(a + 3)$ **18** $(t - 3)(t + 4)$

19 $(x - 4)(x - 1)$ **20** $(r - 3)(r - 2)$ **21** $(m - 3)(m - 1)$

22 $(g - 4)(g - 2)$ **23** $(h - 5)(h - 3)$ **24** $(n - 1)^2$

25 $(x + 5)^2$ **26** $(t + 6)^2$ **27** $(3 - b)(5 + b)$

28 $(5 - y)(1 - y)$ **29** $(p - 4)^2$ **30** $(k - 2)^2$

HINTS AND TIPS

If you need to work out the square of an expression in brackets, always write down the brackets twice.
For example,
$(n - 1)^2 = (n - 1)(n - 1)$.

The expansions of the expressions below follow a pattern. Work out the first few and try to spot the pattern that will allow you immediately to write down the answers to the rest.

31 $(x + 3)(x - 3)$ **32** $(t + 5)(t - 5)$ **33** $(m + 4)(m - 4)$ **34** $(t + 2)(t - 2)$

35 $(y + 8)(y - 8)$ **36** $(p + 1)(p - 1)$ **37** $(5 + x)(5 - x)$ **38** $(7 + g)(7 - g)$

39 $(x - 6)(x + 6)$

7.6 Substitution

In this section you will learn how to:

- substitute numbers for letters in formulae and evaluate the resulting numerical expression
- use a calculator to evaluate numerical expressions

Key words

brackets
calculator
formula
substitution

One of the most important features of algebra is the use of expressions and **formulae**, and the **substitution** of real numbers into them.

The value of an expression, such as $3x + 2$, changes when different values of x are substituted into it. For example, the expression $3x + 2$ has the value:

5 when $x = 1$ 14 when $x = 4$

and so on. A formula expresses the value of one variable as the others in the formula change. For example, the formula for the area, A, of a triangle of base b and height h is:

$$A = \frac{b \times h}{2}$$

When $b = 4$ and $h = 8$:

$$A = \frac{4 \times 8}{2} = 16$$

EXAMPLE 16

The formula for the area of a trapezium is:

$$A = \frac{(a + b)h}{2}$$

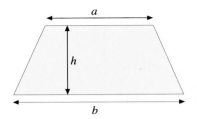

Find the area of the trapezium when $a = 5$, $b = 9$ and $h = 3$.

$$A = \frac{(5 + 9) \times 3}{2} = \frac{14 \times 3}{2} = 21$$

Always substitute the numbers for the letters before trying to work out the value of the expression. You are less likely to make a mistake this way. It is also useful to write **brackets** around each number, especially with negative numbers.

EXERCISE 7H

1 Find the value of $3x + 2$ when:

   a $x = 2$ **b** $x = 5$ **c** $x = 10$

HINTS AND TIPS

It helps to put the numbers in brackets.
$3(2) + 2 = 6 + 2 = 8$
$3(5) + 2 = 15 + 2 = 17$
etc …

2 Find the value of $4k - 1$ when:

   a $k = 1$ **b** $k = 3$ **c** $k = 11$

3 Find the value of $5 + 2t$ when:

   a $t = 2$ **b** $t = 5$ **c** $t = 12$

4 Evaluate $15 - 2f$ when: **a** $f = 3$ **b** $f = 5$ **c** $f = 8$

5 Evaluate $5m + 3$ when: **a** $m = 2$ **b** $m = 6$ **c** $m = 15$

6 Evaluate $3d - 2$ when: **a** $d = 4$ **b** $d = 5$ **c** $d = 20$

7 Find the value of $\frac{8 \times 4h}{5}$ when:

   a $h = 5$ **b** $h = 10$ **c** $h = 25$

8 Find the value of $\frac{25 - 3p}{2}$ when:

   a $p = 4$ **b** $p = 8$ **c** $p = 10$

9 Evaluate $\frac{x}{3}$ when: **a** $x = 6$ **b** $x = 24$ **c** $x = -30$

D

10 Evaluate $\dfrac{A}{4}$ when: **a** $A = 12$ **b** $A = 10$ **c** $A = -20$

11 Find the value of $\dfrac{12}{y}$ when: **a** $y = 2$ **b** $y = 4$ **c** $y = 6$

12 Find the value of $\dfrac{24}{x}$ when: **a** $x = 2$ **b** $x = 3$ **c** $x = 16$

Using your calculator

Now try working out a solution on your calculator, making up values for w and d. Remember to put in the brackets as required.

Look at this expression.

$$t = 5\left(\dfrac{w + 2d}{4}\right)$$

To find t when, for example, $w = 6$ and $d = 3$, key into your calculator:

You should get the answer 15.

Sometimes you need to work out the bottom part (denominator) of a fraction, such as:

$$k = \dfrac{8}{b - d}$$

You will need to use brackets to do this.

For example, to evaluate k when $b = 7$ and $d = 3$, key into your calculator:

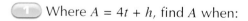

You should get the answer 2.

Notice that the expression does *not* include brackets, but you need to use them on your calculator.

EXERCISE 7I

1 Where $A = 4t + h$, find A when:

    a $t = 2$ and $h = 3$ **b** $t = 3$ and $h = 5$ **c** $t = 1$ and $h = 9$

2 Where $P = 5w - 4y$, find P when:

    a $w = 3$ and $y = 2$ **b** $w = 6$ and $y = 4$ **c** $w = 2$ and $y = 3$

3 Where $A = b^2 + c$, find A when:

    a $b = 2$ and $c = 3$ **b** $b = 5$ and $c = 7$ **c** $b = 1$ and $c = -4$

> **HINTS AND TIPS**
>
> With modern calculators you can type in the calculation as it reads. For example, $(5)^2 + 7$

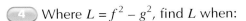

4 Where $L = f^2 - g^2$, find L when:

   a $f = 6$ and $g = 3$ **b** $f = 3$ and $g = 2$ **c** $f = 5$ and $g = 5$

5 Where $T = P - n^2$, find T when:

   a $P = 100$ and $n = 5$ **b** $P = 17$ and $n = 3$ **c** $P = 10$ and $n = 4$

6 Where $A = 180(n - 2)$, find A when:

   a $n = 7$ **b** $n = 3$ **c** $n = 2$

7 Where $t = 10 - \sqrt{P}$, find t when:

   a $P = 25$ **b** $P = 4$ **c** $P = 81$

8 Where $W = v + \dfrac{m}{5}$, find W when:

   a $v = 3$ and $m = 7$ **b** $v = 2$ and $m = 3$ **c** $v = -3$ and $m = 8$

ACTIVITY

In algebra, an *Identity* is an expression which is true for all values of the variable used.

For example:

$$x^2 - 4 \equiv (x - 2)(x + 2)$$

the three horizontal lines indicate an *Identity*.

Whatever value of x is put into the left-hand expression, makes the same value if placed into the right-hand expression.

e.g. $x = 3 : x^2 - 4 = 9 - 4 = 5$ $(x - 2)(x + 2) = 1 \times 5 = 5$

        $x = 7 : x^2 - 4 = 49 - 4 = 45$ $(x - 2)(x + 2) = 5 \times 9 = 45$

Note: Substitution alone will not prove an identity, only show it may be true. Algebra will be the means of sure proof. However a substitution can be used to show an identity is not true if an example can be found showing it not to be.

Find, by substitution or otherwise, which of the following pairs of expressions are identities, may be identities or are not identities.

Those that you feel are (or may be) write them out using the $\equiv$ sign.

a $6n, \quad \dfrac{12n^2}{2n}$

b $n^3 - 1, \quad (n + 1)(n^2 - 1)$

c $x + 1, \quad \dfrac{x^2 - 1}{x - 1}$

d $x^2 - 6, \quad (x + 3)(x - 3)$

e $(x - 2)^2 + 1, \quad x^2 - 4n + 5$

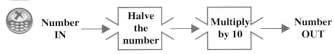

1 Here is a two-step number machine.

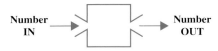
Number IN → Halve the number → Multiply by 10 → Number OUT

a Use the number machine to complete this table.

Number IN	Number OUT
6	30
18	
	170
27	

b The number machine can be simplifed. The two steps can be made into one step. What will this step be?

Number IN → ☐ → Number OUT

c The number IN is n. Write an expression for the Number OUT.

Number IN	Number OUT
n	

2 Simplify each expression.

a $t + 4t - 2t$ **b** $4p \times 3q$

c $8x - 12x$

3 The table shows some expressions.

$2(y + y)$	$2y + y$	$2y \times 2y$	$2y + 2y$	$2 + 2y$

Two of the expressions *always* have the same value as $4y$.

Which two are these?

4 An approximate rule for converting degrees Fahrenheit into degrees Celsius is:

$$C = \frac{F - 30}{2}$$

Use this rule to convert 18 °F into degrees Celsius.

5 **a** At a café, a cup of tea costs 55p. Write down an expression for the cost, in pence, of x cups of tea.

b **i** The cafe sells twice as many cups of coffee as it does cups of tea. Write down an expression for the number of cups of coffee sold when x cups of tea are sold.

   ii Each cup of coffee costs 80p. Write down an expression for the cost, in pence, of the cups of coffee sold.

6 **a** Simplify: $5a + 2b - a + 5b$

b Expand: $5(p + 2q - 3r)$

7 Using the formula $v = 4u - 3t$, calculate the value of v when $u = 12.1$ and $t = 7.2$.

8 **a** Simplify: $2x + 4y - x + 4y$

b Find the value of $3p + 5q$ when $p = 2$ and $q = -1$.

c Find the value of $u^2 + v^2$ when $u = 4$ and $v = -3$.

9 **a** Matt buys 10 boxes of apple juice at 24 pence each.

   i Calculate the total cost.

   ii He pays with a £10 note. How much change will he receive?

b Aisha buys c oranges at 20 pence each.

   i Write down an expression for the total cost in terms of c.

   ii She now buys d apples at 15 pence each. Write down an expression for the total cost of the apples and oranges.

10 Graham is y years old.

Harriet is 5 years older than Graham.

a Write down an expression for Harriet's age.

b Jane is half as old as Harriet. Write down an expression for Jane's age.

11 **a** Find the value of t^3 when $t = 5$.

b Find the value of $3t + 4m$ when $t = -1$ and $m = 3$.

c There are p seats in one single-decker bus and q seats in one double-decker bus. An outing uses four single-decker and six double-decker buses.

Write down an expression in terms of p and q for the number of seats available on the outing.

12 Using $m = 17.6$, $t = 42.3$, $r = 0.2$, work out the value of:

a $m + \dfrac{t}{r}$ **b** $\dfrac{m + t}{r}$

13 $d = 3e + 2h^2$

Calculate the value of d when $e = 3.7$ and $h = 2$.

14 **a** Expand and simplify this expression.
$2(x + 3) + 5(x + 2)$

b Expand and simplify this expression.
$(4x + y) - (2x - y)$

15 **a** Simplify

    i $3a + 4b - 2a - b$

    ii $5x^2 + 2x - 3x^2 - x$

  b Expand the brackets

    i $4(2x - 3)$

    ii $p(q - p^2)$

  c Expand and simplify $5(3p + 2) - 2(5p - 3)$

    Edexcel, Question 5, Paper 3 Intermediate, November 2004

16   **a** Simplify this expression. $3x + 4y + 6x - 3y - 5x$

  b Factorise this expression. $6c + 9$

  c Factorise this expression. $z^2 + 6z$

17   **a** **i** Multiply out and simplify this expression.

       $3(x - 3) + 2(x + 2)$

    ii Multiply out and simplify this expression.

       $(n - 1)^2$

  b Factorise completely the following expressions.

    i $6a^2 + a$

    ii $6x^2y^3 - 4xy^2$

18 **a** Factorise $p^2 + 6p$

  b Expand and simplify $(x + 7)(x - 4)$

    Edexcel, Question 11, Paper 3 Intermediate, June 2005

19   **a** Expand and simplify this expression.

     $3(x - 1) + 2(3x - 5)$

  b Expand and simplify this expression.

     $(x - 3)(x - 2)$

WORKED EXAM QUESTION

a Factorise completely: $6m^2 - 12mp$

b Simplify: $(2mt^2) \times (5tm^3)$

Solution

a $6m^2 - 12mp = 6m \times m - 6m \times 2p$

> Look for a common factor of 6 and 12, e.g. 6.
> Look for a common factor of m^2 and mp, e.g. m.

       $= 6m(m - 2p)$

> Split up the terms, using the common factors.

> Write as a factorised expression.

b $(2mt^2) \times (5tm^3) = 2 \times 5 \times t^2 \times t \times m \times m^3$

> Rearrange the expression to put numbers together and letters together.

       $= 10t^3m^4$

> Work out each part, remembering to add the indices.

A group of friends are planning a five-day walking holiday. The profile of their daily walks is shown below.

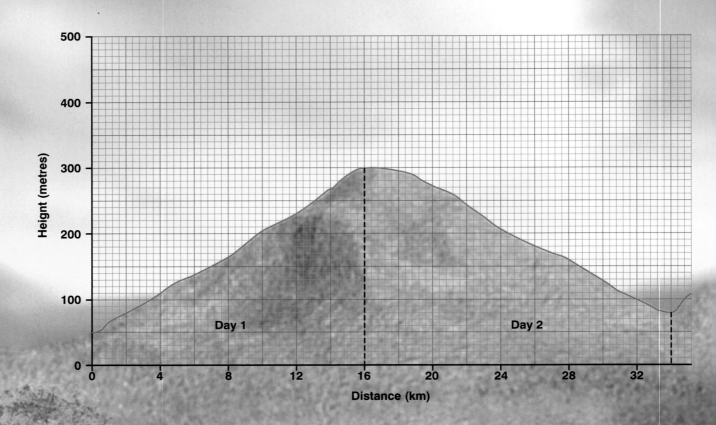

For every day, they work out the horizontal distance they will walk, in kilometres, and the height they climb, in metres. They calculate the length of time that each day's walk will take them, using the formula below.

$$T = 15D + \frac{H}{10}$$

where: T = time, in minutes
D = distance, in kilometres
H = height climbed, in metres

This formula assumes an average walking speed of 4km/h and an extra minute for each 10 metres climbed.

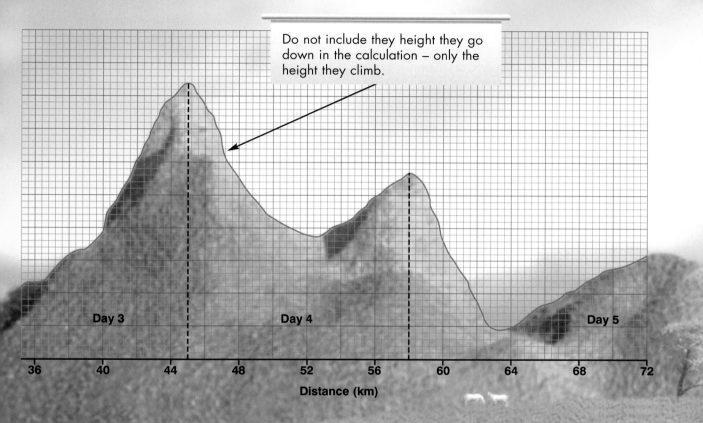

Do not include they height they go down in the calculation – only the height they climb.

Help them to complete the table so that they can work out how much time each day's walk will take, and the time at which they expect to finish.

Day	Distance (km)	Height climbed (m)	Time (minutes)	Time (hours and minutes)	Start time	Time allowed for breaks	Finish time
1					10.00 am	2 hours	
2	18	0	270	4 h 30 min	10.00 am	$1\frac{1}{2}$ hours	4.00 pm
3					9.30 am	$2\frac{1}{2}$ hours	
4					10.30 am	$2\frac{1}{2}$ hours	
5					10.30 am	$2\frac{1}{2}$ hours	

GRADE YOURSELF

G Able to use a formula expressed in words

F Can substitute numbers into expressions and use letters to write a simple algebraic expression

E Able to simplify expressions by collecting like terms

D Know how to use letters to write more complicated expressions, expand expressions with brackets and factorise simple expressions

C Can expand and simplify expressions with brackets, factorise expressions involving letters and numbers, and expand pairs of linear brackets to give quadratic expressions

What you should know now

- How to simplify a variety of algebraic expressions by multiplying, collecting like terms and expanding brackets
- How to factorise expressions by removing common factors
- How to substitute into expressions, using positive or negative whole numbers and decimals

Chapter 8

Further number skills

1 Long multiplication

2 Long division

3 Solving real-life problems

4 Arithmetic with decimal numbers

5 Arithmetic with fractions

6 Multiplying and dividing with negative numbers

7 Approximation of calculations

This chapter will show you ...

- a reminder of the ways you can multiply a three-digit number by a two-digit number
- a reminder of long division
- how to calculate with decimal numbers
- how to interchange decimals and fractions
- further fraction calculations
- how to multiply and divide negative numbers
- how to use decimal places and significant figures to make approximations
- sensible rounding methods

Visual overview

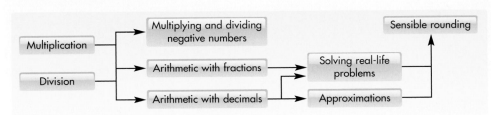

What you should already know

- Times tables up to 10×10
- How to cancel fractions

Quick check

1 Write down the first five multiples of 6.

2 Write down the first five multiples of 8.

3 Write down a number that is both a multiple of 3 and a multiple of 5.

4 Write down the smallest number that is a multiple of 4 and a multiple of 5.

5 Write down the smallest number that is a multiple of 4 and a multiple of 6.

6 Cancel the following fractions.

    a $\dfrac{8}{10}$ **b** $\dfrac{5}{20}$ **c** $\dfrac{4}{16}$ **d** $\dfrac{32}{100}$ **e** $\dfrac{36}{100}$ **f** $\dfrac{16}{24}$ **g** $\dfrac{16}{50}$

In this section you will learn how to:

- multiply a three-digit number (e.g. 358) by a two-digit number (e.g. 74) using
  - the partition method
  - the traditional method
  - the box method

Key words

carry mark
column
partition

When you are asked to do long multiplication on the GCSE non-calculator paper, you will be expected to use an appropriate method. The three most common are:

(1) the **partition** method, see Example 1 below

(2) the traditional method, see Example 2 below

(3) the box method, see Example 3 below.

EXAMPLE 1

Work out 358 × 74 by the partition method.

Set out a grid as shown.

- Put the larger number along the top and the smaller number down the right-hand side.

- Multiply each possible pair in the grid, putting the numbers into each half as shown.

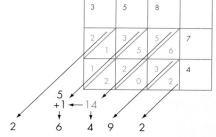

- Add up the numbers in each diagonal. If a total is larger than nine (in this example there is a total of 14), split the number and put the 1 in the next **column** on the left ready to be added in that diagonal.

- When you have completed the totalling, the number you are left with is the answer to the multiplication.

So, 358 × 74 = 26 492

EXAMPLE 2

Work out 357 × 24 without using a calculator.

There are several different ways to do long multiplication, but the following is perhaps the method that is most commonly used.

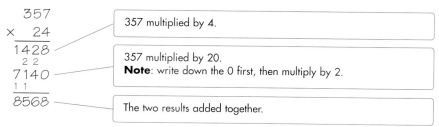

357 multiplied by 4.

357 multiplied by 20.
Note: write down the 0 first, then multiply by 2.

The two results added together.

So 357 × 24 = 8568

Note the use of **carry marks** to help with the calculation. Always try to keep carry marks much smaller than the other numbers, so that you don't confuse them with the main calculation.

EXAMPLE 3

Work out 243×68.

Split the two numbers into hundreds, tens and units and write them in a grid like the one below. Multiply all the pairs of numbers.

✕	200	40	3
60	12 000	2400	180
8	1600	320	24

Add the separate answers to find the total.

```
 12 000
  2 400
    180
  1 600
    320
     24
 ──────
 16 524
   1 1
```

So, $243 \times 68 = 16\,524$

EXERCISE 8A

Use your preferred method to calculate the following without using a calculator.

1 357×34 **2** 724×63 **3** 714×42 **4** 898×23

5 958×54 **6** 676×37 **7** 239×81 **8** 437×29

9 539×37 **10** 477×55 **11** 371×85 **12** 843×93

13 507×34 **14** 810×54 **15** 905×73 **16** 1435×72

17 2504×56 **18** 4037×23 **19** 8009×65 **20** 2070×38

8.2 Long division

In this section you will learn how to:
- divide, without a calculator, a three- or four-digit number by a two-digit number, e.g. $840 \div 24$

Key words
long
    division
remainder

There are several different ways of doing **long division**. It is acceptable to use any of them, provided it gives the correct answer and you can show all your working clearly. Two methods are shown in this book. Example 4 shows the *Italian method*. It is the most commonly used way of doing long division.

Example 5 shows a method of repeated subtraction, which is sometimes called the *chunking method*.

Sometimes, as here, you will not need a whole times table, and so you could jot down only those parts of the table that you will need. But, don't forget, you are going to have to work *without* a calculator, so you do need all the help you can get.

You may do a long division without writing down all the numbers. It will look like this:

$$24\overline{)8\ 4^{12}0}\quad\begin{array}{c}3\ 5\end{array}$$

Notice how the **remainder** from 84 is placed in front of the 0 to make it 120.

EXAMPLE 4

Work out $840 \div 24$.

It is a good idea to jot down the appropriate times table before you start the long division. In this case, it will be the 24 times table.

1	2	3	4	5	6	7	8	9
24	48	72	96	120	144	168	192	216

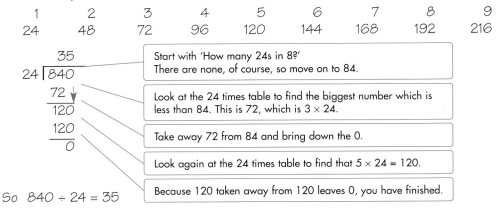

$$\begin{array}{r}35\\24\overline{)840}\\72\downarrow\\\hline120\\120\\\hline0\end{array}$$

Start with 'How many 24s in 8?'
There are none, of course, so move on to 84.

Look at the 24 times table to find the biggest number which is less than 84. This is 72, which is 3×24.

Take away 72 from 84 and bring down the 0.

Look again at the 24 times table to find that $5 \times 24 = 120$.

Because 120 taken away from 120 leaves 0, you have finished.

So $840 \div 24 = 35$

EXAMPLE 5

Work out $1655 \div 35$.

Jot down some of the multiples of 35 that may be useful.

$1 \times 35 = 35 \qquad 2 \times 35 = 70 \qquad 5 \times 35 = 175 \qquad 10 \times 35 = 350 \qquad 20 \times 35 = 700$

$$\begin{array}{r}1655\\-\ 700\quad 20\times35\\\hline955\\-\ 700\quad 20\times35\\\hline255\\-\ 175\quad 5\times35\\\hline80\\-\ 70\quad 2\times35\\\hline10\quad 47\end{array}$$

From 1655, subtract a large multiple of 35, such as $20 \times 35 = 700$.

From 955, subtract a large multiple of 35, such as $20 \times 35 = 700$.

From 255, subtract a multiple of 35, such as $5 \times 35 = 175$.

From 80, subtract a multiple of 35, such as $2 \times 35 = 70$.

Once the remainder of 10 has been found, you cannot subtract any more multiples of 35. Add up the multiples to see how many times 35 has been subtracted.

So, $1655 \div 35 = 47$, remainder 10

EXERCISE 8B

Solve the following by long division.

1. $525 \div 21$
2. $480 \div 32$
3. $925 \div 25$
4. $645 \div 15$
5. $621 \div 23$
6. $576 \div 12$
7. $1643 \div 31$
8. $728 \div 14$
9. $832 \div 26$
10. $2394 \div 42$
11. $829 \div 22$
12. $780 \div 31$
13. $895 \div 26$
14. $873 \div 16$
15. $875 \div 24$
16. $225 \div 13$
17. $759 \div 33$
18. $1478 \div 24$
19. $756 \div 18$
20. $1163 \div 43$

Solving real-life problems

In this section you will learn how to:

- identify which arithmetical process you need to solve some real-life problems

In your GCSE examination, you will not always be given simple, straightforward problems like those in Exercises 8A and 8B but *real* problems that you have to *read carefully*, *think about* and then *sort out* without using a calculator.

EXAMPLE 6

Naseema is organising a coach trip for 640 people. Each coach will carry 46 people. How many coaches are needed?

You need to divide the number of people (640) by the number of people in a coach (46).

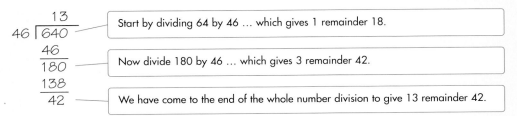

$$
\begin{array}{r}
13 \\
46\,\overline{\smash{)}\,640} \\
\underline{46} \\
180 \\
\underline{138} \\
42
\end{array}
$$

Start by dividing 64 by 46 ... which gives 1 remainder 18.

Now divide 180 by 46 ... which gives 3 remainder 42.

We have come to the end of the whole number division to give 13 remainder 42.

This tells Naseema that 14 coaches are needed to take all 640 passengers.
(There will be 46 − 42 = 4 spare seats)

EXERCISE 8C

1. There are 48 cans of soup in a crate. A supermarket had a delivery of 125 crates of soup. How many cans of soup were there in this delivery?

2. Greystones Primary School has 12 classes, each of which has 26 pupils. How many pupils are there at Greystones Primary School?

3. 3600 supporters of Barnsley Football Club want to go to an away game by coach. Each coach can hold 53 passengers. How many coaches will they need altogether?

4. How many stamps costing 26p each can I buy for £10?

5. Suhail walks to school each day, there and back. The distance to school is 450 metres. How far will he walk in a school term consisting of 64 days?

6. On one page of a newspaper there are seven columns. In each column there are 172 lines, and in each line there are 50 letters. How many letters are there on the page?

7. A tank of water was emptied into casks. Each cask held 81 litres. 71 casks were filled and there were 68 litres left over. How much water was there in the tank to start with?

8. Joy was going to do a sponsored walk to raise money for the Macmillan Nurses. She managed to get 18 people to sponsor her, each for 35p per kilometre. She walked a total of 48 kilometres. How much sponsor money should she expect to collect?

9 Kirsty collects small models of animals. Each one costs 45p. Her pocket money is £15 a month. How many model animals could Kirsty buy with one month's pocket money?

10 Amina wanted to save up to see a concert. The cost of a ticket was £25. She was paid 75p per hour to mind her little sister. For how many hours would Amina have to mind her sister to be able to afford the ticket?

11 The magazine *Teen Dance* comes out every month. The annual (yearly) subscription for the magazine is £21. How much does each magazine cost per month?

12 Paula buys a music centre for her club at a cost of 95p a week for 144 weeks. How much will she actually pay for this music centre?

8.4 Arithmetic with decimal numbers

In this section you will learn how to:
- identify the information that a decimal number shows
- round a decimal number
- identify decimal places
- add and subtract two decimal numbers
- multiply and divide a decimal number by a whole number less than 10
- multiply a decimal number by a two-digit number
- multiply a decimal number by another decimal number

Key words
decimal
   fraction
decimal
   place
decimal
   point
digit

The number system is extended by using decimal numbers to represent fractions.

The **decimal point** separates the **decimal fraction** from the whole-number part.

For example, the number 25.374 means:

Tens	Units		Tenths	Hundredths	Thousandths
10	1		$\frac{1}{10}$	$\frac{1}{100}$	$\frac{1}{1000}$
2	**5**	**.**	**3**	**7**	**4**

You already use decimal notation to express amounts of money. For example:

£32.67   means
$3 \times £10$
$2 \times £1$
$6 \times £0.10$ (10 pence)
$7 \times £0.01$ (1 penny)

Decimal places

When a number is written in decimal form, the **digits** to the right of the decimal point are called **decimal places**. For example:

79.4 is written 'with one decimal place'

6.83 is written 'with two decimal places'

0.526 is written 'with three decimal places'.

To round a decimal number to a particular number of decimal places, take these steps:

- Count along the decimal places from the decimal point and look at the first digit to be removed.

- When the value of this digit is less than 5, just remove the unwanted places.

- When the value of this digit is 5 or more, add 1 onto the digit in the last decimal place then remove the unwanted places.

Here are some examples.

5.852 rounds to 5.85 to two decimal places

7.156 rounds to 7.16 to two decimal places

0.274 rounds to 0.3 to one decimal place

15.3518 rounds to 15.4 to one decimal place

EXERCISE 8D

1 Round each of the following numbers to one decimal place.

a 4.83	**b** 3.79	**c** 2.16	**d** 8.25
e 3.673	**f** 46.935	**g** 23.883	**h** 9.549
i 11.08	**j** 33.509	**k** 7.054	**l** 46.807
m 0.057	**n** 0.109	**o** 0.599	**p** 64.99
q 213.86	**r** 76.07	**s** 455.177	**t** 50.999

> **HINTS AND TIPS**
>
> Just look at the value of the digit in the second decimal place.

2 Round each of the following numbers to two decimal places.

a 5.783	**b** 2.358	**c** 0.977	**d** 33.085
e 6.007	**f** 23.5652	**g** 91.7895	**h** 7.995
i 2.3076	**j** 23.9158	**k** 5.9999	**l** 1.0075
m 3.5137	**n** 96.508	**o** 0.009	**p** 0.065
q 7.8091	**r** 569.897	**s** 300.004	**t** 0.0099

3 Round each of the following to the number of decimal places (dp) indicated.

a 4.568 (1 dp)	**b** 0.0832 (2 dp)	**c** 45.715 93 (3 dp)
d 94.8531 (2 dp)	**e** 602.099 (1 dp)	**f** 671.7629 (2 dp)
g 7.1124 (1 dp)	**h** 6.903 54 (3 dp)	**i** 13.7809 (2 dp)
j 0.075 11 (1 dp)	**k** 4.001 84 (3 dp)	**l** 59.983 (1 dp)
m 11.9854 (2 dp)	**n** 899.995 85 (3 dp)	**o** 0.0699 (1 dp)
p 0.009 87 (2 dp)	**q** 6.0708 (1 dp)	**r** 78.3925 (3 dp)
s 199.9999 (2 dp)	**t** 5.0907 (1 dp)	

 Round each of the following to the nearest whole number.

a 8.7	**b** 9.2	**c** 2.7	**d** 6.5
e 3.28	**f** 7.82	**g** 3.19	**h** 7.55
i 6.172	**j** 3.961	**k** 7.388	**l** 1.514
m 46.78	**n** 23.19	**o** 96.45	**p** 32.77
q 153.9	**r** 342.5	**s** 704.19	**t** 909.5

Adding and subtracting with decimals

When you are working with decimals, you must *always* set out your work properly.

Make sure that the decimal points are in line underneath the first point and each digit is in its correct place or column.

Then you can add or subtract just as you have done before. The decimal point of the answer will be placed directly underneath the other decimal points.

EXAMPLE 7

Work out 4.72 + 13.53

$$\begin{array}{r} 4.72 \\ +\ 13.53 \\ \hline 18.25 \\ \hline {\scriptstyle 1} \end{array}$$

So, 4.72 + 13.53 = 18.25

Notice how to deal with 7 + 5 = 12, the 1 carrying forward into the next column.

EXAMPLE 8

Work out 7.3 − 1.5

$$\begin{array}{r} {}^{6}\!7.{}^{1}3 \\ -\ \ 1.5 \\ \hline 5.8 \end{array}$$

So, 7.3 − 1.5 = 5.8

Notice how to deal with the fact that you cannot take 5 from 3. You have to take one of the units from 7, replace the 7 with a 6 and make the 3 into 13.

Hidden decimal point

Whole numbers are usually written without decimal points. Sometimes you *do* need to show the decimal point in a whole number (see Example 9), in which case it is placed at the right-hand side of the number, followed by a zero.

EXAMPLE 9

Work out 4.2 + 8 + 12.9

$$\begin{array}{r} 4.2 \\ 8.0 \\ + 12.9 \\ \hline 25.1 \\ \hline \scriptstyle 1\ 1 \end{array}$$

So 4.2 + 8 + 12.9 = 25.1

EXERCISE 8E

1 Work out each of these.

a 47.3 + 2.5   b 16.7 + 4.6   c 43.5 + 4.8

d 28.5 + 4.8   e 1.26 + 4.73   f 2.25 + 5.83

g 83.5 + 6.7   h 8.3 + 12.9   i 3.65 + 8.5

j 7.38 + 5.7   k 7.3 + 5.96   l 6.5 + 17.86

2 Work out each of these.

a 3.8 − 2.4   b 4.3 − 2.5   c 7.6 − 2.8

d 8.7 − 4.9   e 8.25 − 4.5   f 19.7 − 13.8

g 9.4 − 5.7   h 8.62 − 4.85   i 8 − 4.3

j 9 − 7.6   k 15 − 3.2   l 24 − 8.7

> **HINTS AND TIPS**
>
> When the numbers to be added or subtracted do not have the same number of decimal places, put in extra zeros, for example:
>
> $$\begin{array}{r} 3.65 \\ + 8.50 \\ \hline \end{array} \qquad \begin{array}{r} 8.25 \\ - 4.50 \\ \hline \end{array}$$

3 Evaluate each of the following. (Take care – they are a mixture.)

a 23.8 + 6.9   b 8.3 − 1.7   c 9 − 5.2

d 12.9 + 3.8   e 17.4 − 5.6   f 23.4 + 6.8

g 35 + 8.3   h 9.54 − 2.81   i 34.8 + 3.15

j 8.1 − 3.4   k 12.5 − 8.7   l 198.5 + 12

Multiplying and dividing decimals by single-digit numbers

You can carry out these operations in exactly the same way as with whole numbers, as long as you remember to put each digit in its correct column.

Again, the decimal point is kept in line underneath or above the first point.

EXAMPLE 10

Work out 4.5 × 3

$$\begin{array}{r} 4.5 \\ \times \quad 3 \\ \hline 13.5 \\ \hline 1 \end{array}$$

So, 4.5 × 3 = 13.5

EXAMPLE 11

Work out 8.25 ÷ 5

$$5\,\overline{\smash{\big)}\,8.^3 2^2 5}\; ^{1.\ 6\ 5}$$

So, 8.25 ÷ 5 = 1.65

EXAMPLE 12

Work out 5.7 ÷ 2

$$2\,\overline{\smash{\big)}\,5.^1 7^1 0}\; ^{2.\ 8\ 5}$$

So, 5.7 ÷ 2 = 2.85

> **HINTS AND TIPS**
>
> We add a 0 after the 5.7 in order to continue dividing.
> We do not use remainders with decimal places.

EXERCISE 8F

1 Evaluate each of these.

a 2.4 × 3	**b** 3.8 × 2	**c** 4.7 × 4	**d** 5.3 × 7
e 6.5 × 5	**f** 3.6 × 8	**g** 2.5 × 4	**h** 9.2 × 6
i 12.3 × 5	**j** 24.4 × 7	**k** 13.6 × 6	**l** 19.3 × 5

2 Evaluate each of these.

a 2.34 × 4	**b** 3.45 × 3	**c** 5.17 × 5	**d** 4.26 × 3
e 0.26 × 7	**f** 0.82 × 4	**g** 0.56 × 5	**h** 0.92 × 6
i 6.03 × 7	**j** 7.02 × 8	**k** 2.55 × 3	**l** 8.16 × 6

3 Evaluate each of these.

a $3.6 \div 2$	**b** $5.6 \div 4$	**c** $4.2 \div 3$	**d** $8.4 \div 7$
e $4.26 \div 2$	**f** $3.45 \div 5$	**g** $8.37 \div 3$	**h** $9.68 \div 8$
i $7.56 \div 4$	**j** $5.43 \div 3$	**k** $1.32 \div 4$	**l** $7.6 \div 4$

4 Evaluate each of these.

a $3.5 \div 2$	**b** $6.4 \div 5$	**c** $7.4 \div 4$	**d** $7.3 \div 2$
e $8.3 \div 5$	**f** $5.8 \div 4$	**g** $7.1 \div 5$	**h** $9.2 \div 8$
i $6.7 \div 2$	**j** $4.9 \div 5$	**k** $9.2 \div 4$	**l** $7.3 \div 5$

HINTS AND TIPS

Remember to keep the decimal points in line.

5 Evaluate each of these.

a $7.56 \div 4$	**b** $4.53 \div 3$	**c** $1.32 \div 5$	**d** $8.53 \div 2$
e $2.448 \div 2$	**f** $1.274 \div 7$	**g** $0.837 \div 9$	**h** $16.336 \div 8$
i $9.54 \div 5$	**j** $14 \div 5$	**k** $17 \div 4$	**l** $37 \div 2$

6 Soup is sold in packs of five for £3.25 and packs of eight for £5. Which is the cheaper way of buying soup?

7 Mike took his wife and four children to a theme park. The tickets were £13.25 for each adult and £5.85 for each child. How much did all the tickets cost Mike?

8 Mary was laying a path through her garden. She bought nine paving stones, each 1.35 m long. She wanted the path to run straight down the garden, which is 10 m long. Has Mary bought too many paving stones? Show all your working.

Long multiplication with decimals

As before, you must put each digit in its correct column and keep the decimal point in line.

EXAMPLE 13

Evaluate 4.27×34

```
       4.27
  ×      34
     17.08
      1 2
    128.10
        2
    145.18
      1
```

So, $4.27 \times 34 = 145.18$

EXERCISE 8G

1 Evaluate each of these.

a 3.72×24 **b** 5.63×53 **c** 1.27×52 **d** 4.54×37

e 67.2×35 **f** 12.4×26 **g** 62.1×18 **h** 81.3×55

i 5.67×82 **j** 0.73×35 **k** 23.8×44 **l** 99.5×19

2 Find the total cost of each of the following purchases.

a Eighteen ties at £12.45 each

b Twenty-five shirts at £8.95 each

c Thirteen pairs of tights at £2.30 a pair

> **HINTS AND TIPS**
>
> When the answer is an amount of money, in pounds, you must write it with two places of decimals. Writing £224.1 may lose you a mark. It should be £224.10.

3 A party of 24 scouts and their leader went into a zoo. The cost of a ticket for each scout was £2.15, and the cost of a ticket for the leader was £2.60. What was the total cost of entering the zoo?

4 A market gardener bought 35 trays of seedlings. Each tray cost £3.45. What was the total cost of the trays of seedlings?

Multiplying two decimal numbers together

Follow these steps to multiply one decimal number by another decimal number.

- First, complete the whole calculation as if the decimal points were not there.

- Then, count the total number of decimal places in the two decimal numbers. This gives the number of decimal places in the answer.

EXAMPLE 14

Evaluate 3.42×2.7

Ignoring the decimal points gives the following calculation:

```
      342
  ×    27
    2394
     2 1
    6840
    9234
     1 1
```

Now, 3.42 has two decimal places (.42) and 2.7 has one decimal place (.7). So, the total number of decimal places in the answer is three.

So $3.42 \times 2.7 = 9.234$

EXERCISE 8H

1 Evaluate each of these.

a 2.4×0.2 **b** 7.3×0.4 **c** 5.6×0.2 **d** 0.3×0.4

e 0.14×0.2 **f** 0.3×0.3 **g** 0.24×0.8 **h** 5.82×0.52

i 5.8×1.23 **j** 5.6×9.1 **k** 0.875×3.5 **l** 9.12×5.1

2 For each of the following:

i estimate the answer by first rounding each number to the nearest whole number

ii calculate the exact answer, and then calculate the difference between this and your answers to part **i**.

a 4.8×7.3 **b** 2.4×7.6 **c** 15.3×3.9 **d** 20.1×8.6

e 4.35×2.8 **f** 8.13×3.2 **g** 7.82×5.2 **h** 19.8×7.1

8.5 Arithmetic with fractions

In this section you will learn how to:
- change a decimal number to a fraction
- change a fraction to a decimal
- add and subtract fractions with different denominators
- multiply a mixed number by a fraction
- divide one fraction by another fraction

Key words
decimal
denominator
fraction
mixed
   number
numerator

Changing a decimal into a fraction

A **decimal** can be changed into a **fraction** by using the place-value table on page 172.

EXAMPLE 15

Express 0.32 as a fraction.

$$0.32 = \frac{32}{100}$$

This cancels to $\frac{8}{25}$

So $0.32 = \frac{8}{25}$

Changing a fraction into a decimal

You can change a fraction into a decimal by dividing the **numerator** by the **denominator**. Example 16 shows how this can be done without a calculator.

EXAMPLE 16

Express $\frac{3}{8}$ as a decimal.

$\frac{3}{8}$ means $3 \div 8$. This is done as a division calculation:

$$\begin{array}{r} 0.\;3\;7\;5 \\ 8\;\overline{)\;3.^30^60^40} \end{array}$$

So $\frac{3}{8} = 0.375$

Notice that extra zeros have been put at the end to be able to complete the division.

EXERCISE 8I

1 Change each of these decimals to fractions, cancelling where possible.

a 0.7   **b** 0.4   **c** 0.5   **d** 0.03   **e** 0.06

f 0.13   **g** 0.25   **h** 0.38   **i** 0.55   **j** 0.64

2 Change each of these fractions to decimals. Where necessary, give your answer correct to three decimal places.

a $\frac{1}{2}$ **b** $\frac{3}{4}$ **c** $\frac{3}{5}$ **d** $\frac{9}{10}$ **e** $\frac{1}{3}$

f $\frac{5}{8}$ **g** $\frac{2}{3}$ **h** $\frac{7}{20}$ **i** $\frac{7}{11}$ **j** $\frac{4}{9}$

3 Put each of the following sets of numbers in order, with the smallest first.

a 0.6, 0.3, $\frac{1}{2}$ **b** $\frac{2}{5}$, 0.8, 0.3

c 0.35, $\frac{1}{4}$, 0.15   **d** $\frac{7}{10}$, 0.72, 0.71

e 0.8, $\frac{3}{4}$, 0.7   **f** 0.08, 0.1, $\frac{1}{20}$

g 0.55, $\frac{1}{2}$, 0.4   **h** $1\frac{1}{4}$, 1.2, 1.23

> **HINTS AND TIPS**
>
> Convert the fractions to decimals first.

Addition and subtraction of fractions

Fractions can only be added or subtracted after you have changed them to equivalent fractions with the same denominator.

For example:

i $\dfrac{2}{3} + \dfrac{1}{5}$

Note you can change both fractions to equivalent fractions with a denominator of 15.

This then becomes:

$$\dfrac{2 \times 5}{3 \times 5} + \dfrac{1 \times 3}{5 \times 3} = \dfrac{10}{15} + \dfrac{3}{15} = \dfrac{13}{15}$$

ii $2\dfrac{3}{4} - 1\dfrac{5}{6}$

Split the calculation into $\left(2 + \dfrac{3}{4}\right) - \left(1 + \dfrac{5}{6}\right)$.

This then becomes:

$2 - 1 + \dfrac{3}{4} - \dfrac{5}{6}$

Note you can change both fractions to equivalent fractions with a denominator of 12.

$= 1 + \dfrac{9}{12} - \dfrac{10}{12} = 1 - \dfrac{1}{12}$

$= \dfrac{11}{12}$

EXERCISE 8J

1 Evaluate the following.

a $\dfrac{1}{3} + \dfrac{1}{5}$

b $\dfrac{1}{3} + \dfrac{1}{4}$

c $\dfrac{1}{5} + \dfrac{1}{10}$

d $\dfrac{2}{3} + \dfrac{1}{4}$

e $\dfrac{3}{4} + \dfrac{1}{8}$

f $\dfrac{1}{3} + \dfrac{1}{6}$

g $\dfrac{1}{2} - \dfrac{1}{3}$

h $\dfrac{1}{4} - \dfrac{1}{5}$

i $\dfrac{1}{5} - \dfrac{1}{10}$

j $\dfrac{7}{8} - \dfrac{3}{4}$

k $\dfrac{5}{6} - \dfrac{3}{4}$

l $\dfrac{5}{6} - \dfrac{1}{2}$

m $\dfrac{5}{12} - \dfrac{1}{4}$

n $\dfrac{1}{3} + \dfrac{4}{9}$

o $\dfrac{1}{4} + \dfrac{3}{8}$

p $\dfrac{7}{8} - \dfrac{1}{2}$

q $\dfrac{3}{5} - \dfrac{8}{15}$

r $\dfrac{11}{12} + \dfrac{5}{8}$

s $\dfrac{7}{16} + \dfrac{3}{10}$

t $\dfrac{4}{9} - \dfrac{2}{21}$

u $\dfrac{5}{6} - \dfrac{4}{27}$

2 Evaluate the following.

a $2\frac{1}{7} + 1\frac{3}{14}$

b $6\frac{3}{10} + 1\frac{4}{5} + 2\frac{1}{2}$

c $3\frac{1}{2} - 1\frac{1}{3}$

d $1\frac{7}{18} + 2\frac{3}{10}$

e $3\frac{2}{6} + 1\frac{9}{20}$

f $1\frac{1}{8} - \frac{5}{9}$

g $1\frac{3}{16} - \frac{7}{12}$

h $\frac{5}{6} + \frac{7}{16} + \frac{5}{8}$

i $\frac{7}{10} + \frac{3}{8} + \frac{5}{6}$

j $1\frac{1}{3} + \frac{7}{10} - \frac{4}{15}$

k $\frac{5}{14} + 1\frac{3}{7} - \frac{5}{12}$

3 In a class of children, three-quarters are Chinese, one-fifth are Malay and the rest are Indian. What fraction of the class are Indian?

4 In a class election, half of the people voted for Aminah, one-third voted for Janet and the rest voted for Peter. What fraction of the class voted for Peter?

5 A group of people travelled from Hope to Castletown. One-twentieth of them decided to walk, one-twelfth went by car and all the rest went by bus. What fraction went by bus?

6 A one-litre flask filled with milk is used to fill two glasses, one of capacity half a litre and the other of capacity one-sixth of a litre. What fraction of a litre will remain in the flask?

7 Katie spent three-eighths of her income on rent, and two-fifths of what was left on food. What fraction of her income was left after buying her food?

Multiplication of fractions

Remember:

- To multiply two fractions, multiply the numerators (top numbers) and multiply the denominators (bottom numbers) and cancel if possible.

- When multiplying a **mixed number**, change the mixed number to a top-heavy fraction before you start multiplying.

EXAMPLE 17

Work out $\qquad 1\frac{3}{4} \times \frac{2}{5}$.

Change the mixed number to a top-heavy fraction.

$1\frac{3}{4}$ to $\frac{7}{4}$

The problem is now:

$\frac{7}{4} \times \frac{2}{5}$

So, $\frac{7}{4} \times \frac{2}{5} = \frac{14}{20}$ which cancels to $\frac{7}{10}$.

EXAMPLE 18

A boy had 930 stamps in his collection. $\frac{2}{15}$ of them were British stamps. How many British stamps did he have?

The problem is:

$$\frac{2}{15} \times 930$$

First, calculate $\frac{1}{15}$ of 930.

$$\frac{1}{15} \times 930 = 930 \div 15 = 62$$

So, $\frac{2}{15}$ of 930 = 2 × 62 = 124

He has 124 British stamps.

EXERCISE 8K

1 Evaluate the following, leaving each answer in its simplest form.

a $\frac{1}{2} \times \frac{1}{3}$ **b** $\frac{1}{4} \times \frac{2}{5}$ **c** $\frac{3}{4} \times \frac{1}{2}$ **d** $\frac{3}{7} \times \frac{1}{2}$

e $\frac{2}{3} \times \frac{4}{5}$ **f** $\frac{1}{3} \times \frac{3}{5}$ **g** $\frac{1}{3} \times \frac{6}{7}$ **h** $\frac{3}{4} \times \frac{2}{5}$

i $\frac{5}{16} \times \frac{3}{10}$ **j** $\frac{2}{3} \times \frac{3}{4}$ **k** $\frac{1}{2} \times \frac{4}{5}$ **l** $\frac{9}{10} \times \frac{5}{12}$

m $\frac{14}{15} \times \frac{3}{8}$ **n** $\frac{8}{9} \times \frac{6}{15}$ **o** $\frac{6}{7} \times \frac{21}{30}$ **p** $\frac{9}{14} \times \frac{35}{36}$

2 I walked two-thirds of the way along Pungol Road which is four and a half kilometres long. How far have I walked?

3 One-quarter of Alan's stamp collection was given to him by his sister. Unfortunately two-thirds of these were torn. What fraction of his collection was given to him by his sister and were not torn?

4 Bilal eats one-quarter of a cake, and then half of what is left. How much cake is left uneaten?

5 A merchant buys 28 crates, each containing three-quarters of a tonne of waste metal. What is the total weight of this order?

6 Because of illness, on one day $\frac{2}{5}$ of a school was absent. If the school had 650 pupils on the register, how many were absent that day?

7 To increase sales, a shop reduced the price of a car stereo radio by $\frac{2}{5}$. If the original price was £85, what was the new price?

8 Two-fifths of a class were boys. If the class contained 30 children, how many were girls?

9 Evaluate the following, giving each answer as a mixed number where possible.

a $1\frac{1}{4} \times \frac{1}{3}$

b $1\frac{2}{3} \times 1\frac{1}{4}$

c $2\frac{1}{2} \times 2\frac{1}{2}$

d $1\frac{3}{4} \times 1\frac{2}{3}$

e $3\frac{1}{4} \times 1\frac{1}{5}$

f $1\frac{1}{4} \times 2\frac{2}{3}$

g $2\frac{1}{2} \times 5$

h $7\frac{1}{2} \times 4$

10 Which is larger, $\frac{3}{4}$ of $2\frac{1}{2}$ or $\frac{2}{5}$ of $6\frac{1}{2}$?

11 After James spent $\frac{2}{5}$ of his pocket money on magazines, and $\frac{1}{4}$ of his pocket money at a football match, he had £1.75 left. How much pocket money did he have in the beginning?

12 Which is the biggest: half of 96, one-third of 141, two-fifths of 120, or three-quarters of 68?

13 At a burger-eating competition, Lionel ate 34 burgers in 20 minutes while Ahmed ate 26 burgers in 20 minutes. How long after the start of the competition would they have consumed a total of 21 burgers between them?

14 If £5.20 is two-thirds of three-quarters of a sum of money, what is the sum?

15 Emily lost $\frac{3}{4}$ of her money in the market, but then found $\frac{3}{5}$ of what she had lost. She now had £21 altogether. How much did she start with?

Dividing fractions

Look at the problem $3 \div \frac{3}{4}$. This is like asking, 'How many $\frac{3}{4}$s are there in 3?'

Look at the diagram.

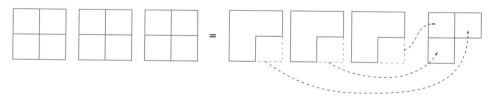

Each of the three whole shapes is divided into quarters. How many 3s go into the total number of quarters?

Can you see that you could fit the four shapes on the right-hand side of the = sign into the three shapes on the left-hand side?

i.e. $3 \div \frac{3}{4} = 4$

or $3 \div \frac{3}{4} = 3 \times \frac{4}{3} = \frac{3 \times 4}{3} = \frac{12}{3} = 4$

So, to divide by a fraction, you turn the fraction upside down (finding its reciprocal), and then multiply.

EXERCISE 8L

1 Evaluate the following, giving your answer as a mixed number where possible.

a $\dfrac{1}{4} \div \dfrac{1}{3}$ **b** $\dfrac{2}{5} \div \dfrac{2}{7}$ **c** $\dfrac{4}{5} \div \dfrac{3}{4}$ **d** $\dfrac{3}{7} \div \dfrac{2}{5}$

e $5 \div 1\dfrac{1}{4}$ **f** $6 \div 1\dfrac{1}{2}$ **g** $7\dfrac{1}{2} \div 1\dfrac{1}{2}$ **h** $3 \div 1\dfrac{3}{4}$

i $1\dfrac{5}{12} \div 3\dfrac{3}{16}$ **j** $3\dfrac{3}{5} \div 2\dfrac{1}{4}$

2 A grain merchant has only thirteen and a half tonnes in stock. He has several customers who are all ordering three-quarters of a tonne. How many customers can he supply?

3 For a party, Zahar made twelve and a half litres of lemonade. His glasses could each hold $\dfrac{5}{16}$ of a litre. How many of the glasses could he fill from the twelve and a half litres of lemonade?

4 How many strips of ribbon, each three and a half centimetres long, can I cut from a roll of ribbon that is fifty-two and a half centimetres long?

5 Joe's stride is three-quarters of a metre long. How many strides does he take to walk the length of a bus twelve metres long?

6 Evaluate the following, giving your answers as a mixed number where possible.

a $2\dfrac{2}{9} \times 2\dfrac{1}{10} \times \dfrac{16}{35}$ **b** $3\dfrac{1}{5} \times 2\dfrac{1}{2} \times 4\dfrac{3}{4}$

c $1\dfrac{1}{4} \times 1\dfrac{2}{7} \times 1\dfrac{1}{6}$ **d** $\dfrac{18}{25} \times \dfrac{15}{16} \div 2\dfrac{2}{5}$

e $\left(\dfrac{2}{5} \times \dfrac{2}{5}\right) \times \left(\dfrac{5}{6} \times \dfrac{5}{6}\right) \times \left(\dfrac{3}{4} \times \dfrac{3}{4}\right)$ **f** $\left(\dfrac{4}{5} \times \dfrac{4}{5}\right) \div \left(1\dfrac{1}{4} \times 1\dfrac{1}{4}\right)$

8.6 Multiplying and dividing with negative numbers

In this section you will learn how to:

- multiply and divide with negative numbers

The rules for multiplying and dividing with negative numbers are very easy.

- When the signs of the numbers are the *same*, the answer is *positive*.

- When the signs of the numbers are *different*, the answer is *negative*.

Here are some examples.

$2 \times 4 = 8$ $12 \div -3 = -4$ $-2 \times -3 = 6$ $-12 \div -3 = 4$

EXERCISE 8M

1 Write down the answers to the following.

a −3 × 5	**b** −2 × 7	**c** −4 × 6	**d** −2 × −3	**e** −7 × −2
f −12 ÷ −6	**g** −16 ÷ 8	**h** 24 ÷ −3	**i** 16 ÷ −4	**j** −6 ÷ −2
k 4 × −6	**l** 5 × −2	**m** 6 × −3	**n** −2 × −8	**o** −9 × −4
p 24 ÷ −6	**q** 12 ÷ −1	**r** −36 ÷ 9	**s** −14 ÷ −2	**t** 100 ÷ 4
u −2 × −9	**v** 32 ÷ −4	**w** 5 × −9	**x** −21 ÷ −7	**y** −5 × 8

2 Write down the answers to the following.

a −3 + −6	**b** −2 × −8	**c** 2 + −5	**d** 8 × −4	**e** −36 ÷ −2
f −3 × −6	**g** −3 − −9	**h** 48 ÷ −12	**i** −5 × −4	**j** 7 − −9
k −40 ÷ −5	**l** −40 + −8	**m** 4 − −9	**n** 5 − 18	**o** 72 ÷ −9
p −7 − −7	**q** 8 − −8	**r** 6 × −7	**s** −6 ÷ −1	**t** −5 ÷ −5
u −9 − 5	**v** 4 − −2	**w** 4 ÷ −1	**x** −7 ÷ −1	**y** −4 × 0

3 What number do you multiply by −3 to get the following?

a 6	**b** −90	**c** −45	**d** 81	**e** 21

4 What number do you divide −36 by to get the following?

a −9	**b** 4	**c** 12	**d** −6	**e** 9

5 Evaluate the following.

a −6 + (4 − 7)	**b** −3 − (−9 − −3)	**c** 8 + (2 − 9)

6 Evaluate the following.

a 4 × (−8 ÷ −2)	**b** −8 −(3 × −2)	**c** −1 × (8 − −4)

7 What do you get if you divide −48 by the following?

a −2	**b** −8	**c** 12	**d** 24

8 Write down six different multiplications that give the answer −12.

9 Write down six different divisions that give the answer −4.

10 Find the answers to the following.

a −3 × −7	**b** 3 + −7	**c** −4 ÷ −2	**d** −7 − 9	**e** −12 ÷ −6
f −12 − −7	**g** 5 × −7	**h** −8 + −9	**i** −4 + −8	**j** −3 + 9
k −5 × −9	**l** −16 ÷ 8	**m** −8 − −8	**n** 6 ÷ −6	**o** −4 + −3
p −9 × 4	**q** −36 ÷ −4	**r** −4 × −8	**s** −1 − −1	**t** 2 − 67

Approximation of calculations

In this section you will learn how to:

- identify significant figures
- round to one significant figure
- approximate the result before multiplying two numbers together
- approximate the result before dividing two numbers
- round a calculation, at the end of a problem, to give what is considered to be a sensible answer

Key words

approximate
round
significant
    figure

Rounding to significant figures

You will often use **significant figures** when you want to **approximate** a number with quite a few digits in it.

The following table illustrates some numbers written correct to one, two and three significant figures (sf).

One sf	8	50	200	90 000	0.000 07	0.003	0.4
Two sf	67	4.8	0.76	45 000	730	0.006 7	0.40
Three sf	312	65.9	40.3	0.0761	7.05	0.003 01	0.400

In the GCSE exam you only have to **round** numbers correct to one significant figure.

The steps taken to round a number to one significant figure are very similar to those used for decimal places.

- From the left, find the second digit. If the original number is less than 1, start counting from the first non-zero digit.

- When the value of the second digit is less than 5, leave the first digit as it is.

- When the value of the second digit is equal to or greater than 5, add 1 to the first digit.

- Put in enough zeros at the end to keep the number the right size.

For example, the following tables show some numbers rounded to one significant figure.

Number	Rounded to 1 sf
78	80
32	30
0.69	0.7
1.89	2
998	1000
0.432	0.4

Number	Rounded to 1 sf
45 281	50 000
568	600
8054	8000
7.837	8
99.8	100
0.078	0.08

EXERCISE 8N

1 Round each of the following numbers to 1 significant figure.

a 46 313	**b** 57 123	**c** 30 569	**d** 94 558	**e** 85 299
f 54.26	**g** 85.18	**h** 27.09	**i** 96.432	**j** 167.77
k 0.5388	**l** 0.2823	**m** 0.005 84	**n** 0.047 85	**o** 0.000 876
p 9.9	**q** 89.5	**r** 90.78	**s** 199	**t** 999.99

2 Write down the smallest and the greatest numbers of sweets that can be found in each of these jars.

a   **b**  **c**

3 Write down the smallest and the greatest numbers of people that might live in these towns.

Elsecar   population 800 (to 1 significant figure)

Hoyland   population 1000 (to 1 significant figure)

Barnsley   population 200 000 (to 1 significant figure)

4 Round each of the following numbers to 1 significant figure.

a 56 147	**b** 26 813	**c** 79 611	**d** 30 578	**e** 14 009
f 5876	**g** 1065	**h** 847	**i** 109	**j** 638.7
k 1.689	**l** 4.0854	**m** 2.658	**n** 8.0089	**o** 41.564
p 0.8006	**q** 0.458	**r** 0.0658	**s** 0.9996	**t** 0.009 82

Approximation of calculations

How would you approximate the value of a calculation? What would you actually do when you try to approximate an answer to a problem?

For example, what is the approximate answer to 35.1×6.58?

To find the approximate answer, you simply round each number to 1 significant figure, then complete the calculation. So in this case, the approximation is:

$$35.1 \times 6.58 \approx 40 \times 7 = 280$$

Sometimes, especially when dividing, it is more sensible to round to 2 sf instead of 1 sf. For example:

$$57.3 \div 6.87$$

Since 6.87 rounds to 7, round 57.3 to 56 because 7 divides exactly into 56. Hence:

$$57.3 \div 6.87 \approx 56 \div 7 = 8$$

A quick approximation is always a great help in any calculation since it often stops you giving a silly answer.

EXERCISE 8P

1 Find approximate answers to the following.

   a 5435×7.31 **b** 5280×3.211 **c** $63.24 \times 3.514 \times 4.2$

   d 3508×2.79 **e** $72.1 \times 3.225 \times 5.23$ **f** $470 \times 7.85 \times 0.99$

   g $354 \div 79.8$ **h** $36.8 \div 1.876$ **i** $5974 \div 5.29$

Check your answers on a calculator to see how close you were.

2 Find the approximate monthly pay of the following people whose annual salaries are given.

   a Paul £35 200   **b** Michael £25 600   **c** Jennifer £18 125   **d** Ross £8420

3 Find the approximate annual pay of the following people who earn:

   a Kevin £270 a week   **b** Malcolm £1528 a month   **c** David £347 a week

4 A litre of paint will cover an area of about 8.7 m². Approximately how many litre cans will I need to buy to paint a room with a total surface area of 73 m²?

5 A farmer bought 2713 kg of seed at a cost of £7.34 per kg. Find the approximate total cost of this seed.

6 By rounding, find an approximate answer to each of the following.

   a $\dfrac{573 + 783}{107}$ **b** $\dfrac{783 - 572}{24}$ **c** $\dfrac{354 + 656}{997 - 656}$ **d** $\dfrac{1124 - 661}{355 + 570}$

   e $\dfrac{28.3 \times 19.5}{97.4}$ **f** $\dfrac{78.3 \times 22.6}{3.69}$ **g** $\dfrac{3.52 \times 7.95}{15.9}$ **h** $\dfrac{11.78 \times 77.8}{39.4}$

7 It took me 6 hours and 40 minutes to drive from Sheffield to Bude, a distance of 295 miles. My car uses petrol at the rate of about 32 miles per gallon. The petrol cost £3.51 per gallon.

   a Approximately how many miles did I travel each hour?

   b Approximately how many gallons of petrol did I use in going from Sheffield to Bude?

   c What was the approximate cost of all the petrol I used in the journey to Bude and back again?

8 Kirsty arranges for magazines to be put into envelopes. She sorts out 178 magazines between 10.00 am and 1.00 pm. Approximately how many magazines will she be able to sort in a week in which she works for 17 hours?

9 An athlete's training routine is to run 3.75 km every day. Approximately how far does he run in:

   a a week   **b** a month   **c** a year?

10 A box full of magazines weighs 8 kg. One magazine weighs about 15 g. Approximately how many magazines are there in the box?

11 An apple weighs about 280 grams.

    a What is the approximate weight of a bag containing a dozen apples?

    b Approximately how many apples will there be in a sack weighing 50 kg?

12 One marble weighs 8 grams to the nearest gram.

    a What is **i** the greatest **ii** the least possible weight of 100 marbles identical to this one?

    b I buy 1 kg of these identical marbles, what is **i** the greatest **ii** the least number of marbles I might have bought?

Sensible rounding

In your GCSE examination you will be required to round off answers to problems to a suitable degree of accuracy without being told specifically what that is.

Generally, you can use common sense. For example, you would not give the length of a pencil as 14.574 cm; you would round off to something like 14.6 cm. If you were asked how many tins you need to buy to do a particular job, then you would give a whole-number answer and not a decimal fraction such as 5.91 tins.

It is hard to make rules about this, as there is much disagreement even among the 'experts' as to how you ought to do it. But, generally, when you are in any doubt as to how many significant figures to use for the final answer to a problem, round to the same accuracy as the numbers used in the original data.

Remember too, that measurements given to the nearest whole unit may be inaccurate by up to one half in either direction.

EXERCISE 8Q

1 Round each of the following figures to a suitable degree of accuracy.

    a I am 1.7359 metres tall.

    b It took me 5 minutes 44.83 seconds to mend the television.

    c My kitten weighs 237.97 grams.

    d The correct temperature at which to drink Earl Grey tea is 82.739 °C.

    e There were 34 827 people at the Test Match yesterday.

    f The distance from Wath to Sheffield is 15.528 miles.

    g My telephone number is 284 519.

    h The area of the floor is 13.673 m^2.

2 Rewrite the following article, rounding all the numbers to a suitable degree of accuracy if necessary.

It was a hot day, the temperature was 81.699 °F and still rising. I had now walked 5.3289 km in just over 113.98 minutes. But I didn't care since I knew that the 43 275 people watching the race were cheering me on. I won by clipping 6.2 seconds off the record time. This was the 67th time the race had taken place since records first began in 1788. Well, next year I will only have 15 practice walks beforehand as I strive to beat the record by at least another 4.9 seconds.

1 **a** Copy and complete the shopping bill for Dean.

4 kg potatoes	at £0.85 per kg	
3 kg apples	at £1.45 per kg	
2 bottles of orange	at £1.15 each	
	Total	

b The shop assistant gives Dean 10p off for every £2 he spends. How much is Dean given off his bill?

c Dean buys six balloons at 45p each. He pays with a £10 note. How much change should he receive?

2 450 people go on a Football trip. Each coach will seat 54 people.

a How many coaches are needed?

b How many seats will be empty?

3 Every day, a quarter of a million babies are born in the world.

a Write a quarter of a million using figures.

b Work out the number of babies born in 28 days. Give your answer in millions.

Edexcel, Question 14, Paper 2 Foundation, June 2003

4 **a** Write $\frac{5}{8}$ as a decimal.

b Write 0.6 as a fraction. Give your answer in its lowest terms.

5 Nick takes 26 boxes out of his van. The weight of each box is 32.9 kg.

Work out the *total* weight of the 26 boxes.

Edexcel, Question 3, Paper 3 Intermediate, June 2004

6 Estimate the value of each expression:

a 15.7×29.2 **b** 143.1×17.8

7 **a** Work out $13 \times 17 - 11 \times 17$.

b Find an approximate value of $\frac{51 \times 250}{82}$.

You *must* show all your working.

8 John says 'For all prime numbers, n, the value of $n^2 + 3$ is always an even number'. Give an example to show that John is *not* correct.

9 Three pupils use calculators to work out $\frac{32.7 + 14.3}{1.28 - 0.49}$

Arnie gets 43.4, Bert gets 36.2 and Chuck gets 59.5. Use approximations to show which one of them is correct.

10 Work out $3\frac{2}{5} - 1\frac{2}{3}$

11 Use approximations to estimate the value of

$$\sqrt{\frac{323\,407}{0.48}}$$

12 Each term of a sequence is formed by multiplying the previous term by −2 and then subtracting 1.
The first three terms are

2, −5, 9 …

a Write down the next two terms of the sequence

b A later term in the sequence is 119. What was the previous term?

WORKED EXAM QUESTION

In a survey the number of visitors to a Theme Park was recorded daily. Altogether 20 million visitors went to the Theme Park. Each day there were approximately 400 000 visitors.
Based on this information, for how many days did the survey last?

> Read the question to decide what you have to do.
> You need to find the number of days: total times visited ÷ number of visits a day

Solution

$20\,000\,000 \div 400\,000 = \dfrac{20\,000\,000}{400\,000}$

> Show the calculation, you get a mark for this.

> You can cancel the five zeros on the top and the bottom.

$= \dfrac{200}{4} = 50 \text{ days}$

> Check the final answer is sensible. Here, it is.

The gym

A health and fitness club has six new members.

The manager measures their heights and weights and uses the height–weight chart to identify the category into which each of them falls.

Help him to complete the table.

Person	Weight category
Dave	
Pete	
Andy	OK
Sue	
Sally	
Lynn	

Height–Weight chart

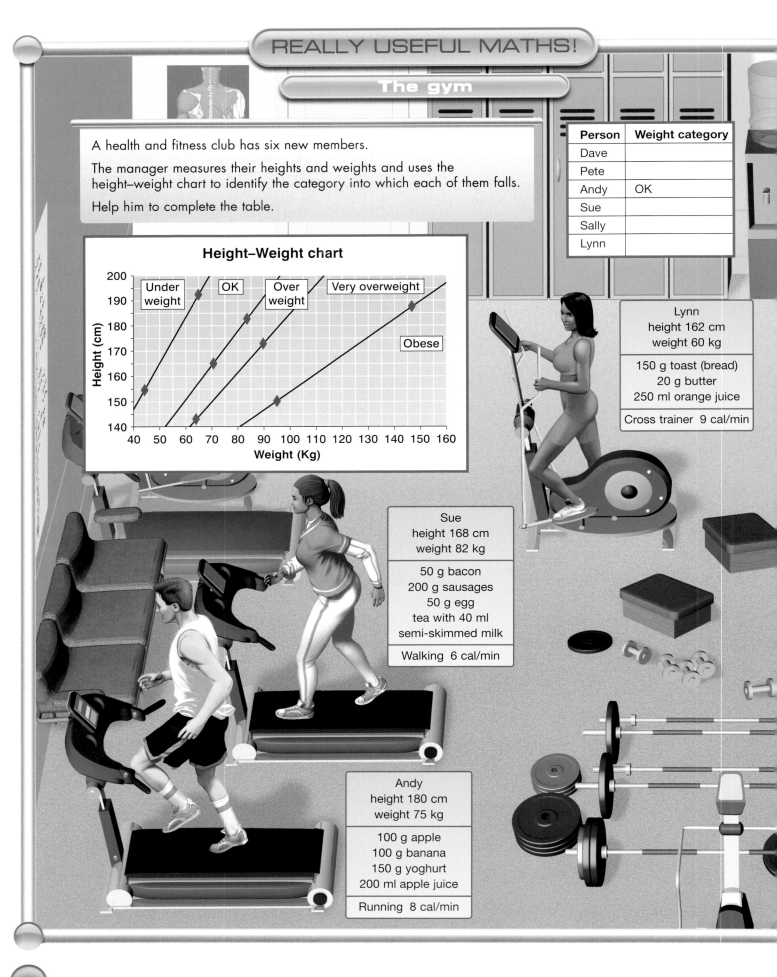

Lynn
height 162 cm
weight 60 kg

150 g toast (bread)
20 g butter
250 ml orange juice

Cross trainer 9 cal/min

Sue
height 168 cm
weight 82 kg

50 g bacon
200 g sausages
50 g egg
tea with 40 ml
semi-skimmed milk

Walking 6 cal/min

Andy
height 180 cm
weight 75 kg

100 g apple
100 g banana
150 g yoghurt
200 ml apple juice

Running 8 cal/min

Calories per 100 g of food	
apple	46
bacon	440
banana	76
bread	246
butter	740
cornflakes	370
eggs	148
porridge	368
sausages	186
yoghurt	62
apple juice (100 ml)	41
orange juice (100 ml)	36
semi-skimmed milk (100 ml)	48
skimmed milk (100 ml)	34
sugar (1 teaspoonful)	20
tea or coffee (black)	0

Pete
height 175 cm
weight 60 kg

30 g cornflakes
300 ml semi-skimmed milk
tea with 40 ml skimmed milk
2 teaspoons sugar

Step machine 9 cal/min

Dave
height 192 cm
weight 95 kg

50 g bacon
150 g bread
20 g butter
200 ml semi-skimmed milk

Exercise bike 7 cal/min

Person	Calories in breakfast	Minutes exercising
Dave		
Pete		
Andy		
Sue		
Sally	440	55
Lynn		

Sally
height 165 cm
weight 45 kg

75 g porridge
300 ml semi-skimmed milk
black coffee
1 teaspoon sugar

Rowing 8 cal/min

Each new member writes down what they usually have for breakfast. The manager uses the calorie table to work out how many calories there are in each breakfast.

He also selects an exercise machine for each of them to use.

Copy and complete the table to show how many calories there are in each breakfast and how many minutes on the exercise machine it would take each member to burn off these calories. Round each time up to the nearest minute.

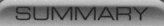

GRADE YOURSELF

F Multiply a three-digit number by a two-digit number without using a calculator

F Divide a three- or four-digit number by a two-digit number

F Solve real problems involving multiplication and division

F Round decimal numbers to a specific number of places

E Evaluate calculations involving decimal numbers

E Change decimals to fractions

E Change fractions to decimals

D Estimate the approximate value of a calculation before calculating

D Order a list containing decimals and fractions

D Round numbers to one significant figure

C Multiply and divide by negative numbers

C Round answers to a suitable degree of accuracy

C Multiply and divide fractions

What you should know now

- How to do long multiplication
- How to do long division
- How to perform calculations with decimal numbers
- How to round to a specific number of decimal places
- How to round to a specific number of significant figures
- How to add fractions with different denominators
- How to multiply and divide fractions
- How to multiply and divide with negative numbers
- How to interchange decimals and fractions
- How to make estimates by suitable rounding

1 Ratio

2 Speed, time and distance

3 Direct proportion problems

4 Best buys

This chapter will show you ...

- what a ratio is
- how to divide an amount according to a given ratio
- how to solve problems involving direct proportion
- how to compare prices of products
- how to calculate speed

Visual overview

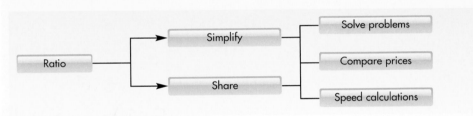

What you should already know

- Times tables up to 10×10
- How to cancel fractions
- How to find a fraction of a quantity
- How to multiply and divide, with and without a calculator

Quick check

1 Cancel the following fractions.

a $\dfrac{6}{10}$ **b** $\dfrac{4}{20}$ **c** $\dfrac{4}{12}$ **d** $\dfrac{32}{50}$ **e** $\dfrac{36}{90}$ **f** $\dfrac{18}{24}$ **g** $\dfrac{16}{48}$

2 Find the following quantities.

a $\dfrac{2}{5}$ of £30 **b** $\dfrac{3}{4}$ of £88 **c** $\dfrac{7}{10}$ of 250 litres **d** $\dfrac{5}{8}$ of 24 kg

e $\dfrac{2}{3}$ of 60 m **f** $\dfrac{5}{6}$ of £42 **g** $\dfrac{9}{20}$ of 300 g **h** $\dfrac{3}{10}$ of 3.5 litres

In this section you will learn how to:

- simplify a ratio
- express a ratio as a fraction
- divide amounts according to ratios
- complete calculations from a given ratio and partial information

Key words

cancel
common
  unit
ratio
simplest
  form

A **ratio** is a way of comparing the sizes of two or more quantities.

A ratio can be expressed in a number of ways. For example, if Joy is five years old and James is 20 years old, the ratio of their ages is:

	Joy's age : James's age
which is:	5 : 20
which simplifies to:	1 : 4 (dividing both sides by 5)

A ratio is usually given in one of these three ways.

Joy's age : James's age	or	5 : 20	or	1 : 4
Joy's age to James's age	or	5 to 20	or	1 to 4
$\dfrac{\text{Joy's age}}{\text{James's age}}$	or	$\dfrac{5}{20}$	or	$\dfrac{1}{4}$

Common units

When working with a ratio involving different units, *always change them to a **common unit***. A ratio can be simplified only when the units of each quantity are the *same*, because the ratio itself has no units. Once the units are the same, the ratio can be simplified or **cancelled**.

For example, the ratio 125 g to 2 kg must be changed to 125 g to 2000 g, so that you can simplify it.

	125 : 2000
Divide both sides by 25:	5 : 80
Divide both sides by 5:	1 : 16

The ratio 125 : 2000 can be cancelled to 1 : 16.

Ratios as fractions

A ratio in its **simplest form** can be expressed as portions by changing the whole numbers in the ratio into fractions with the same denominator (bottom number).

For example, in a garden that is divided into lawn and shrubs in the ratio 3 : 2, you should see that:

the lawn covers $\frac{3}{5}$ of the garden
and the shrubs cover $\frac{2}{5}$ of the garden.

The common denominator (bottom number) 5 is the *sum of the numbers in the ratio*.

EXERCISE 9A

1 Express each of the following ratios in its simplest form.

a 6 : 18   **b** 15 : 20   **c** 16 : 24   **d** 24 : 36

e 20 to 50   **f** 12 to 30   **g** 25 to 40   **h** 125 to 30

i 15 : 10   **j** 32 : 12   **k** 28 to 12   **l** 100 to 40

m 0.5 to 3   **n** 1.5 to 4   **o** 2.5 to 1.5   **p** 3.2 to 4

2 Express each of the following ratios of quantities in its simplest form. (Remember always to express both parts in a common unit before you simplify.)

a £5 to £15   **b** £24 to £16

c 125 g to 300 g   **d** 40 minutes : 5 minutes

e 34 kg to 30 kg   **f** £2.50 to 70p

g 3 kg to 750 g   **h** 50 minutes to 1 hour

i 1 hour to 1 day   **j** 12 cm to 2.5 mm

k 1.25 kg : 500 g   **l** 75p : £3.50

m 4 weeks : 14 days   **n** 600 m: 2 km

o 465 mm : 3 m   **p** 15 hours : 1 day

3 A length of wood is cut into two pieces in the ratio 3 : 7. What fraction of the original length is the longer piece?

4 Jack and Thomas find a bag of marbles that they share between them in the ratio of their ages. Jack is 10 years old and Thomas is 15. What fraction of the marbles did Jack get?

5 Dave and Sue share a pizza in the ratio 2 : 3. They eat it all.

a What fraction of the pizza did Dave eat?   **b** What fraction of the pizza did Sue eat?

6 A camp site allocates space to caravans and tents in the ratio 7 : 3. What fraction of the total space is given to:

a the caravans   **b** the tents?

7 Two sisters, Amy and Katie, share a packet of sweets in the ratio of their ages. Amy is 15 and Katie is 10. What fraction of the sweets does each sister get?

8 The recipe for a fruit punch is 1.25 litres of fruit crush to 6.75 litres of lemonade. What fraction of the punch is each ingredient?

9 One morning a farmer notices that her hens, Gertrude, Gladys and Henrietta, have laid eggs in the ratio 2 : 3 : 4.

   a What fraction of the eggs did Gertrude lay?

   b What fraction of the eggs did Gladys lay?

   c How many more eggs did Henrietta lay than Gertrude?

10 In a safari park at feeding time, the elephants, the lions and the chimpanzees are given food in the ratio 10 to 7 to 3. What fraction of the total food is given to:

   a the elephants   **b** the lions   **c** the chimpanzees?

11 Three brothers, James, John and Joseph, share a huge block of chocolate in the ratio of their ages. James is 20, John is 12 and Joseph is 8. What fraction of the bar of chocolate does each brother get?

12 The recipe for a pudding is 125 g of sugar, 150 g of flour, 100 g of margarine and 175 g of fruit. What fraction of the pudding is each ingredient?

Dividing amounts according to ratios

To divide an amount into portions according to a given ratio, you first change the whole numbers in the ratio into fractions with the same common denominator. Then you multiply the amount by each fraction.

EXAMPLE 1

Divide £40 between Peter and Hitan in the ratio 2 : 3

Changing the ratio to fractions gives:

$$\text{Peter's share} = \frac{2}{(2+3)} = \frac{2}{5}$$

$$\text{Hitan's share} = \frac{3}{(2+3)} = \frac{3}{5}$$

So Peter receives £40 × $\frac{2}{5}$ = £16 and Hitan receives £40 × $\frac{3}{5}$ = £24.

EXERCISE 9B

1 Divide the following amounts according to the given ratios.

   a 400 g in the ratio 2 : 3   **b** 280 kg in the ratio 2 : 5

   c 500 in the ratio 3 : 7   **d** 1 km in the ratio 19 : 1

   e 5 hours in the ratio 7 : 5   **f** £100 in the ratio 2 : 3 : 5

   g £240 in the ratio 3 : 5 : 12   **h** 600 g in the ratio 1 : 5 : 6

   i £5 in the ratio 7 : 10 : 8   **j** 200 kg in the ratio 15 : 9 : 1

2 The ratio of female to male members of Lakeside Gardening Club is 5 : 3. The total number of members of the group is 256.

   a How many members are female?   **b** What percentage of members are male?

3 A supermarket aims to stock branded goods and their own goods in the ratio 2 : 5. They stock 350 kg of breakfast cereal.

   a What percentage of the cereal stock is branded?

   b How much of the cereal stock is their own?

4 The Illinois Department of Health reported that, for the years 1981 to 1992 when they tested a total of 357 horses for rabies, the ratio of horses with rabies to those without was 1 : 16.

   a How many of these horses had rabies?

   b What percentage of the horses did not have rabies?

5 Being overweight increases the chances of an adult suffering from heart disease. A way to test whether an adult has an increased risk is shown below:

   For women, increased risk when $W/H > 0.8$

   For men, increased risk when $W/H > 1.0$

> W = waist measurement
>
> H = hip measurement

   a Find whether the following people have an increased risk of heart disease.

      Miss Mott: waist 26 inches, hips 35 inches

      Mrs Wright: waist 32 inches, hips 37 inches

      Mr Brennan: waist 32 inches, hips 34 inches

      Ms Smith: waist 31 inches, hips 40 inches

      Mr Kaye: waist 34 inches, hips 33 inches

   b Give three examples of waist and hip measurements that would suggest no risk of heart disease for a man, but would suggest a risk for a woman.

6 Rewrite the following scales as ratios as simply as possible.

   a 1 cm to 4 km   **b** 4 cm to 5 km   **c** 2 cm to 5 km

   d 4 cm to 1 km   **e** 5 cm to 1 km   **f** 2.5 cm to 1 km

   g 8 cm to 5 km   **h** 10 cm to 1 km   **i** 5 cm to 3 km

7 A map has a scale of 1 cm to 10 km.

   a Rewrite the scale as a ratio in its simplest form.

   b What is the actual length of a lake that is 4.7 cm long on the map?

   c How long will a road be on the map if its actual length is 8 km?

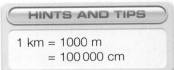

> **HINTS AND TIPS**
>
> 1 km = 1000 m
>   = 100 000 cm

8 A map has a scale of 2 cm to 5 km.

   a Rewrite the scale as a ratio in its simplest form.

   b How long is a path that measures 0.8 cm on the map?

   c How long should a 12 km road be on the map?

9 The scale of a map is 5 cm to 1 km.

   a Rewrite the scale as a ratio in its simplest form.

   b How long is a wall that is shown as 2.7 cm on the map?

   c The distance between two points is 8 km; how far will this be on the map?

10 You can simplify a ratio by changing it into the form 1 : n. For example, 5 : 7 can be rewritten as

$$\frac{5}{5} : \frac{7}{5} = 1 : 1.4$$

Rewrite each of the following ratios in the form 1 : n.

   a 5 : 8   **b** 4 : 13   **c** 8 : 9

   d 25 : 36   **e** 5 : 27   **f** 12 : 18

   g 5 hours : 1 day   **h** 4 hours : 1 week   **i** £4 : £5

Calculating according to a ratio when only part of the information is known

EXAMPLE 2

Two business partners, Lubna and Adama, divided their total profit in the ratio 3 : 5. Lubna received £2100. How much did Adama get?

Lubna's £2100 was $\frac{3}{8}$ of the total profit. (Check that you know why.)

$\frac{1}{8}$ of the total profit = £2100 ÷ 3 = £700

So Adama's share, which was $\frac{5}{8}$, amounted to £700 × 5 = £3500.

EXERCISE 9C

1 Derek, aged 15, and Ricki, aged 10, shared all the conkers they found in the woods in the same ratio as their ages. Derek had 48 conkers.

   a Simplify the ratio of their ages.

   b How many conkers did Ricki have?

   c How many conkers did they find altogether?

C

2 Two types of crisps, plain and salt 'n' vinegar, were bought for a school party in the ratio 5 : 3. The school bought 60 packets of salt 'n' vinegar crisps.

   a How many packets of plain crisps did they buy?

   b How many packets of crisps altogether did they buy?

3 Robin is making a drink from orange juice and lemon juice in the ratio 9 : 1. If Robin has only 3.6 litres of orange juice, how much lemon juice does he need to make the drink?

4 When I picked my strawberries, I found some had been spoilt by snails. The rest were good. These were in the ratio 3 : 17. Eighteen of my strawberries had been spoilt by snails. How many good strawberries did I find?

5 A blend of tea is made by mixing Lapsang with Assam in the ratio 3 : 5. I have a lot of Assam tea but only 600 g of Lapsang. How much Assam do I need to make the blend using all the Lapsang?

6 The ratio of male to female spectators at ice hockey games is 4 : 5. At the Steelers' last match, 4500 men watched the match. What was the total attendance at the game?

7 'Proper tea' is made by putting milk and tea together in the ratio 2 : 9. How much 'proper tea' can be made if you have 1 litre of milk?

8 A teacher always arranged the content of each of his lessons to Y10 as 'teaching' and 'practising learnt skills' in the ratio 2 : 3.

   a If a lesson lasted 35 minutes, how much teaching would he do?

   b If he decided to teach for 30 minutes, how long would the lesson be?

9 A 'good' children's book is supposed to have pictures and text in the ratio 17 : 8. In a book I have just looked at, the pictures occupy 23 pages. Approximately how many pages of text should this book have to be deemed a 'good' children's book?

10 Three business partners, Kevin, John and Margaret, put money into a venture in the ratio 3 : 4 : 5. They shared any profits in the same ratio. Last year, Margaret made £3400 out of the profits. How much did Kevin and John make last year?

11 The soft drinks Coke, Orange and Vimto were bought for the school disco in the ratio 10 : 5 : 3. The school bought 80 cans of Orange.

   a How much Coke did they buy?   **b** How much Vimto did they buy?

12 Iqra is making a drink from lemonade, orange and ginger in the ratio 40 : 9 : 1. If Iqra has only 4.5 litres of orange, how much of the other two ingredients does she need to make the drink?

13 When I harvested my apples I found some had been eaten by wasps, some were rotten and some were good. These were in the ratio 6 : 5 : 25. Eighteen of my apples had been eaten by wasps.

   a What fraction of my apples were rotten?   **b** How many good apples did I get?

In this section you will learn how to:

- recognise the relationship between speed, distance and time
- calculate average speed from distance and time
- calculate distance travelled from the speed and the time taken
- calculate the time taken on a journey from the speed and the distance

Key word

average

The relationship between speed, time and distance can be expressed in three ways:

$$\text{speed} = \frac{\text{distance}}{\text{time}} \qquad \text{distance} = \text{speed} \times \text{time} \qquad \text{time} = \frac{\text{distance}}{\text{speed}}$$

In problems relating to speed, you usually mean **average** speed, as it would be unusual to maintain one exact speed for the whole of a journey.

This diagram will help you remember the relationships between distance (D), time (T) and speed (S).

$$D = S \times T \qquad S = \frac{D}{T} \qquad T = \frac{D}{S}$$

EXAMPLE 3

Paula drove a distance of 270 miles in 5 hours. What was her average speed?

$$\text{Paula's average speed} = \frac{\text{distance she drove}}{\text{time she took}} = \frac{270}{5} = 54 \text{ miles/h}$$

EXAMPLE 4

Sarah drove from Sheffield to Peebles in $3\frac{1}{2}$ hours at an average speed of 60 miles/h. How far is it from Sheffield to Peebles?

Since:

distance = speed × time

the distance from Sheffield to Peebles is given by:

60 × 3.5 = 210 miles

Note: You need to change the time to a decimal number and use 3.5 (*not* 3.30).

EXAMPLE 5

Sean is going to drive from Newcastle upon Tyne to Nottingham, a distance of 190 miles. He estimates that he will drive at an average speed of 50 miles/h. How long will it take him?

$$\text{Sean's time} = \frac{\text{distance he covers}}{\text{his average speed}} = \frac{190}{50} = 3.8 \text{ hours}$$

Change the 0.8 hour to minutes by multiplying by 60, to give 48 minutes.

So, the time for Sean's journey will be 3 hours 48 minutes. A sensible rounding would give 4 hours.

Remember: When you calculate a time and get a decimal answer, as in Example 5, *do not mistake* the decimal part for minutes. You must either:

- leave the time as a decimal number and give the unit as hours, or

- change the decimal part to minutes by multiplying it by 60 (1 hour = 60 minutes) and give the answer in hours and minutes.

EXERCISE 9D

1 A cyclist travels a distance of 90 miles in 5 hours. What was her average speed?

2 How far along a motorway would you travel if you drove at 70 mph for 4 hours?

3 I drive to Bude in Cornwall from Sheffield in about 6 hours. The distance from Sheffield to Bude is 315 miles. What is my average speed?

4 The distance from Leeds to London is 210 miles. The train travels at an average speed of 90 mph. If I catch the 9.30 am train in London, at what time should I expect to arrive in Leeds?

5 How long will an athlete take to run 2000 metres at an average speed of 4 metres per second?

6 Copy and complete the following table.

> **HINTS AND TIPS**
>
> Remember to convert time to a decimal if you are using a calculator, for example, 8 hours 30 minutes is 8.5 hours.

	Distance travelled	Time taken	Average speed
a	150 miles	2 hours	
b	260 miles		40 mph
c		5 hours	35 mph
d		3 hours	80 km/h
e	544 km	8 hours 30 minutes	
f		3 hours 15 minutes	100 km/h
g	215 km		50 km/h

D

7 A train travels at 50 km/h for 2 hours, then slows down to do the last 30 minutes of its journey at 40 km/h.

    a What is the total distance of this journey?

    b What is the average speed of the train over the whole journey?

8 Jade runs and walks the 3 miles from home to work each day. She runs the first 2 miles at a speed of 8 mph, then walks the next mile at a steady 4 mph.

    a How long does it take Jade to get to work?   **b** What is her average speed?

9 Eliot drove from Sheffield to Inverness, a distance of 410 miles, in 7 hours 45 minutes.

    a Change the time 7 hours 45 minutes to a decimal.

    b What was the average speed of the journey? Round your answer to 1 decimal place.

10 Colin drives home from his son's house in 2 hours 15 minutes. He says that he drives at an average speed of 44 mph.

    a Change the 2 hours 15 minutes to a decimal.

    b How far is it from Colin's home to his son's house?

11 The distance between Paris and Le Mans is 200 km. The express train between Paris and Le Mans travels at an average speed of 160 km/h.

    a Calculate the time taken for the journey from Paris to Le Mans, giving your answer as a decimal number of hours.

    b Change your answer to part **a** to hours and minutes.

C

12 The distance between Sheffield and Land's End is 420 miles.

    a What is the average speed of a journey from Sheffield to Land's End that takes 8 hours 45 minutes?

    b If Sam covered the distance at an average speed of 63 mph, how long would it take him?

13 Change the following speeds to metres per second.

    a 36 km/h   **b** 12 km/h   **c** 60 km/h

    d 150 km/h   **e** 75 km/h

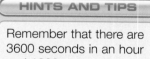

HINTS AND TIPS

Remember that there are 3600 seconds in an hour and 1000 metres in a kilometre.

14 Change the following speeds to kilometres per hour.

    a 25 m/s   **b** 12 m/s   **c** 4 m/s

    d 30 m/s   **e** 0.5 m/s

15 A train travels at an average speed of 18 m/s.

    a Express its average speed in km/h.

    b Find the approximate time the train would take to travel 500 m.

    c The train set off at 7.30 on a 40 km journey. At approximately what time will it reach its destination?

HINTS AND TIPS

To convert a decimal fraction of an hour to minutes, just multiply by 60.

16 A cyclist is travelling at an average speed of 24 km/h.

    a What is this speed in metres per second?

    b What distance does he travel in 2 hours 45 minutes?

    c How long does it take him to travel 2 km?

    d How far does he travel in 20 seconds?

9.3 Direct proportion problems

In this section you will learn how to:

- recognise and solve problems using direct proportion

Key words

direct
   proportion
unit cost
unitary method

Suppose you buy 12 items which each cost the *same*. The total amount you spend is 12 times the cost of one item.

That is, the total cost is said to be in **direct proportion** to the number of items bought. The cost of a single item (the **unit cost**) is the constant factor that links the two quantities.

Direct proportion is concerned not only with costs. Any two related quantities can be in direct proportion to each other.

The best way to solve all problems involving direct proportion is to start by finding the single unit value. This method is called the **unitary method**, because it involves referring to a single unit value. Work through Examples 6 and 7 to see how it is done.

Remember: Before solving a direct proportion problem, think about it carefully to make sure that you know how to find the required single unit value.

EXAMPLE 6

If eight pens cost £2.64, what is the cost of five pens?

First, find the cost of one pen. This is £2.64 ÷ 8 = £0.33

So, the cost of five pens is £0.33 × 5 = £1.65

EXAMPLE 7

Eight loaves of bread will make packed lunches for 18 people. How many packed lunches can be made from 20 loaves?

First, find how many lunches one loaf will make.

One loaf will make 18 ÷ 8 = 2.25 lunches.

So, 20 loaves will make 2.25 × 20 = 45 lunches.

EXERCISE 9E

1 If 30 matches weigh 45 g, what would 40 matches weigh?

2 Five bars of chocolate cost £2.90. Find the cost of nine bars.

3 Eight men can chop down 18 trees in a day. How many trees can 20 men chop down in a day?

4 Find the cost of 48 eggs when 15 eggs can be bought for £2.10.

5 Seventy maths textbooks cost £875.

    a How much will 25 maths textbooks cost?

    b How many maths textbooks can you buy for £100?

HINTS AND TIPS

Remember to work out the value of one unit each time. Always check that answers are sensible.

6 A lorry uses 80 litres of diesel fuel on a trip of 280 miles.

    a How much diesel would the same lorry use on a trip of 196 miles?

    b How far would the lorry get on a full tank of 100 litres of diesel?

7 During the winter, I find that 200 kg of coal keeps my open fire burning for 12 weeks.

    a If I want an open fire all through the winter (18 weeks), how much coal will I need to buy?

    b Last year I bought 150 kg of coal. For how many weeks did I have an open fire?

8 It takes a photocopier 16 seconds to produce 12 copies. How long will it take to produce 30 copies?

9 A recipe for 12 biscuits uses:

    200 g margarine

    400 g sugar

    500 g flour

    300 g ground rice

    a What quantities are needed for:

      i 6 biscuits   **ii** 9 biscuits   **iii** 15 biscuits?

    b What is the maximum number of biscuits I could make if I had just 1 kg of each ingredient?

Best buys

In this section you will learn how to:
- find the cost per unit weight
- find the weight per unit cost
- use the above to find which product is the cheaper

Key words
best buy
value for
 money

When you wander around a supermarket and see all the different prices for the many different-sized packets, it is rarely obvious which are the '**best buys**'. However, with a calculator you can easily compare **value for money** by finding either:

the cost per unit weight   **or**   the weight per unit cost

To find:

- *cost per unit weight*, divide *cost by weight*

- *weight per unit cost*, divide *weight by cost*.

The next two examples show you how to do this.

EXAMPLE 8

A 300 g tin of cocoa costs £1.20. Find the cost per unit weight and the weight per unit cost.

First change £1.20 to 120p. Then divide, using a calculator, to get:

Cost per unit weight $120 \div 300 = 0.4p$ per gram

Weight per unit cost $300 \div 120 = 2.5$ g per penny

EXAMPLE 9

A supermarket sells two different-sized packets of Whito soap powder. The medium size contains 800 g and costs £1.60 and the large size contains 2.5 kg and costs £4.75. Which is the better buy?

Find the weight per unit cost for both packets.

Medium: $800 \div 160 = 5$ g per penny

Large: $2500 \div 475 = 5.26$ g per penny

From these it is clear that there is more weight per penny with the large size, which means that the large size is the better buy.

EXERCISE 9F

D

1 Compare the following pairs of products and state which is the better buy. Explain why.

   a Coffee: a medium jar which contains 140 g for £1.10 or a large jar which contains 300 g for £2.18

   b Beans: a 125 g tin at 16p or a 600 g tin at 59p

   c Flour: a 3 kg bag at 75p or a 5 kg bag at £1.20

   d Toothpaste: a large tube containing 110 ml for £1.79 or a medium tube containing 75 ml for £1.15

   e Frosties: a large box which contains 750 g for £1.64 or a medium box which contains 500 g for £1.10

   f Rice Crispies: a medium box which contains 440 g for £1.64 or a large box which contains 600 g for £2.13

   g Hair shampoo: a bottle containing 400 ml for £1.15 or a bottle containing 550 ml for £1.60

2 Julie wants to respray her car with yellow paint. In the local automart, she sees the following tins:

   Small tin   350 ml at a cost of £1.79
   Medium tin   500 ml at a cost of £2.40
   Large tin   1.5 litres at a cost of £6.70

   a What is the cost per litre of paint in the small tin?

   b Which tin is offered at the lowest price per litre?

3 Tisco's sells bottled water in three sizes.

   a Work out the cost per litre of the 'handy' size.

   b Which bottle is the best value for money?

Handy size 40 cl   Family size 2 l   Giant size 5 l
£0.38   £0.98   £2.50

4 Two drivers are comparing the petrol consumption of their cars.

   Ahmed says, 'I get 320 miles on a tank of 45 litres.'

   Bashir says, 'I get 230 miles on a tank of 32 litres.'

   Whose car is the more economical?

5 Mary and Jane are arguing about which of them is better at mathematics.

   Mary scored 49 out of 80 on a test.

   Jane scored 60 out of 100 on a test of the same standard.

   Who is better at mathematics?

6 Paula and Kelly are comparing their running times.

   Paula completed a 10-mile run in 65 minutes.

   Kelly completed a 10-kilometre run in 40 minutes.

   Given that 8 kilometres are equal to 5 miles, which girl has the greater average speed?

1 Breakfast cereal is sold in two sizes of packet.

The small packet holds 500 grams and costs £2.10.

The large packet holds 875 grams and costs £3.85.

500 g £2.10

875 g £3.85

Which packet is better value for money? You *must* show all your working.

 2 a Brian travels 234 miles by train. His journey takes $2\frac{1}{2}$ hours.

What is the average speed of the train?

b Val drives 234 miles at an average speed of 45 mph.

How long does her journey take?

 3 A country walk is 15 miles long. A leaflet states that this walk can be done in 4 hours.

a Calculate the average speed required to complete the walk in the time stated.

b A walker completes the route in 4 hours. She averages 5 miles an hour for the first hour.

Calculate her average speed for the remainder of the journey.

 4 The only pets a pet shop sells are hamsters and fish. The ratio of the number of hamsters to the number of fish is 12 : 28

a What fraction of these pets are hamsters? Give your fraction in its simplest form.

The only fish the pet shop sells are goldfish and tropical fish.

The ratio of goldfish to tropical fish is 1 : 4.

The shop has 280 fish.

b Work out the number of goldfish the shop has.

Edexcel, Question 2, Paper 12A Intermediate, March 2005

  5 The length of a coach is 15 metres. Jonathan makes a model of the coach. He uses a scale of 1 : 24

Work out the length, in centimetres, of the model coach.

Edexcel, Question 2, Paper 4 Intermediate, June 2005

 6 Mr Bandle wins £18 000. He divides the £18 000 between his three children, Charlotte, James and Louise, in the ratio 4 : 5 : 6, respectively.

How much does Charlotte receive?

 7 a The most popular picture frames are those for which the ratio of width to length is 5 : 8.

Which frames are in the ratio 5 : 8?

15 cm | **A** | 30 cm | **B** | 10 cm | **C**
25 cm | 48 cm | 16 cm

b There are 52 cards in a normal pack of cards. For a game, Dad shares the pack between Jack and Kenny in the ratio of 6 : 7.

How many cards does each player receive?

 8 There are 40 chocolates in a box. 12 chocolates are plain chocolates. The remaining chocolates are milk chocolates.

a Work out the ratio of the number of plain chocolates to the number of milk chocolates in the box. Give your ratio in its simplest form.

Some plain chocolates are added to the box so that the ratio of the number of plain chocolates to the number of milk chocolates is 1 : 2

b Work out how many plain chocolates are added to the box.

Edexcel, Question 3, Paper 12B Intermediate, January 2005

  9 In a school the ratio of teachers to pupils is 5 : 92. There are 644 pupils. How many teachers are there?

WORKED EXAM QUESTION

Cream is sold in small pots and large pots.

The ratio of the weight of a small pot to the weight of a large pot is 5 : 14. The weight of a small pot is 110 g.

What is the weight of a large pot?

Read the question.
Let W be the weight of the large pot.
The ratio of the weights of the pots is 110 : W, which is equal to 5 : 14.

Set up the equation $\frac{W}{110} = \frac{14}{5}$.
You get 1 mark for this.

Solution

$W = \dfrac{14 \times 110}{5}$

$= \dfrac{14 \times 22}{1} = 308$ g

Perform the final calculation (after maybe cancelling the fraction).
Check the final answer is sensible.

Party time!

Alison and Bob have invited four friends to a dinner party.

They choose a menu but they have to change all the recipes to serve six people.

Copy their notebook pages and fill in the correct amounts.

Menu

* * * * *

Marinated mushrooms

* * * * *

Leek and macaroni bake
Mixed salad

* * * * *

Crème caramel

Marinated mushrooms (serves 2)
225 g mushrooms
15 ml wine vinegar
45 ml olive oil

Marinated mushrooms
(serves 6)
mushrooms _____ g
wine vinegar _____ ml
olive oil _____ ml

Leek and macaroni bake (serves 4)
130 g macaroni
50 g butter
270 g leeks
30 g flour
600 ml milk
180 g cheese
20 g breadcrumbs

Leek and macaroni bake
(serves 6)
macaroni _____ g
butter _____ g
leeks _____ g
flour _____ g
milk _____ ml
cheese _____ g
breadcrumbs _____ g

Crème caramel (serves 8)
240 g sugar
8 eggs
1.2 litres milk

Crème caramel (serves 6)
sugar _____ g
eggs _____
milk _____ litres

Ratios, fractions, speed and proportion

Bob arranges the seating plan for the table.

He sits everyone in order, male, female, male, female, and so on.

The plan shows where he places Alison and himself.

How many different ways are there to seat Claire, Derek, Elizabeth and Frank?

Bob

Alison

Bob estimates how many bottles of wine they will need.

A wine glass holds 150 ml. A bottle of wine holds 75 cl.

If each person at the party drinks two glasses of wine, apart from Frank who is driving, how many bottles will they need?

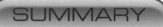

GRADE YOURSELF

E Simplify a ratio

D Calculate average speeds from data

D Calculate distance from speed and time

D Calculate time from speed and distance

D Compare prices of products to find the 'best buy'

C Solve problems, using ratio in appropriate situations

What you should know now

- How to divide any amount according to a given ratio
- The relationships between speed, time and distance
- How to solve problems involving direct proportion
- How to compare the prices of products

Symmetry

1 Lines of symmetry

2 Rotational symmetry

3 Planes of symmetry

This chapter will show you ...

- how to draw the lines of symmetry on a 2-D shape
- how to find the order of rotational symmetry for a 2-D shape
- how to find the planes of symmetry for a 3-D shape

Visual overview

What you should already know

- The names of these 2-D shapes: isosceles triangle, equilateral triangle, right-angled triangle, square, rectangle, parallelogram, rhombus, trapezium and kite
- The names of these 3-D shapes: cone, cube, cuboid, cylinder, prism, sphere

Quick check

Name these 3-D shapes.

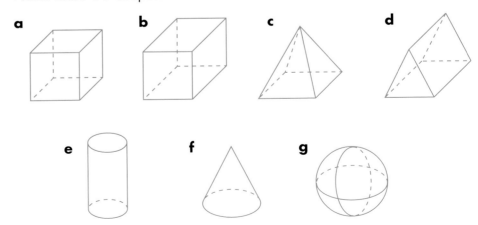

Mirror writing

You need a plane mirror and some plain or squared paper.

You probably know that certain styles of some upright capital letters have one or more lines of symmetry. For example, the upright A given below has one line of symmetry (shown here as a dashed line).

Draw a large A on your paper and put the mirror along the line of symmetry.

What do you notice when you look in the mirror?

Upright capital letters such as A, O and M have a vertical line of symmetry. Can you find any others?

Other upright capital letters (E, for example) have a horizontal line of symmetry. Can you find any others?

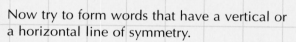

Now try to form words that have a vertical or a horizontal line of symmetry.

Here are two examples:

Make a display of all the different words you have found.

In this section you will learn how to:
- draw the lines of symmetry on a 2-D shape
- recognise shapes with reflective symmetry

Key words
line of symmetry
mirror line
symmetry

Many 2-D shapes have one or more lines of **symmetry**.

A **line of symmetry** is a line that can be drawn through a shape so that what can be seen on one side of the line is the mirror image of what is on the other side. This is why a line of symmetry is sometimes called a **mirror line**.

It is also the line along which a shape can be folded exactly onto itself.

Finding lines of symmetry

In an examination, you cannot use a mirror to find lines of symmetry but it is just as easy to use tracing paper, which is always available in any mathematics examination.

For example, to find the lines of symmetry for a rectangle, follow these steps.

1   Trace the rectangle.

2   Draw a line on the tracing paper where you think there is a line of symmetry.

3   Fold the tracing paper along this line. If the parts match, you have found a line of symmetry. If they do not match, try a line in another position.

4   Next, find out whether this is also a line of symmetry. You will find that it is.

5   Now see whether this is a line of symmetry. You will find that it is *not* a line of symmetry.

6   Your completed diagram should look like this. It shows that a rectangle has *two* lines of symmetry.

EXAMPLE 1

Find the number of lines of symmetry for this cross.

First, follow steps 1 to 4, which give the vertical and horizontal lines of symmetry.

Then, search for any other lines of symmetry in the same way.

There are two more, as the diagram shows.

So, this cross has a total of four lines of symmetry.

EXERCISE 10A

1 Copy these shapes and draw on the lines of symmetry for each one. If it will help you, use tracing paper or a mirror to check your results.

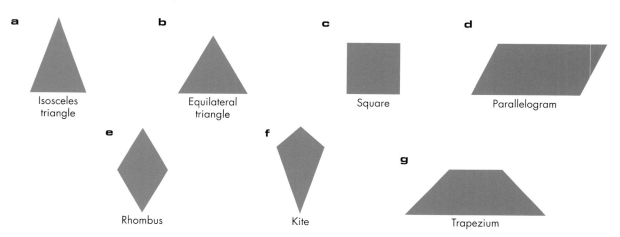

a Isosceles triangle

b Equilateral triangle

c Square

d Parallelogram

e Rhombus

f Kite

g Trapezium

2 a Find the number of lines of symmetry for each of these regular polygons.

i Regular pentagon

ii Regular hexagon

iii Regular octagon

b How many lines of symmetry do you think a regular decagon has? (A decagon is a ten-sided polygon.)

3 Copy these star shapes and draw in all the lines of symmetry for each one.

a   **b**   **c**

4 Copy these patterns and draw in all the lines of symmetry for each one.

a

b

c

d

e

f
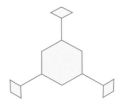

5 Write down the number of lines of symmetry for each of these flags.

    Austria   Canada   Iceland   Switzerland   Greece

6 a These road signs all have lines of symmetry. Copy them and draw on the lines of symmetry for each one.

  b Draw sketches of other common signs that also have lines of symmetry. State the number of lines of symmetry in each case.

7 The animal and plant kingdoms are full of symmetry. Four examples are given below. Sketch them and state the number of lines of symmetry for each one. Can you find other examples? Find suitable pictures, copy them and state the number of lines of symmetry each one has.

a

b

c

d

8 a Draw a circle with a radius of 3 cm.

  b Draw on any lines of symmetry. What do you notice?

  c How many lines of symmetry does a circle have?

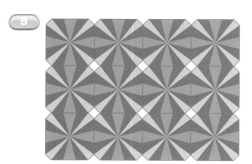

This decorative pattern is made by repeating shapes that have lines of symmetry. By using squared or isometric paper, try to make a similar pattern of your own.

10.2 Rotational symmetry

In this section you will learn how to:
- find the order of rotational symmetry for a 2-D shape
- recognise shapes with rotational symmetry

Key words
order of rotational symmetry
rotational symmetry

A 2-D shape has **rotational symmetry** if it can be rotated about a point to look exactly the same in a new position.

The **order of rotational symmetry** is the number of different positions in which the shape looks the same when it is rotated about the point.

The easiest way to find the order of rotational symmetry for any shape is to trace it and count the number of times that the shape stays the same as you turn the tracing paper through one complete turn.

EXAMPLE 2

Find the order of rotational symmetry for this shape.

First, hold the tracing paper on top of the shape and trace the shape. Then rotate the tracing paper and count the number of times the tracing matches the original shape in one complete turn.

You will find three different positions.

So, the order of rotational symmetry for the shape is 3.

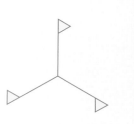

EXERCISE 10B

1 Copy these shapes and write below each one the order of rotational symmetry. If it will help you, use tracing paper.

a

Square

b

Rectangle

c

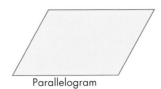

Parallelogram

d

Equilateral triangle

e

Regular hexagon

2 Find the order of rotational symmetry for each of these shapes.

a 　**b** 　**c** 　**d** 　**e**

3 The following are Greek capital letters. Write down the order of rotational symmetry for each one.

a Φ　　**b** H　　**c** Z　　**d** Θ　　**e** Ξ

4 Copy these shapes on tracing paper and find the order of rotational symmetry for each one.

a

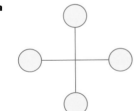

b

c

d

e

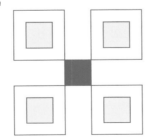

f

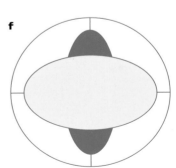

5 The upright capital letter A fits exactly onto itself only *once*. So, its order of rotational symmetry is 1. This means that it has *no* rotational symmetry. Write down all the upright capital letters of the alphabet that have rotational symmetry of order 1.

6 Find the order of rotational symmetry for a circle.

7 Obtain a pack of playing cards or a set of dominoes. Which cards or dominoes have rotational symmetry? Can you find any patterns? Write down everything you discover about the symmetry of the cards or dominoes.

ACTIVITY

Pentomino patterns

Pentominoes are shapes made with five squares that touch edge to edge.

Investigate line symmetry and rotational symmetry for different pentominoes.

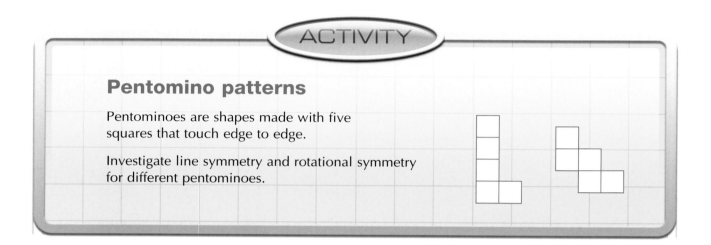

10.3 Planes of symmetry

In this section you will learn how to:
- find the number of planes of symmetry for a 3-D shape
- recognise shapes with planes of symmetry

Key words
plane of
  symmetry

Because of their 'depth', 3-D shapes have **planes of symmetry**, instead of the lines of symmetry found in 2-D shapes.

A plane of symmetry divides a 3-D shape into two identical parts or halves.

That is, one half of the shape is the reflection of the other half in the plane of symmetry.

EXAMPLE 3

How many planes of symmetry does this cuboid have?

A cuboid has three planes of symmetry because it can be sliced into halves in three different ways.

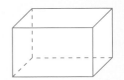

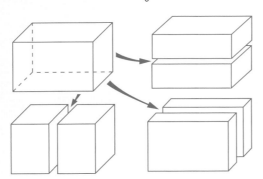

EXERCISE 10C

1 Find the number of planes of symmetry in each of these 3-D shapes.

a

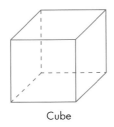

Cube

b

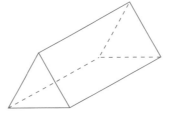

Triangular prism

c

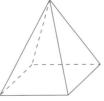

Square-based pyramid

2 This 3-D shape has five planes of symmetry.
Draw diagrams to show where they are.

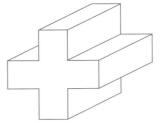

3 a The diagram shows half of a 3-D shape. Draw the complete shape so that the shaded part forms a plane of symmetry. What name do we give to this 3-D shape?

b Draw similar diagrams to show a plane of symmetry for a cylinder and for a cone.

4 How many planes of symmetry does each of the following have?

    a brick   **b** shovel   **c** chair

    d spoon   **e** milk bottle   **f** kettle

1 The diagram shows a pentagon. It has one line of symmetry.

Copy the diagram and draw the line of symmetry.

  2 a Copy this rectangle and draw the lines of symmetry on it.

b What is the order of rotational symmetry of a rectangle?

  3 Here is a list of 8 numbers.

| 11 | 16 | 18 | 36 |
| 68 | 69 | 82 | 88 |

From these numbers, write down a number which has

a exactly *one* line of symmetry,

b 2 lines of symmetry *and* rotational symmetry of order 2,

c rotational symmetry of order 2 but *no* lines of symmetry.

Edexcel, Question 5d, Paper 1 Foundation, June 2005

  4 A pattern is to be drawn. It will have rotational symmetry of order 4. The pattern has been started.

Copy the diagram and shade *six* more squares to complete the pattern.

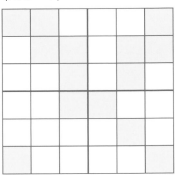

Edexcel, Question 6, Paper 8A Foundation, January 2003

  5

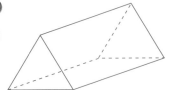

The diagram shows a triangular prism. The cross-section of the prism is an equilateral triangle.

Copy the diagram and draw in one plane of symmetry for the triangular prism.

Edexcel, Question 19a, Paper 2 Foundation, June 2005

  6 The diagram shows a square-based pyramid.

How many planes of symmetry does the pyramid have?

WORKED EXAM QUESTIONS

B A T H S

1   Which of the letters above has
    a line symmetry
    b rotational symmetry of order 2?

Solution

a    These letters have line symmetry as shown

b **H S**

2   A pattern has rotational symmetry of order 4 and no line symmetry. Part of the pattern is shown below.
    Complete the pattern.

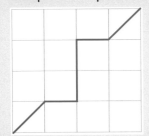

Solution

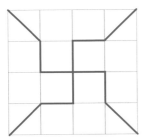

Trace the part of the pattern and rotate it about the centre of the grid three times through 90° to form the pattern.

GRADE YOURSELF

G Able to draw lines of symmetry on basic 2-D shapes

F Able to find the order of rotational symmetry for basic 2-D shapes

E Able to draw lines of symmetry on more complex 2-D shapes

E Able to find the order of rotational symmetry for more complex 2-D shapes

D Able to identify the number of planes of symmetry for 3-D shapes

What you should know now

- How to recognise lines of symmetry and draw them on 2-D shapes
- How to recognise whether a 2-D shape has rotational symmetry and find its order of rotational symmetry
- How to find the number of planes of symmetry for a 3-D shape

Averages

This chapter will show you ...

- how to calculate the mode, median, mean and range of small sets of discrete data
- how to calculate the mode, median, mean and range from frequency tables of discrete data
- how to decide which is the best average for different types of data
- how to use and recognise the modal class and calculate an estimate of the mean from frequency tables of grouped data
- how to draw frequency polygons

Visual overview

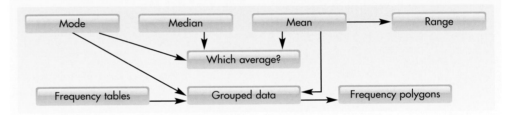

What you should already know

- How to collect and organise data
- How to draw frequency tables
- How to extract information from tables and diagrams

Quick check

The marks for 15 students in a maths test are:

2, 3, 4, 5, 5, 6, 6, 6, 7, 7, 7, 7, 7, 8, 10

a What is the most common mark?

b What is the middle value in the list?

c Find the difference between the highest mark and the lowest mark.

d Find the total of all 15 marks.

Average is a term often used when describing or comparing sets of data, for example, the average rainfall in Britain, the average score of a batsman, an average weekly wage or the average mark in an examination.

In each of the above examples, you are representing the whole set of many values by just a single, 'typical' value, which is called the average.

The idea of an average is extremely useful, because it enables you to compare one set of data with another set by comparing just two values – their averages.

There are several ways of expressing an average, but the most commonly used averages are the **mode**, the **median** and the **mean**.

11.1 The mode

In this section you will learn how to:
- find the mode from lists of data and from frequency tables

Key words
frequency
modal class
modal value
mode

The **mode** is the value that occurs the most in a set of data. That is, it is the value with the highest **frequency**.

The mode is a useful average because it is very easy to find and it can be applied to non-numerical data (qualitative data). For example, you could find the modal style of skirts sold in a particular month.

EXAMPLE 1

Suhail scored the following number of goals in 12 school football matches:

1 2 1 0 1 0 0 1 2 1 0 2

What is the mode of his scores?

The number which occurs most often in this list is 1. So, the mode is 1.

You can also say that the modal score or **modal value** is 1.

EXAMPLE 2

Barbara asked her friends how many books they had each taken out of the school library during the previous month. Their responses were:

2 1 3 4 6 4 1 3 0 2 6 0

Find the mode.

Here, there is *no mode*, because no number occurs more than the others.

EXERCISE 11A

1 Find the mode for each set of data.

a 3, 4, 7, 3, 2, 4, 5, 3, 4, 6, 8, 4, 2, 7

b 47, 49, 45, 50, 47, 48, 51, 48, 51, 48, 52, 48

c −1, 1, 0, −1, 2, −2, −2, −1, 0, 1, −1, 1, 0, −1, 2, −1, 2

d $\frac{1}{2}$, $\frac{1}{4}$, 1, $\frac{1}{2}$, $\frac{3}{4}$, $\frac{1}{4}$, 0, 1, $\frac{3}{4}$, $\frac{1}{4}$, 1, $\frac{1}{4}$, $\frac{3}{4}$, $\frac{1}{4}$, $\frac{1}{2}$

e 100, 10, 1000, 10, 100, 1000, 10, 1000, 100, 1000, 100, 10

f 1.23, 3.21, 2.31, 3.21, 1.23, 3.12, 2.31, 1.32, 3.21, 2.31, 3.21

2 Find the modal category for each set of data.

a red, green, red, amber, green, red, amber, green, red, amber

b rain, sun, cloud, sun, rain, fog, snow, rain, fog, sun, snow, sun

c α, γ, α, β, γ, α, α, γ, β, α, β, γ, β, β, α, β, γ, β

d ❋, ☆, ★, ★, ☆, ❋, ★, ✩, ★, ✩, ✱, ❋, ✪, ✩, ★, ✱, ☆

> **HINTS AND TIPS**
>
> It helps to put the data in order or group all the same things together.

3 Joan did a survey to find the shoe sizes of pupils in her class. The bar chart illustrates her data.

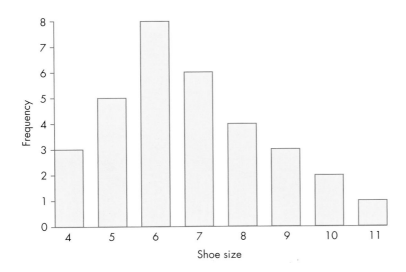

a How many pupils are in Joan's class?

b What is the modal shoe size?

c Can you tell from the bar chart which are the boys or which are the girls in her class?

d Joan then decided to draw a bar chart to show the shoe sizes of the boys and the girls separately. Do you think that the mode for the boys and the mode for the girls will be the same as the mode for the whole class? Explain your answer.

4 The frequency table shows the marks that Form 10MP obtained in a spelling test.

Mark	3	4	5	6	7	8	9	10
Frequency	1	2	6	5	5	4	3	4

a Write down the mode for their marks.

b Do you think this is a typical mark for the form? Explain your answer.

5 The grouped frequency table shows the number of e-mails each household in Corporation Street received during one week.

No. of e-mails	0–4	5–9	10–14	15–19	20–24	25–29	30–34	35–39
Frequency	9	12	14	11	10	8	4	2

a Draw a bar chart to illustrate the data.

b How many households are there in Corporation Street?

c How many households received 20 or more e-mails?

d How many households did not receive any e-mails during the week? Explain your answer.

e Write down the modal class for the data in the table.

HINTS AND TIPS

You cannot find the mode of the data in a grouped frequency table. So, instead, you need to find the **modal class**, which is the class interval with the highest frequency.

6 Explain why the mode is often referred to as the 'shopkeeper's average'.

7 This table shows the colours of eyes for the pupils in form 7P.

	Blue	Brown	Green
Boys	4	8	1
Girls	8	5	2

a How many pupils are in form 7P?

b What is the modal eye colour for:

  i boys   **ii** girls   **iii** the whole form?

c After two pupils join the form the modal eye colour for the whole form is blue. Which of the following statements is true?

  • Both pupils had green eyes.

  • Both pupils had brown eyes.

  • Both pupils had blue eyes.

  • You cannot tell what their eye colours were.

The median

In this section you will learn how to:
- find the median from a list of data, a table of data and a stem-and-leaf diagram

Key words
median
middle
value

The **median** is the **middle value** of a list of values when they are put in *order* of size, from lowest to highest.

The advantage of using the median as an average is that half the data-values are below the median value and half are above it. Therefore, the average is only slightly affected by the presence of any particularly high or low values that are not typical of the data as a whole.

EXAMPLE 3

Find the median for the following list of numbers:

2, 3, 5, 6, 1, 2, 3, 4, 5, 4, 6

Putting the list in numerical order gives:

1, 2, 2, 3, 3, **4**, 4, 5, 5, 6, 6

There are 11 numbers in the list, so the middle of the list is the 6th number.
Therefore, the median is 4.

EXAMPLE 4

Find the median of the data shown in the frequency table.

Value	2	3	4	5	6	7
Frequency	2	4	6	7	8	3

First, add up the frequencies to find out how many pieces of data there are.

The total is 30 so the median value will be between the 15th and 16th values.

Now, add up the frequencies to give a running total, to find out where the 15th and 16th values are.

Value	2	3	4	5	6	7
Frequency	2	4	6	7	8	3
Total frequency	2	6	12	19	27	30

There are 12 data-values up to the value 4 and 19 up to the value 5.

Both the 15th and 16th values are 5, so the median is 5.

To find the median in a list of n values, written in order, use the rule:

$$\text{median} = \frac{n+1}{2}\text{th value}$$

For a set of data that has a lot of values, it is sometimes more convenient and quicker to draw a stem-and-leaf diagram. Example 5 shows you how to do this.

EXAMPLE 5

The ages of 20 people attending a conference were as follows:

28, 34, 46, 23, 28, 34, 52, 61, 45, 34, 39, 50, 26, 44, 60, 53, 31, 25, 37, 48

Find the modal age and median age of the group.

Taking the tens to be the 'stem' and the units to be the 'leaves', draw the stem-and-leaf diagram as shown below.

```
2 | 3  5  6  8  8
3 | 1  4  4  4  7  9
4 | 4  5  6  8
5 | 0  2  3
6 | 0  1
```
Key 2 | 3 represents 23 people

The most common value is 34, so the mode is 34.

There is an even number of values in this list, so the middle of the list is between the two central values, which are the 10th and 11th values. To find the central values count *up* 10 from the lowest value, 23, 25, 26, 28, 28, 31 ... or *down* 10 from the highest value 61, 60, 53, 52, 50, 48 ...

Therefore, the median is exactly midway between 37 and 39.

Hence, the median is 38.

EXERCISE 11B

1 Find the median for each set of data.

a 7, 6, 2, 3, 1, 9, 5, 4, 8

b 26, 34, 45, 28, 27, 38, 40, 24, 27, 33, 32, 41, 38

c 4, 12, 7, 6, 10, 5, 11, 8, 14, 3, 2, 9

d 12, 16, 12, 32, 28, 24, 20, 28, 24, 32, 36, 16

e 10, 6, 0, 5, 7, 13, 11, 14, 6, 13, 15, 1, 4, 15

f −1, −8, 5, −3, 0, 1, −2, 4, 0, 2, −4, −3, 2

g 5.5, 5.05, 5.15, 5.2, 5.3, 5.35, 5.08, 5.9, 5.25

HINTS AND TIPS

Remember to put the data in order before finding the median.

HINTS AND TIPS

If there is an even number of pieces of data, the median will be halfway between the two middle values.

2 A group of 15 sixth-formers had lunch in the school's cafeteria. Given below are the amounts that they spent.

£2.30, £2.20, £2, £2.50, £2.20, £3.50, £2.20, £2.25, £2.20, £2.30, £2.40, £2.20, £2.30, £2, £2.35

a Find the mode for the data.

b Find the median for the data.

c Which is the better average to use? Explain your answer.

3 **a** Find the median of 7, 4, 3, 8, 2, 6, 5, 2, 9, 8, 3.

b Without putting them in numerical order, write down the median for each of these sets.

i 17, 14, 13, 18, 12, 16, 15, 12, 19, 18, 13

ii 217, 214, 213, 218, 212, 216, 215, 212, 219, 218, 213

iii 12, 9, 8, 13, 7, 11, 10, 7, 14, 13, 8

iv 14, 8, 6, 16, 4, 12, 10, 4, 18, 16, 6

HINTS AND TIPS

Look for a connection between the original data and the new data. For example, in **i**, the numbers are each 10 more than those in part **a**.

---

4 Given below are the age, height and weight of each of the seven players in a netball team.

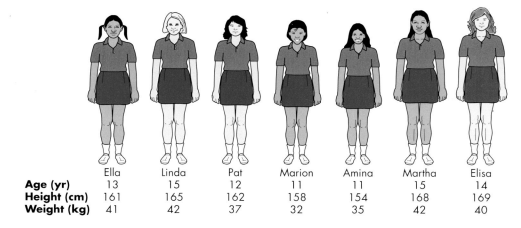

	Ella	Linda	Pat	Marion	Amina	Martha	Elisa
Age (yr)	13	15	12	11	11	15	14
Height (cm)	161	165	162	158	154	168	169
Weight (kg)	41	42	37	32	35	42	40

a Find the median age of the team. Which player has the median age?

b Find the median height of the team. Which player has the median height?

c Find the median weight of the team. Which player has the median weight?

d Who would you choose as the average player in the team? Give a reason for your answer.

5 The table shows the number of sandwiches sold in a corner shop over 25 days.

Sandwiches sold	10	11	12	13	14	15	16
Frequency	2	3	6	4	3	4	3

a What is the modal number of sandwiches sold?

b What is the median number of sandwiches sold?

6 The bar chart shows the marks that Mrs Woodhead gave her students for their first mathematics coursework task.

a How many students are there in Mrs Woodhead's class?

b What is the modal mark?

c Copy and complete this frequency table.

Mark	12	13	14	15	16	17	18
Frequency	1	3					

d What is the median mark?

7 **a** Write down a list of nine numbers that has a median of 12.

b Write down a list of ten numbers that has a median of 12.

c Write down a list of nine numbers that has a median of 12 and a mode of 8.

d Write down a list of ten numbers that has a median of 12 and a mode of 8.

8 The following stem-and-leaf diagram shows the times taken for 15 students to complete a mathematical puzzle.

```
1 | 7   8   8   9
2 | 2   2   2   5   6   9
3 | 3   4   5   5   8
```
Key 1 | 7 represents 17 seconds

a What is the modal time taken to complete the puzzle?

b What is the median time taken to complete the puzzle?

9 The stem-and-leaf diagram shows the marks for 13 boys and 12 girls in form 7E in a science test.

Key 2 | 3 represents 32 marks for boys
3 | 5 represents 35 marks for girls

```
           Boys | | Girls
       6   4   2 | 3 | 5   7   9
       9   9   6   2 | 4 | 2   2   3   8   8   8
   7   6   6   6   5   3 | 5 | 1   1   5
```

HINTS AND TIPS

Read the boys' marks from right to left.

a What was the modal mark for the boys?

b What was the modal mark for the girls?

c What was the median mark for the boys?

d What was the median mark for the girls?

HINTS AND TIPS

To find the middle value of two numbers, add them together and divide the result by 2. For example, for 43 and 48, 43 + 48 = 91, 91 ÷ 2 = 45.5.

e Who did better in the test, the boys or the girls? Give a reason for your answer.

10 A list contains seven even numbers. The largest number is 24. The smallest number is half the largest. The mode is 14 and the median is 16. Two of the numbers add up to 42. What are the seven numbers?

11 The marks of 25 students in an English examination were as follows:

55, 63, 24, 47, 60, 45, 50, 89, 39, 47, 38, 42, 69, 73, 38, 47, 53, 64, 58, 71, 41, 48, 68, 64, 75

Draw a stem-and-leaf diagram to find the median.

11.3 The mean

In this section you will learn how to:
● calculate the mean of a set of data

Key words
average
mean

The **mean** of a set of data is the sum of all the values in the set divided by the total number of values in the set. That is:

$$\text{mean} = \frac{\text{sum of all values}}{\text{total number of values}}$$

This is what most people mean when they use the term '**average**'.

The advantage of using the mean as an average is that it takes into account all the values in the set of data.

EXAMPLE 6

Find the mean of 4, 8, 7, 5, 9, 4, 8, 3.

Sum of all the values = 4 + 8 + 7 + 5 + 9 + 4 + 8 + 3 = 48

Total number of values = 8

Therefore, mean = $\frac{48}{8}$ = 6

EXAMPLE 7

The ages of 11 players in a football squad are:

21, 23, 20, 27, 25, 24, 25, 30, 21, 22, 28

What is the mean age of the squad?

Sum of all the ages = 266

Total number in squad = 11

Therefore, mean age = $\dfrac{266}{11}$ = 24.1818... = 24.2 (1 decimal place)

When the answer is not exact, it is usual to round the mean to 1 decimal place.

Using a calculator

If your calculator has a statistical mode, the mean of a set of numbers can be found by simply entering the numbers and then pressing the $\bar{x}$ key. On some calculators, the statistical mode is represented by SD.

Try this example. Find the mean of 2, 3, 7, 8 and 10.

First put your calculator into statistical mode. Then press the following keys:

2 DATA 3 DATA 7 DATA 8 DATA 1 0 DATA $\bar{x}$

You should find that the mean is given by $\bar{x}$ = 6.

You can also find the number of data-values by pressing the n key.

EXERCISE 11C

1 Find, without the help of a calculator, the mean for each set of data.

  a 7, 8, 3, 6, 7, 3, 8, 5, 4, 9

  b 47, 3, 23, 19, 30, 22

  c 42, 53, 47, 41, 37, 55, 40, 39, 44, 52

  d 1.53, 1.51, 1.64, 1.55, 1.48, 1.62, 1.58, 1.65

  e 1, 2, 0, 2, 5, 3, 1, 0, 1, 2, 3, 4

2 Calculate the mean for each set of data, giving your answer correct to 1 decimal place. You may use your calculator.

  a 34, 56, 89, 34, 37, 56, 72, 60, 35, 66, 67

  b 235, 256, 345, 267, 398, 456, 376, 307, 282

  c 50, 70, 60, 50, 40, 80, 70, 60, 80, 40, 50, 40, 70

  d 43.2, 56.5, 40.5, 37.9, 44.8, 49.7, 38.1, 41.6, 51.4

  e 2, 3, 1, 0, 2, 5, 4, 3, 2, 0, 1, 3, 4, 5, 0, 3, 1, 2

3 The table shows the marks that ten students obtained in mathematics, English and science in their Year 10 examinations.

Student	Abigail	Brian	Chloe	David	Eric	Frances	Graham	Howard	Ingrid	Jane
Maths	45	56	47	77	82	39	78	32	92	62
English	54	55	59	69	66	49	60	56	88	44
Science	62	58	48	41	80	56	72	40	81	52

a Calculate the mean mark for mathematics.

b Calculate the mean mark for English.

c Calculate the mean mark for science.

d Which student obtained marks closest to the mean in all three subjects?

e How many students were above the average mark in all three subjects?

4 Heather kept a record of the amount of time she spent on her homework over 10 days:

$\frac{1}{2}$ h, 20 min, 35 min, $\frac{1}{4}$ h, 1 h, $\frac{1}{2}$ h, $1\frac{1}{2}$ h, 40 min, $\frac{3}{4}$ h, 55 min

Calculate the mean time, in minutes, that Heather spent on her homework.

HINTS AND TIPS

Convert all times to minutes, for example, $\frac{1}{4}$ h = 15 minutes.

5 The weekly wages of ten people working in an office are:

£350   £200   £180   £200   £350   £200   £240   £480   £300   £280

a Find the modal wage.

b Find the median wage.

c Calculate the mean wage.

HINTS AND TIPS

Remember that the mean can be distorted by extreme values.

d Which of the three averages best represents the office staff's wages? Give a reason for your answer.

6 The ages of five people in a group of walkers are 38, 28, 30, 42 and 37.

a Calculate the mean age of the group.

b Steve, who is 41, joins the group. Calculate the new mean age of the group.

7 a Calculate the mean of 3, 7, 5, 8, 4, 6, 7, 8, 9 and 3.

b Calculate the mean of 13, 17, 15, 18, 14, 16, 17, 18, 19 and 13. What do you notice?

c Write down, without calculating, the mean for each of the following sets of data.

i 53, 57, 55, 58, 54, 56, 57, 58, 59, 53

ii 103, 107, 105, 108, 104, 106, 107, 108, 109, 103

iii 4, 8, 6, 9, 5, 7, 8, 9, 10, 4

HINTS AND TIPS

Look for a connection between the original data and the new data. For example in **i** the numbers are 50 more.

8 The mean age of a group of eight walkers is 42. Joanne joins the group and the mean age changes to 40. How old is Joanne?

11.4 The range

In this section you will learn how to:
- find the range of a set of data and compare different sets of data using the mean and the range

Key words
consistency
range
spread

The **range** for a set of data is the highest value of the set minus the lowest value.

The range is *not* an average. It shows the **spread** of the data. It is, therefore, used when comparing two or more sets of similar data. You can also use it to comment on the **consistency** of two or more sets of data.

EXAMPLE 8

Rachel's marks in ten mental arithmetic tests were 4, 4, 7, 6, 6, 5, 7, 6, 9 and 6.

Therefore, her mean mark is 60 ÷ 10 = 6 and the range is 9 − 4 = 5.

Adil's marks in the same tests were 6, 7, 6, 8, 5, 6, 5, 6, 5 and 6.

Therefore, his mean mark is 60 ÷ 10 = 6 and the range is 8 − 5 = 3.

Although the means are the same, Adil has a smaller range. This shows that Adil's results are more consistent.

EXERCISE 11D
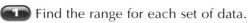

1 Find the range for each set of data.

a 3, 8, 7, 4, 5, 9, 10, 6, 7, 4

b 62, 59, 81, 56, 70, 66, 82, 78, 62, 75

c 1, 0, 4, 5, 3, 2, 5, 4, 2, 1, 0, 1, 4, 4

d 3.5, 4.2, 5.5, 3.7, 3.2, 4.8, 5.6, 3.9, 5.5, 3.8

e 2, −1, 0, 3, −1, −2, 1, −4, 2, 3, 0, 2, −2, 0, −3

2 The table shows the maximum and minimum temperatures at midday for five cities in England during a week in August.

	Birmingham	Leeds	London	Newcastle	Sheffield
Maximum temperature (°C)	28	25	26	27	24
Minimum temperature (°C)	23	22	24	20	21

a Write down the range of the temperatures for each city.

b What do the ranges tell you about the weather for England during the week?

3 Over a three-week period, the school tuck shop took the following amounts.

	Monday	Tuesday	Wednesday	Thursday	Friday
Week 1	£32	£29	£36	£30	£28
Week 2	£34	£33	£25	£28	£20
Week 3	£35	£34	£31	£33	£32

a Calculate the mean amount taken each week.

b Find the range for each week.

c What can you say about the total amounts taken for each of the three weeks?

4 In a ladies' golf tournament, the club chairperson had to choose either Sheila or Fay to play in the first round. In the previous eight rounds, their scores were as follows:

Sheila's scores: 75, 92, 80, 73, 72, 88, 86, 90

Fay's scores: 80, 87, 85, 76, 85, 79, 84, 88

a Calculate the mean score for each golfer.

b Find the range for each golfer.

c Which golfer would you choose to play in the tournament? Explain why.

HINTS AND TIPS

The best person to choose may not be the one with the biggest mean but could be the most consistent player.

5 Dan has a choice of two buses to get to school: Number 50 or Number 63. Over a month, he kept a record of the number of minutes each bus was late when it set off from his home bus stop.

No. 50: 4, 2, 0, 6, 4, 8, 8, 6, 3, 9

No. 63: 3, 4, 0, 10, 3, 5, 13, 1, 0, 1

a For each bus, calculate the mean number of minutes late.

b Find the range for each bus.

c Which bus would you advise Dan to catch? Give a reason for your answer.

Your time is up

You are going to find out how good you are at estimating 1 minute.

You need a stopwatch and a calculator.

This is a group activity. One person in the group acts as a timekeeper, says 'Start' and starts the stopwatch.

When someone thinks 1 minute has passed, they say 'Stop', and the timekeeper writes down the actual time, in seconds, that has passed. The timekeeper should try to record everyone's estimate.

Repeat the activity, with every member of the group taking a turn as the timekeeper.

Collate all the times and, from the data, find the mean (to the nearest second) and the range.

- How close is the mean to 1 minute?
- Why is the range useful?
- What strategies did people use to estimate 1 minute?

Repeat the activity for estimating different times, for example, 30 seconds or 2 minutes.

Write a brief report on what you find out about people's ability to estimate time.

11.5 Which average to use

In this section you will learn how to:

- understand the advantages and disadvantages of each type of average and decide which one to use in different situations

Key words

appropriate
extreme values
representative

An average must be truly **representative** of a set of data. So, when you have to find an average, it is crucial to choose the **appropriate** type of average for this particular set of data.

If you use the wrong average, your results will be distorted and give misleading information.

This table, which compares the advantages and disadvantages of each type of average, will help you to make the correct decision.

	Mode	Median	Mean
Advantages	Very easy to find Not affected by **extreme values** Can be used for non-numerical data	Easy to find for ungrouped data Not affected by extreme values	Easy to find Uses all the values The total for a given number of values can be calculated from it
Disadvantages	Does not use all the values May not exist	Does not use all the values Often not understood	Extreme values can distort it Has to be calculated
Use for	Non-numerical data Finding the most likely value	Data with extreme values	Data with values that are spread in a balanced way

EXERCISE 11E

1 The ages of the members of a hockey team were:

29   26   21   24   26   28   35   23   29   28   29

a What is:

  i the modal age?   **ii** the median age?   **iii** the mean age?

b What is the range of the ages?

2 **a** For each set of data, find the mode, the median and the mean.

  i 6, 10, 3, 4, 3, 6, 2, 9, 3, 4

  ii 6, 8, 6, 10, 6, 9, 6, 10, 6, 8

  iii 7, 4, 5, 3, 28, 8, 2, 4, 10, 9

b For each set of data, decide which average is the best one to use and give a reason.

3 A newsagent sold the following number of copies of *The Evening Star* on 12 consecutive evenings during a promotion exercise organised by the newspaper's publisher:

65   73   75   86   90   112   92   87   77   73   68   62

a Find the mode, the median and the mean for the sales.

b The newsagent had to report the average sale to the publisher after the promotion. Which of the three averages would you advise the newsagent to use? Explain why.

4 The mean age of a group of ten young people was 15.

a What do all their ages add up to?

b What will be their mean age in five years' time?

5 **a** Find the median of each list below.

    i 2, 4, 6, 7, 9   **ii** 12, 14, 16, 17, 19

    iii 22, 24, 26, 27, 29   **iv** 52, 54, 56, 57, 59

    v 92, 94, 96, 97, 99

b What do you notice about the lists and your answers?

c Use your answer above to help find the medians of the following lists.

    i 132, 134, 136, 137, 139   **ii** 577, 576, 572, 574, 579

    iii 431, 438, 439, 432, 435   **iv** 855, 859, 856, 851, 857

d Find the mean of each of the sets of numbers in part **a**.

6 Decide which average you would use for each of the following. Give a reason for your answer.

a The average mark in an examination

b The average pocket money for a group of 16-year-old students

c The average shoe size for all the girls in Year 10

d The average height for all the artistes on tour with a circus

e The average hair colour for pupils in your school

f The average weight of all newborn babies in a hospital's maternity ward

7 A pack of matches consisted of 12 boxes. The contents of each box were counted as:

    34   31   29   35   33   30   31   28   29   35   32   31

On the box it stated 'Average contents 32 matches'. Is this correct?

8 A firm showed the annual salaries for its employees as:

Chairman	£43 000
Managing director	£37 000
Floor manager	£25 000
Skilled worker 1	£24 000
Skilled worker 2	£24 000
Machinist	£18 000
Computer engineer	£18 000
Secretary	£18 000
Office junior	£7 000

a What is:

   i the modal salary?   **ii** the median salary?   **iii** the mean salary?

b The management suggested a pay rise of 6% for all employees. The shopfloor workers suggested a pay rise of £1500 for all employees.

   i One of the suggestions would cause problems for the firm. Which one is that and why?

   ii What difference would each suggestion make to the modal, median and mean salaries?

9 Mr Brennan, a caring maths teacher, told each pupil their test mark and only gave the test statistics to the whole class. He gave the class the modal mark, the median mark and the mean mark.

   a Which average would tell a pupil whether they were in the top half or the bottom half of the class?

   b Which average tells the pupils nothing really?

   c Which average allows a pupil to gauge how well they have done compared with everyone else?

10 A list of nine numbers has a mean of 7.6. What number must be added to the list to give a new mean of 8?

11 A dance group of 17 teenagers had a mean weight of 44.5 kg. To enter a competition there needed to be 18 teenagers with an average weight of 44.4 kg or less. What is the maximum weight that the eighteenth person must be?

11.6 Frequency tables

In this section you will:
- revise finding the mode and median from a frequency table
- learn how to calculate the mean from a frequency table

Key words
frequency
table

When a lot of information has been gathered, it is often convenient to put it together in a **frequency table**. From this table you can then find the values of the three averages and the range.

EXAMPLE 9

A survey was done on the number of people in each car leaving the Meadowhall Shopping Centre, in Sheffield. The results are summarised in the table below.

Number of people in each car	1	2	3	4	5	6
Frequency	45	198	121	76	52	13

For the number of people in a car, calculate the following.

a the mode   **b** the median   **c** the mean

a The modal number of people in a car is easy to spot. It is the number with the largest frequency, that is 198. Hence, the modal number of people in a car is 2.

b The median number of people in a car is found by working out where the middle of the set of numbers is located. First, add up frequencies to get the total number of cars surveyed, which comes to 505. Next, calculate the middle position:

$$(505 + 1) \div 2 = 253$$

Now add the frequencies across the table to find which group contains the 253rd item. The 243rd item is the end of the group with 2 in a car. Therefore, the 253rd item must be in the group with 3 in a car. Hence, the median number of people in a car is 3.

c To calculate the mean number of people in a car, multiply the number of people in the car by the frequency. This is best done in an extra column. Add these to find the total number of people and divide by the total frequency (the number of cars surveyed).

Number in car	Frequency	Number in these cars
1	45	1 × 45 = 45
2	198	2 × 198 = 396
3	121	3 × 121 = 363
4	76	4 × 76 = 304
5	52	5 × 52 = 260
6	13	6 × 13 = 78
Totals	505	1446

Hence, the mean number of people in a car is 1446 ÷ 505 = 2.9 (to 1 decimal place).

Using your calculator

The previous example can also be done by using the statistical mode which is available on some calculators. However, not all calculators are the same, so you will have to either read your instruction manual or experiment with the statistical keys on your calculator.

You may find one labelled:

DATA or **M+** or **Σ+** or **$\bar{x}$** , where $\bar{x}$ is printed in blue.

Try the following key strokes:

1 **×** **4** **5** **DATA**   **2** **×** **1** **9** **8** **DATA** ... **6** **×** **1** **3** **DATA** **$\bar{x}$**

EXERCISE 11F

1 Find **i** the mode, **ii** the median and **iii** the mean from each frequency tables below.

a A survey of the shoe sizes of all the Y10 boys in a school gave these results.

Shoe size	4	5	6	7	8	9	10
Number of pupils	12	30	34	35	23	8	3

b A survey of the number of eggs laid by hens over a period of one week gave these results.

Number of eggs	0	1	2	3	4	5	6
Frequency	6	8	15	35	48	37	12

c This is a record of the number of babies born each week over one year in a small maternity unit.

Number of babies	0	1	2	3	4	5	6	7	8	9	10	11	12	13	14
Frequency	1	1	1	2	2	2	3	5	9	8	6	4	5	2	1

d A school did a survey on how many times in a week pupils arrived late at school. These are the findings.

Number of times late	0	1	2	3	4	5
Frequency	481	34	23	15	3	4

2 A survey of the number of children in each family of a school's intake gave these results.

Number of children	1	2	3	4	5
Frequency	214	328	97	26	3

a Assuming each child at the school is shown in the data, how many children are at the school?

b Calculate the mean number of children in a family.

c How many families have this mean number of children?

d How many families would consider themselves average from this survey?

3 A dentist kept records of how many teeth he extracted from his patients.

In 1980 he extracted 598 teeth from 271 patients.

In 1990 he extracted 332 teeth from 196 patients.

In 2000 he extracted 374 teeth from 288 patients.

a Calculate the average number of teeth taken from each patient in each year.

b Explain why you think the average number of teeth extracted falls each year.

4 One hundred cases of apples delivered to a supermarket were inspected and the numbers of bad apples were recorded.

Bad apples	0	1	2	3	4	5	6	7	8	9
Frequency	52	29	9	3	2	1	3	0	0	1

What is:

a the modal number of bad apples per case?

b the mean number of bad apples per case?

5 Two dice are thrown together 60 times. The sum of the scores is shown below.

Score	2	3	4	5	6	7	8	9	10	11	12
Frequency	1	2	6	9	12	15	6	5	2	1	1

Find **a** the modal score, **b** the median score and **c** the mean score.

6 During a one-month period, the number of days off by 100 workers in a factory were noted as follows.

Number of days off	0	1	2	3	4
Number of workers	35	42	16	4	3

Calculate the following.

a the modal number of days off

b the median number of days off

c the mean number of days off

7 Two friends often played golf together. They recorded their scores for each hole over the last five games to compare who was more consistent and who was the better player. Their results were summarised in the following table.

No. of shots to hole ball	1	2	3	4	5	6	7	8	9
Roger	0	0	0	14	37	27	12	0	0
Brian	5	12	15	18	14	8	8	8	2

a What is the modal score for each player?

b What is the range of scores for each player?

c What is the median score for each player?

d What is the mean score for each player?

e Which player is the more consistent and why?

f Who would you say is the better player and why?

In this section you will learn how to:
- identify the modal class
- calculate an estimate of the mean from a grouped table

Sometimes the information you are given is grouped in some way (called **grouped data**), as in Example 10, which shows the range of weekly pocket money given to Y10 students in a particular class.

Normally, grouped tables use continuous data, which is data that can have any value within a range of values, for example, height, weight, time, area and capacity. In these situations, the **mean** can only be **estimated** as you do not have all the information.

Discrete data is data that consists of separate numbers, for example, goals scored, marks in a test, number of children and shoe sizes.

In both cases, when using a grouped table to estimate the mean, first find the midpoint of the interval by adding the two end values and then dividing by two.

EXAMPLE 10

Pocket money, p (£)	$0 < p \leq 1$	$1 < p \leq 2$	$2 < p \leq 3$	$3 < p \leq 4$	$4 < p \leq 5$
No. of students	2	5	5	9	15

a Write down the **modal class**.   b Calculate an estimate of the mean weekly pocket money.

a The modal class is easy to pick out, since it is simply the one with the largest frequency. Here the modal class is £4 to £5.

b To estimate the mean, assume that each person in each class has the 'midpoint' amount, then build up the following table.

To find the midpoint value, the two end values are added together and then divided by two.

Pocket money, p (£)	Frequency (f)	Midpoint (m)	$f \times m$
$0 < p \leq 1$	2	0.50	1.00
$1 < p \leq 2$	5	1.50	7.50
$2 < p \leq 3$	5	2.50	12.50
$3 < p \leq 4$	9	3.50	31.50
$4 < p \leq 5$	15	4.50	67.50
Totals	36		120

The estimated mean will be £120 ÷ 36 = £3.33 (rounded to the nearest penny).

Note the notation for the classes:

$0 < p \leq 1$ means any amount above 0p up to and including £1.

$1 < p \leq 2$ means any amount above £1 up to and including £2, and so on.

If you had written 0.01 – 1.00, 1.01 – 2.00 and so on for the groups, then the midpoints would have been 0.505, 1.505 and so on. This would not have had a significant effect on the final answer as it is only an estimate.

EXERCISE 11G

1 For each table of values given below, find:

i the modal group

ii an estimate for the mean.

a

x	$0 < x \leqslant 10$	$10 < x \leqslant 20$	$20 < x \leqslant 30$	$30 < x \leqslant 40$	$40 < x \leqslant 50$
Frequency	4	6	11	17	9

b

y	$0 < y \leqslant 100$	$100 < y \leqslant 200$	$200 < y \leqslant 300$	$300 < y \leqslant 400$	$400 < y \leqslant 500$	$500 < x \leqslant 600$
Frequency	95	56	32	21	9	3

c

z	$0 < z \leqslant 5$	$5 < z \leqslant 10$	$10 < z \leqslant 15$	$15 < z \leqslant 20$
Frequency	16	27	19	13

> **HINTS AND TIPS**
>
> When you copy the tables, drawn them vertically as in Example 10.

d

Weeks	1–3	4–6	7–9	10–12	13–15
Frequency	5	8	14	10	7

2 Jason brought 100 pebbles back from the beach and weighed them all, recording each weight to the nearest gram. His results are summarised in the table below.

Weight, w (g)	$40 < w \leqslant 60$	$60 < w \leqslant 80$	$80 < w \leqslant 100$	$100 < w \leqslant 120$	$120 < w \leqslant 140$	$140 < w \leqslant 160$
Frequency	5	9	22	27	26	11

Find the following.

a the modal weight of the pebbles

b an estimate of the total weight of all the pebbles

c an estimate of the mean weight of the pebbles

3 A gardener measured the heights of all his daffodils to the nearest centimetre and summarised his results as follows.

Height (cm)	10–14	15–18	19–22	23–26	27–40
Frequency	21	57	65	52	12

a How many daffodils did the gardener have?

b What is the modal height of the daffodils?

c What is the estimated mean height of the daffodils?

4 A survey was made to see how quickly the AA attended calls that were not on a motorway. The following table summarises the results.

Time (min)	1–15	16–30	31–45	46–60	61–75	76–90	91–105
Frequency	2	23	48	31	27	18	11

a How many calls were used in the survey?

b Estimate the mean time taken per call.

c Which average would the AA use for the average call-out time?

d What percentage of calls do the AA get to within the hour?

5 One hundred light bulbs were tested by their manufacturer to see whether the average life-span of the manufacturer's bulbs was over 200 hours. The following table summarises the results.

Life span, *h* (hours)	$150 < h \leqslant 175$	$175 < h \leqslant 200$	$200 < h \leqslant 225$	$225 < h \leqslant 250$	$250 < h \leqslant 275$
Frequency	24	45	18	10	3

a What is the modal length of time a bulb lasts?

b What percentage of bulbs last longer than 200 hours?

c Estimate the mean life-span of the light bulbs.

d Do you think the test shows that the average life-span is over 200 hours? Fully explain your answer.

6 Three supermarkets each claimed to have the lowest average price increase over the year. The following table summarises their price increases.

Price increase (p)	1–5	6–10	11–15	16–20	21–25	26–30	31–35
Soundbuy	4	10	14	23	19	8	2
Springfields	5	11	12	19	25	9	6
Setco	3	8	15	31	21	7	3

Using their average price increases, make a comparison of the supermarkets and write a report on which supermarket, in your opinion, has the lowest price increases over the year. Do not forget to justify your answers.

7 The table shows the distances run, over a month, by an athlete who is training for a marathon.

Distance, *d* (miles)	$0 < d \leqslant 5$	$5 < d \leqslant 10$	$10 < d \leqslant 15$	$15 < d \leqslant 20$	$20 < d \leqslant 25$
Frequency	3	8	13	5	2

a A marathon is 26.2 miles. It is recommended that an athlete's daily average mileage should be at least a third of the distance of the race for which they are training. Is this athlete doing enough training?

b The athlete records the times of some runs and calculates that her average pace for all runs is $6\frac{1}{2}$ minutes to a mile. Explain why she is wrong to expect a finishing time for the marathon of $26.2 \times 6\frac{1}{2}$ minutes ≈ 170 minutes.

c The runner claims that the difference in length between her shortest and longest run is 21 miles. Could this be correct? Explain your answer.

Frequency polygons

In this section you will learn how to:

- draw frequency polygons for discrete and continuous data

Key words

frequency
    polygon
discrete data
continuous
    data

To help people understand it, statistical information is often presented in pictorial or diagrammatic form, which includes the pie chart, the line graph, the bar chart and stem-and-leaf diagrams. These were covered in Chapter 6. Another method of showing data is by **frequency polygons**.

Frequency polygons can be used to represent both ungrouped data and grouped data, as shown in Example 11 and Example 12 respectively and are appropriate for both **discrete data** and **continuous data**.

Frequency polygons show the shapes of distributions and can be used to compare distributions.

EXAMPLE 11

No. of children	0	1	2	3	4	5
Frequency	12	23	36	28	16	11

This is the frequency polygon for the ungrouped data in the table.

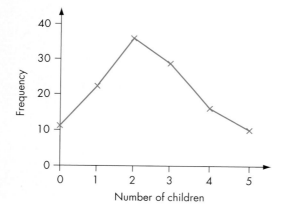

Note:

- The coordinates are plotted from each ordered pair in the table.

- The polygon is completed by joining up the plotted points with straight lines.

EXAMPLE 12

Weight, w (kg)	$0 < w \leqslant 5$	$5 < w \leqslant 10$	$10 < w \leqslant 15$	$15 < w \leqslant 20$	$20 < w \leqslant 25$	$25 < w \leqslant 30$
Frequency	4	13	25	32	17	9

This is the frequency polygon for the grouped data in the table.

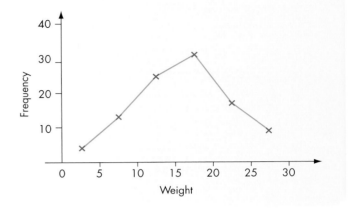

Note:

● The midpoint of each group is used, just as it was in estimating the mean.

● The ordered pairs of midpoints with frequency are plotted, namely:

(2.5, 4), (7.5, 13), (12.5, 25), (17.5, 32), (22.5, 17), (27.5, 9)

● The polygon should be left like this. Any lines you draw before and after this have no meaning.

EXERCISE 11H

1 The following table shows how many students were absent from one particular class throughout the year.

Students absent	1	2	3	4	5
Frequency	48	32	12	3	1

a Draw a frequency polygon to illustrate the data.

b Estimate the mean number of absences each lesson.

2 The table below shows the number of goals scored by a hockey team in one season.

Goals	1	2	3	4	5
Frequency	3	9	7	5	2

a Draw the frequency polygon for this data.

b Estimate the mean number of goals scored per game this season.

3 After a spelling test, all the results were collated for girls and boys as below.

Number correct	1–4	5–8	9–12	13–16	17–20
Boys	3	7	21	26	15
Girls	4	8	17	23	20

HINTS AND TIPS

The highest point of the frequency polygon is the modal value.

a Draw frequency polygons to illustrate the differences between the boys' scores and the girls' scores.

b Estimate the mean score for boys and girls separately, and comment on the results.

4 A doctor was concerned at the length of time her patients had to wait to see her when they came to the morning surgery. The survey she did gave her the following results.

Time, m (min)	$0 < m \leqslant 10$	$10 < m \leqslant 20$	$20 < m \leqslant 30$	$30 < m \leqslant 40$	$40 < m \leqslant 50$	$50 < m \leqslant 60$
Monday	5	8	17	9	7	4
Tuesday	9	8	16	3	2	1
Wednesday	7	6	18	2	1	1

a Using the same pair of axes, draw a frequency polygon for each day.

b What is the average amount of time spent waiting each day?

c Why might the average time for each day be different?

5 The frequency polygon shows the amounts of money spent in a corner shop by the first 40 customers one morning.

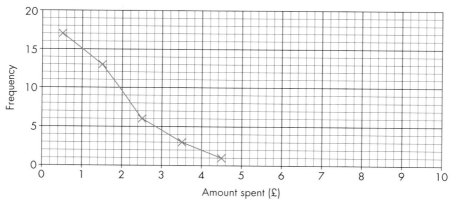

a i Use the frequency polygon to complete the table for the amounts spent by the first 40 customers.

Amount spent, m (£)	$0 < m \leqslant 1$	$1 < m \leqslant 2$	$2 < m \leqslant 3$	$3 < m \leqslant 4$	$4 < m \leqslant 5$
Frequency					

ii Work out the mean amount of money spent by these 40 customers.

b Mid-morning another 40 customers visit the shop and the shopkeeper records the amounts they spend. The table below shows the data.

Amount spent, m (£)	$0 < m \leqslant 2$	$2 < m \leqslant 4$	$4 < m \leqslant 6$	$6 < m \leqslant 8$	$8 < m \leqslant 10$
Frequency	3	5	18	10	4

i Copy the graph above and draw the frequency polygon to show this data.

ii Calculate the mean amount spent by the 40 mid-morning customers.

c Comment on the differences between the frequency polygons and the average amounts spent by the different groups of customers.

1 The table shows how many children there were in the family of each member of a class.

Number of children	Frequency
1	6
2	10
3	4
4	3
5	1

a How many children were in the class?

b What is the modal number of children per family?

c What is the median number of children per family?

d What is the mean number of children per family?

 2 Find: **a** the mode   **b** the median of:

6, 6, 6, 8, 9, 10, 11, 12, 13

 3 Here are the test marks of 6 girls and 4 boys.

Girls: 5   3   10   2   7   3

Boys: 2   5   9   3

a Write down the mode of the 10 marks.

b Work out the median mark of the boys.

c Work out the range of the girls' marks.

d Work out the mean mark of all 10 students.

Edexcel, Question 4, Paper 8B Foundation, January 2004

 4 Find the mean of 5, 7, 8, 9, 10, 10, 11, 12, 13 and 35.

 5 Use your calculator to work out the value of

$$\frac{5.4 \times 8.1}{12.3 - 5.9}$$

Write down all the figures on your calculator display.

Edexcel, Question 2, Paper 12B Intermediate, March 2005

 6 a Work out:

i the mean   **ii** the range

of 61, 63, 61, 86, 78, 75, 80, 68, 84 and 84.

b Fred wants to plant a conifer hedge. At the local garden centre he looks at 10 plants from two different varieties of conifer.

All the plants have been growing for six months. The Sprucy Pine plants have a mean height of 74 cm and a range of 25 cm.

The Evergreen plants have a mean height of 52 cm and a range of 5 cm.

i Give one reason why Fred might decide to plant a hedge of Sprucy Pine trees.

ii Give one reason why Fred might decide to plant a hedge of Evergreen trees.

 7 The stem-and leaf-diagram shows the number of packages 15 drivers delivered.

Key   3 | 5   means 35 packages

```
3 | 5  7
4 | 1  3  8  8
5 | 0  2  5  6  7  9
6 | 6  9
7 | 2
```

a What is the range of the packets delivered?

b What is the median of the packets delivered?

c What is the mode of the packets delivered?

 8 The weights, in kilograms, of each passenger in a minibus are:

86, 76, 84, 84, 81, 85, 80, 86, 33

a Calculate:

i their median weight

ii the range of their weights

iii their mean weight.

b Which of the two averages, mean or median, better describes the data above? Give a reason for your answer.

 9 A company puts this advert in the local paper.

> **NCS Engineers**
> **Mechanic needed**
> Average wage over £500 per week

The following people work for the company.

Job	Wage per week (£)
Apprentice	210
Cleaner	210
Foreman	360
Manager	850
Mechanic	255
Parts Manager	650
Sales Manager	680

a What is the mode of these wages?

b What is the median wage?

c Calculate the mean wage.

d Explain why the advert is misleading.

10 The numbers of people in 50 cars are recorded.

Number of people	Frequency
1	24
2	13
3	8
4	4
5	1

Calculate the mean number of people per car.

11 The table shows the distances travelled to work by 40 office workers.

Distance travelled, d (km)	Frequency
$0 < d \leqslant 2$	10
$2 < d \leqslant 4$	16
$4 < d \leqslant 6$	8
$6 < d \leqslant 8$	5
$8 < d \leqslant 10$	1

Calculate an estimate of the mean distance travelled to work by these office workers.

12 Tom and Barbara grew tomatoes. They compared their tomatoes by selecting 100 of each one weekend. The table shows the mean weight of Tom's tomatoes.

Weight, w (grams)	Tom's Tomatoes
$50 \leqslant w < 100$	21
$100 \leqslant w < 150$	28
$150 \leqslant w < 200$	26
$200 \leqslant w < 250$	14
$250 \leqslant w < 300$	9
$300 \leqslant w < 350$	2

a Which class interval contains the median weight for Tom's Tomatoes?

b The frequency polygon for Barbara's Tomatoes is drawn on the following grid. Copy it on to graph paper. On the same grid draw the frequency polygon for Tom's Tomatoes.

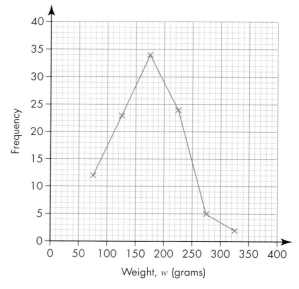

c Use the frequency polygons to write down one comparison between Tom and Barbara's Tomatoes.

13 The mean weight of five rowers is 49.2 kg.

a Find the total weight of the rowers.

b The mean weight of the five rowers and the reserve is 50.5 kg.
Calculate the weight of the reserve.

14 The table shows information about the number of hours that 120 children used a computer last week.

Number of hours (h)	Frequency
$0 < h \leqslant 2$	10
$2 < h \leqslant 4$	15
$4 < h \leqslant 6$	30
$6 < h \leqslant 8$	35
$8 < h \leqslant 10$	25
$10 < h \leqslant 12$	5

Work out an estimate for the mean number of hours that the children used a computer. Give your answer correct to 2 decimal places.

Edexcel, Question 10, Paper 17 Intermediate, June 2005

WORKED EXAM QUESTIONS

1   A teacher asks all his class: 'How many children are there in your family?' Their replies are given below.

Number of children in a family	Number of replies
1	7
2	12
3	5
4	2
5	0

a   How many children are in the class?

b   What is the modal number of children in a family?

c   What is the median number in a family?

d   What is the mean number in a family?

Solution

1   a   7 + 12 + 5 + 2 + 0 = 26

   The total number of children is 26.

   b   The modal number of children is 2.

   c   The median number of children is 2.

   d   The mean number of children = 54 ÷ 26 = 2.1

> Add up the frequencies.

> The largest frequency is 12 so the modal number is 2.

> The median will be between the 13th and 14th values. Adding up the frequencies gives 7, 19, 24, 26, 26. So the required value is in the second row.

> Add an extra column to the table and multiply the number of children by the number of replies. This gives 7, 24, 15, 8, 0.
> Add these to get 54.
> Divide 54 by 26.

2   A teacher shows her class 25 objects on a tray. She leaves it in view for one minute.

She then covers the objects and asks the class to write down the names of as many objects as they can remember.

The results are shown in the table.

What is the mean number of objects recalled by the class?

Number of objects recalled, x	Frequency, f
$0 < x \leqslant 5$	2
$5 < x \leqslant 10$	5
$10 < x \leqslant 15$	13
$15 < x \leqslant 20$	8
$20 < x \leqslant 25$	2
	30

Solution

2

Number of objects recalled, x	Frequency, f	Midpoint, m	$m \times f$
$0 < x \leqslant 5$	2	2.5	5
$5 < x \leqslant 10$	5	7.5	37.5
$10 < x \leqslant 15$	13	12.5	162.5
$15 < x \leqslant 20$	8	17.5	140
$20 < x \leqslant 25$	2	22.5	45
	30		390

> First add a column for the midpoints. This is the two end values added and divided by 2.

> Next, add a column for midpoint multiplied by frequency.

> Next, work out the totals for the frequency and the $m \times f$ columns.

Mean = 390 ÷ 30

= 13

> Finally, divide the total of the $m \times f$ column by the total frequency.

Mr Davies is a dairy farmer. Every month he records how many thousands of litres of milk are produced by his cows.

For his business plan he compares the amount of milk produced in 2004 with the amount in 2005.

Monthly milk production (thousands of litres)

Month	2004	2005
Jan	51	62
Feb	53	65
Mar	55	62
Apr	56	67
May	64	72
Jun	72	83
Jul	70	81
Aug	75	86
Sep	64	75
Oct	64	73
Nov	62	70
Dec	58	68

Copy and comple the table below.

Monthly milk production (thousands of litres)

	2004	2005
mean		
median		
mode		
range		

Copy this bar chart into your book and complete it for Mr Davies' milk production in 2005.

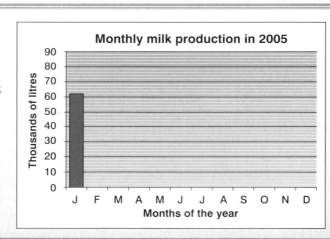

Monthly milk production in 2005

For his business plan Mr Davies compares the amount of milk he produces in 2005 with the graphs showing the hours of sunshine and amount of rain that year.

Compare your milk production bar chart with the rainfall bar chart.

What do you notice?

Compare your milk production bar chart with the hours of sunshine bar chart.

What do you notice?

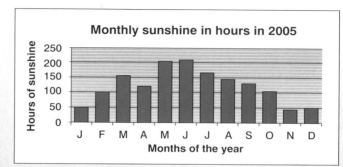

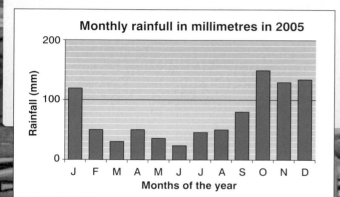

GRADE YOURSELF

G Able to find the mode and median of a list of data

F Able to find the range of a set of data and find the mean of a small set of data

E Able to find the mean and range from a stem-and-leaf diagram

D Able to find the mean from a frequency table of discrete data and draw a frequency polygon for discrete data

D Able to find the median from a stem-and-leaf diagram

C Able to find an estimate of the mean from a grouped table of continuous data and draw a frequency polygon for continuous data

What you should know now

- How to find the range, mode, median and mean of sets of discrete data
- Which average to use in different situations
- How to find the modal class and an estimated mean for continuous data
- How to draw frequency polygons for discrete and continuous data

1 Equivalent percentages, fractions and decimals

2 Calculating a percentage of a quantity

3 Calculating a percentage increase or decrease

4 Expressing one quantity as a percentage of another

This chapter will show you ...

- what is meant by percentage
- how to do calculations involving percentages
- how to use your calculator to work out percentages by using a multiplier
- how to work out percentage increases and decreases

Visual overview

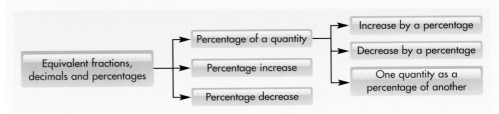

What you should already know

- How to cancel fractions
- How to calculate with fractions
- How to multiply decimals by 100 (move the digits two places to the left)
- How to divide decimals by 100 (move the digits two places to the right)

Quick check

1 Cancel these fractions.

a $\dfrac{12}{32}$ **b** $\dfrac{20}{45}$ **c** $\dfrac{28}{48}$ **d** $\dfrac{36}{60}$

2 Work out these amounts.

a $\dfrac{2}{3}$ of 27   **b** $\dfrac{5}{8}$ of 32   **c** $\dfrac{1}{4} \times 76$ **d** $\dfrac{3}{5} \times 45$

3 Work out these amounts.

a 12×100 **b** $34 \div 100$ **c** 0.23×100 **d** $4.7 \div 100$

In this section you will learn how to:

● convert percentages to fractions and decimals and vice versa

Key words

decimal
decimal equivalents
fraction
percentage

Per cent means 'out of 100'. So, any **percentage** can be expressed as a **fraction** with denominator 100. For example:

$$32\% = \frac{32}{100}$$ which can be cancelled to $\frac{8}{25}$

Also, any percentage can be expressed as a **decimal** by dividing by 100. This means moving the digits two places to the right. For example:

$$65\% = 65 \div 100 = 0.65$$

Any decimal can be expressed as a percentage simply by multiplying by 100.

Any fraction can be expressed as a percentage either by making the denominator into 100 or dividing the numerator by the denominator and multiplying by 100.

Knowing the percentage and **decimal equivalents** of the common fractions is extremely useful. So, do try to learn them.

$$\frac{1}{2} = 0.5 = 50\% \qquad \frac{1}{4} = 0.25 = 25\% \qquad \frac{3}{4} = 0.75 = 75\% \qquad \frac{1}{8} = 0.125 = 12.5\%$$

$$\frac{1}{10} = 0.1 = 10\% \qquad \frac{1}{5} = 0.2 = 20\% \qquad \frac{1}{3} = 0.33 = 33\frac{1}{3}\% \qquad \frac{2}{3} = 0.67 = 67\%$$

The following table shows how to convert from one to the other.

Convert from percentage to:	
Decimal	**Fraction**
Divide the percentage by 100, for example, 52% = 52 ÷ 100 = 0.52	Make the percentage into a fraction with a denominator of 100 and cancel down if possible, for example, $52\% = \frac{52}{100} = \frac{13}{25}$

Convert from decimal to:	
Percentage	**Fraction**
Multiply the decimal by 100, for example, 0.65 = 0.65 × 100 = 65%	If the decimal has 1 decimal place put it over the denominator 10, if it has 2 decimal places put it over the denominator 100, etc. Then cancel down if possible, for example, $0.65 = \frac{65}{100} = \frac{13}{20}$

Convert from fraction to:	
Percentage	**Decimal**
If the denominator is a factor of 100 multiply numerator and denominator to make the denominator 100, then the numerator is the percentage, for example, $\frac{3}{20} = \frac{15}{100} = 15\%$, or convert to a decimal and change the decimal to a percentage, for example, $\frac{7}{8} = 7 \div 8 = 0.875 = 87.5\%$	Divide the numerator by the denominator, for example, $\frac{9}{40} = 9 \div 40 = 0.225$

100% means the *whole* of something. So, if you want to, you can express *part* of the whole as a percentage.

EXAMPLE 1

Change the following to decimals. **a** 78% **b** 35% **c** $\frac{3}{25}$ **d** $\frac{7}{40}$

a $78 \div 100 = 0.78$ **b** $35 \div 100 = 0.35$

c $3 \div 25 = 0.12$ **d** $7 \div 40 = 0.175$

EXAMPLE 2

Change the following to percentages. **a** 0.85 **b** 0.125 **c** $\frac{7}{20}$ **d** $\frac{3}{8}$

a $0.85 \times 100 = 85\%$ **b** $0.125 \times 100 = 12.5\%$

c $\frac{7}{20} = \frac{35}{100} = 35\%$ **d** $\frac{3}{8} = 3 \div 8 = 0.375 = 37.5\%$

EXAMPLE 3

Change the following to fractions. **a** 0.45 **b** 0.4 **c** 32% **d** 15%

a $0.45 = \frac{45}{100} = \frac{9}{20}$ **b** $0.4 = \frac{4}{10} = \frac{2}{5}$

c $32\% = \frac{32}{100} = \frac{8}{25}$ **d** $15\% = \frac{15}{100} = \frac{3}{20}$

EXAMPLE 4

Put the following set of fractions into order, putting the smallest on the left hand side.

$25\%, \frac{1}{10}, 0.2, 0.195$

Change each fraction into a decimal for easier comparison

$25\% = 0.25, \frac{1}{10} = 0.1, 0.2, 0.195$

Re-order as: 0.1, 0.195, 0.2, 0.25
          smallest

> **HINTS AND TIPS**
>
> It will help to think of
>   0.1   as   0.100
> and 0.2   as   0.20

G

EXERCISE 12A

 1 Write each percentage as a fraction in its lowest terms.

    a 8%   **b** 50%   **c** 25%

    d 35%   **e** 90%   **f** 75%

 2 Write each percentage as a decimal.

    a 27%   **b** 85%   **c** 13%

    d 6%   **e** 80%   **f** 32%

 3 Write each decimal as a fraction in its lowest terms.

    a 0.12   **b** 0.4   **c** 0.45

    d 0.68   **e** 0.25   **f** 0.625

 4 Write each decimal as a percentage.

    a 0.29   **b** 0.55   **c** 0.03

    d 0.16   **e** 0.6   **f** 1.25

 5 Write each fraction as a percentage.

    a $\frac{7}{25}$ **b** $\frac{3}{10}$ **c** $\frac{19}{20}$

    d $\frac{17}{50}$ **e** $\frac{11}{40}$ **f** $\frac{7}{8}$

 6 Write each fraction as a decimal.

    a $\frac{9}{15}$ **b** $\frac{3}{40}$ **c** $\frac{19}{25}$

    d $\frac{5}{16}$ **e** $\frac{1}{20}$ **f** $\frac{1}{8}$

 7 Of the 300 members of a social club 50% are men. How many members are women?

 8 Gillian came home and told her dad that she got 100% of her spellings correct. She told her mum that there were 25 spellings to learn. How many spellings did Gillian get wrong?

 9 Every year a school library likes to replace 1% of its books. One year the library had 2000 books. How many did it replace?

 10 a If 23% of pupils go home for lunch, what percentage do not go home for lunch?

    b If 61% of the population takes part in the National Lottery, what percentage do not take part?

    c If 37% of members of a gym are males, what percentage of the members are females?

 11 I calculated that 28% of my time is spent sleeping and 45% is spent working. How much time is left to spend doing something else?

 12 In one country, 24.7% of the population is below the age of 16 and 13.8% of the population is aged over 65. How much of the population is aged from 16 to 65 inclusive?

13 Approximately what percentage of each bottle is filled with water?

a    b    c

 14 Helen made a cake for James. The amount of cake left each day is shown in the diagram.

   a What percentage is left each day?

   b What percentage has been eaten each day?

   Monday   Tuesday   Wednesday   Thursday   Friday

 15 Change each of these fractions into a percentage.

   a $\frac{1}{5}$ b $\frac{1}{4}$ c $\frac{3}{4}$ d $\frac{9}{20}$ e $\frac{7}{50}$

   f $\frac{1}{2}$ g $\frac{3}{5}$ h $\frac{7}{40}$ i $\frac{11}{20}$ j $\frac{13}{10}$

 16 Change each of these fractions into a percentage. Give your answers to one decimal place.

   a $\frac{1}{3}$ b $\frac{1}{6}$ c $\frac{2}{3}$ d $\frac{5}{6}$ e $\frac{2}{7}$

   f $\frac{47}{60}$ g $\frac{31}{45}$ h $\frac{8}{9}$ i $\frac{73}{90}$ j $\frac{23}{110}$

 17 Change each of these decimals into a percentage.

   a 0.07   b 0.8   c 0.66   d 0.25   e 0.545

   f 0.82   g 0.3   h 0.891   i 1.2   j 2.78

 18 Chris scored 24 marks out of a possible 40 in a maths test.

   a Write this score as a fraction.

   b Write this score as a decimal.

   c Write this score as a percentage.

 19 Convert each of the following test scores into a percentage. Give each answer to the nearest whole number.

Subject	Result	Percentage
Mathematics	38 out of 60	
English	29 out of 35	
Science	27 out of 70	
History	56 out of 90	
Technology	58 out of 75	

20 The air you breathe consists of about $\frac{4}{5}$ nitrogen and $\frac{1}{5}$ oxygen. What percentage of the air is **a** nitrogen **b** oxygen?

21 There were two students missing from my class of 30. What percentage of my class were away?

22 In one season, Robbie Keane had 110 shots at goal. He scored with 28 of these shots. What percentage of his shots resulted in goals?

23 Copy and complete the table.

Percentage	Decimal	Fraction
34%		
	0.85	
		$\frac{3}{40}$

24 Put the following sets of fractions into order, the smallest being on the left.

    a   0.8, 0.35, 0.3, 0.75

    b   0.15, $\frac{1}{2}$, 10%, $\frac{1}{5}$

    c   30%, $\frac{1}{4}$, 0.275, 26%

    d $\frac{3}{4}$, 0.32, 3%, $\frac{3}{8}$

    e   0.6, 45%, $\frac{1}{2}$, 0.55

    f   9%, $\frac{1}{8}$, 0.111, $\frac{1}{10}$

    g   28%, 0.23, $\frac{1}{4}$, 0.275

    h   0.8, 8%, $\frac{1}{8}$, 0.88

    i   0.3, 35%, $\frac{1}{3}$, 0.325

    j $\frac{1}{5}$, 50%, $\frac{3}{5}$, 0.35

Calculating a percentage of a quantity

In this section you will learn how to:

- calculate a percentage of a quantity

Key word

multiplier

To calculate a percentage of a quantity, you multiply the quantity by the percentage. The percentage may be expressed as either a fraction or a decimal. When finding percentages without a calculator, base the calculation on 10% (or 1%) as these are easy to calculate.

EXAMPLE 5

Calculate: **a** 10%   **b** 15% of 54 kg.

a   10% is $\frac{1}{10}$ so divide 54 by 10. $54 \div 10 = 5.4$ kg

b   15% is 10% + 5% = 5.4 + 2.7 = 8.1 kg

EXAMPLE 6

Calculate 12% of £80.

10% of £80 is £8 and 1% of £80 is £0.80

12% = 10% + 1% + 1% = £8 + £0.80 + £0.80 = £9.60

Using a percentage multiplier

You have already seen that percentages and decimals are equivalent so it is easier, particularly when using a calculator, to express a percentage as a decimal and use this to do the calculation.

For example, 13% is a multiplier of 0.13, 20% is a multiplier of 0.2 (or 0.20) and so on.

EXAMPLE 7

Calculate 45% of 16 cm.

45% = 0.45, so 45% of 160 = 0.45 × 160 = 72 cm

 **EXERCISE 12B**

1 What multiplier is equivalent to a percentage of:

   a 88%   **b** 30%   **c** 25%   **d** 8%   **e** 115%?

2 What percentage is equivalent to a multiplier of:

   a 0.78   **b** 0.4   **c** 0.75   **d** 0.05   **e** 1.1?

E

3 Calculate the following.

    a 15% of £300   **b** 6% of £105   **c** 23% of 560 kg

    d 45% of 2.5 kg   **e** 12% of 9 hours   **f** 21% of 180 cm

    g 4% of £3   **h** 35% of 8.4 m   **i** 95% of £8

    j 11% of 308 minutes   **k** 20% of 680 kg   **l** 45% of £360

4 In a school 15% of the pupils bring sandwiches with them. If there are 640 pupils in the school, how many bring sandwiches?

5 An estate agent charges 2% commission on every house he sells. How much commission will he earn on a house that he sells for £60 250?

6 A department store had 250 employees. During one week of a flu epidemic, 14% of the store's employees were absent.

    a What percentage of the employees went into work?

    b How many of the employees went into work?

7 It is thought that about 20% of fans at a rugby match are women. For a match at Twickenham there were 42 600 fans. How many of these do you think would be women?

8 At St Pancras Railway Station, in one week 350 trains arrived. Of these trains, 5% arrived early and 13% arrived late. How many arrived on time?

9 For the FA Cup Final that was held at Wembley, each year the 75 000 tickets were split up as follows.

Each of the teams playing received 30% of the tickets.

The referees' association received 1% of the tickets.

The other 90 teams received 10% of the tickets among them.

The FA associates received 20% of the tickets among them.

The rest were for the special celebrities.

How many tickets went to each set of people?

> **HINTS AND TIPS**
>
> Always read the question carefully. **Each** team received 30% of the tickets.

10 A school estimates that during a parents' evening it will see the parents of 60% of all the students. Year 10 consists of 190 students. How many of them expected to be represented by their parents?

11 A school had 850 pupils and the attendance record in the week before Christmas was:

Monday 96%   Tuesday 98%   Wednesday 100%   Thursday 94%   Friday 88%

How many pupils were present each day?

12 Soft solder consists of 60% lead, 35% tin and 5% bismuth (by weight). How much of each metal is there in 250 grams of solder?

E

13 Calculate the following.

a 12.5% of £26

b 6.5% of 34 kg

c 26.8% of £2100

d 7.75% of £84

e 16.2% of 265 m

f 0.8% of £3000

14 Air consists of 80% nitrogen and 20% oxygen (by volume). A man's lungs have a capacity of 600 cm^3. How much of each gas will he have in his lungs when he has just taken a deep breath?

15 A factory estimates that 1.5% of all the garments it produces will have a fault in them. One week the factory produces 850 garments. How many are likely to have a fault?

16 An insurance firm sells house insurance and the annual premiums are usually set at 0.3% of the value of the house. What will be the annual premium for a house valued at £90 000?

12.3 Calculating a percentage increase or decrease

In this section you will learn how to:
- calculate percentage increases and decreases

Key word
multiplier

Increase

There are two methods for increasing by a percentage.

Method 1
Find the increase and add it to the original amount.

EXAMPLE 8

Increase £6 by 5%.

Find 5% of £6: (5 ÷ 100) × 6 = £0.30

Add the £0.30 to the original amount: £6 + £0.30 = £6.30

Method 2
Use a **multiplier**. An increase of 6% is equivalent to the original 100% *plus* the extra 6%. This is a total of 106% and is equivalent to the multiplier 1.06.

EXAMPLE 9

Increase £6.80 by 5%.

A 5% increase is a multiplier of 1.05.

So £6.80 increased by 5% is 6.80 × 1.05 = £7.14

EXERCISE 12C

1 What multiplier is equivalent to a percentage increase of:

   a 10%   **b** 3%   **c** 20%   **d** 7%   **e** 12%?

2 Increase each of the following by the given percentage. (Use any method you like.)

   a £60 by 4%   **b** 12 kg by 8%   **c** 450 g by 5%   **d** 545 m by 10%

   e £34 by 12%   **f** £75 by 20%   **g** 340 kg by 15%   **h** 670 cm by 23%

   i 130 g by 95%   **j** £82 by 75%   **k** 640 m by 15%   **l** £28 by 8%

3 Kevin, who was on a salary of £27 500, was given a pay rise of 7%. What was his new salary?

4 In 2000 the population of Melchester was 1 565 000. By 2005 it had increased by 8%. What was the population of Melchester in 2005?

5 A small firm made the same pay increase of 5% for all its employees.

   a Calculate the new pay of each employee listed below. Each of their salaries before the increase is given.

   Bob, caretaker, £16 500   Jean, supervisor, £19 500
   Anne, tea lady, £17 300   Brian, manager, £25 300

   b Is the actual pay increase the same for each worker?

6 A bank pays 7% interest on the money that each saver keeps in the bank for a year. Allison keeps £385 in this bank for a year. How much will she have in the bank after the year?

7 In 1980 the number of cars on the roads of Sheffield was about 102 000. Since then it has increased by 90%. Approximately how many cars are there on the roads of Sheffield now?

8 An advertisement for a breakfast cereal states that a special offer packet contains 15% more cereal for the same price as a normal 500 g packet. How much breakfast cereal is there in a special offer packet?

9 A headteacher was proud to point out that, since he had arrived at the school, the number of students had increased by 35%. How many students are now in the school, if there were 680 when the headteacher started at the school?

10 At a school disco there are always about 20% more girls than boys. If there were 50 boys at a recent disco, how many girls were there?

11 The Government adds a tax called VAT to the price of most goods in shops. At the moment, it is 17.5% on all electrical equipment.

   Calculate the price of the following electrical equipment after VAT of 17.5% has been added.

Equipment	Pre-VAT price
TV set	£245
Microwave oven	£72
CD player	£115
Personal stereo	£29.50

Decrease

There are two methods for decreasing by a percentage.

Method 1
Find the decrease and take it away from the original amount.

EXAMPLE 10

Decrease £8 by 4%.

Find 4% of £8: (4 ÷ 100) × 8 = £0.32

Take the £0.32 away from the original amount: £8 − £0.32 = £7.68

Method 2
Use a multiplier. A 7% decrease is 7% less than the original 100% so it represents 100 − 7 = 93% of the original. This is a multiplier of 0.93.

EXAMPLE 11

Decrease £8.60 by 5%.

A decrease of 5% is a multiplier of 0.95.

So £8.60 decreased by 5% is 8.60 × 0.95 = £8.17

EXERCISE 12D

1 What multiplier is equivalent to a percentage decrease of:

    a 8%   **b** 15%   **c** 25%   **d** 9%   **e** 12%?

2 Decrease each of the following by the given percentage. (Use any method you like.)

    a £10 by 6%   **b** 25 kg by 8%   **c** 236 g by 10%

    d 350 m by 3%   **e** £5 by 2%   **f** 45 m by 12%

    g 860 m by 15%   **h** 96 g by 13%   **i** 480 cm by 25%

    j 180 minutes by 35% **k** 86 kg by 5%   **l** £65 by 42%

3 A car valued at £6500 last year is now worth 15% less. What is its value now?

4 A new P-plan diet guarantees that you will lose 12% of your weight in the first month. How much should the following people weigh after one month on the diet?

    a Gillian, who started at 60 kg

    b Peter, who started at 75 kg

    c Margaret, who started at 52 kg

D

5 A motor insurance firm offers no-claims discounts off the given premium, as follows.

1 year no claim	15% discount
2 years no claim	25% discount
3 years no claim	45% discount
4 years no claim	60% discount

Mr Speed and his family are all offered motor insurance from this firm:

Mr Speed, who has four years' no-claim discount, is quoted a premium of £440.

Mrs Speed, who has one year's no-claim discount, is quoted a premium of £350.

James, who has three years' no-claim discount, is quoted a premium of £620.

John, who has two years' no-claim discount, is quoted a premium of £750.

Calculate the actual amount each member of the family has to pay for the motor insurance.

6 A large factory employed 640 people. It had to streamline its workforce and lose 30% of the workers. How big is the workforce now?

7 On the last day of the Christmas term, a school expects to have an absence rate of 6%. If the school population is 750 pupils, how many pupils will the school expect to see on the last day of the Christmas term?

8 A particular charity called *Young Ones* said that since the start of the National Lottery they have had a decrease of 45% in the amount of money raised by scratch cards. If before the Lottery the charity had an annual income of £34 500 from their scratch cards, how much do they collect now?

9 Most speedometers in cars have an error of about 5% from the true reading. When my speedometer says I am driving at 70 mph:

a what is the lowest speed I could be doing

b what is the highest speed I could be doing?

10 You are a member of a club that allows you to claim a 12% discount off any marked price in shops. What will you pay in total for the following goods?

| Sweatshirt | £19 |
| Track suit | £26 |

11 I read an advertisement in my local newspaper last week that stated: "By lagging your roof and hot water system you will use 18% less fuel." Since I was using an average of 640 units of gas a year, I thought I would lag my roof and my hot water system. How much gas would I expect to use now?

12 Shops add VAT to the basic price of goods to find the selling price that customers will be asked to pay. In a sale, a shop reduces the selling price by a certain percentage to set the sale price. Calculate the sale price of each of these items.

Item	Basic price	VAT rate	Sale discount	Sale price
TV	£220	17.5%	14%	
DVD player	£180	17.5%	20%	

C

Expressing one quantity as a percentage of another

In this section you will learn how to:

- express one quantity as a percentage of another

You can express one quantity as a percentage of another by setting up the first quantity as a fraction of the second, making sure that the *units of each are the same*. Then, you convert that fraction to a percentage by simply multiplying it by 100.

EXAMPLE 12

Express £6 as a percentage of £40.

Set up the fraction and multiply it by 100. This gives:

$(6 \div 40) \times 100 = 15\%$

EXAMPLE 13

Express 75 cm as a percentage of 2.5 m.

First, change 2.5 m to 250 cm to work in a common unit.

Hence, the problem becomes 75 cm as a percentage of 250 cm.

Set up the fraction and multiply it by 100. This gives:

$(75 \div 250) \times 100 = 30\%$

You can use this method to calculate percentage gain or loss in a financial transaction.

EXAMPLE 14

Jabeer buys a car for £1500 and sells it for £1800. What is Jabeer's percentage gain?

Jabeer's gain is £300, so his percentage gain is:

$$\frac{300}{1500} \times 100 = 20\%$$

Notice how the percentage gain is found as: $\dfrac{\text{difference}}{\text{original}} \times 100$

Using a multiplier

Find the multiplier by dividing the increase by the original quantity, then change the resulting decimal to a percentage.

EXAMPLE 15

Express 5 as a percentage of 40.

$5 \div 40 = 0.125$

$0.125 = 12.5\%$

EXERCISE 12E

1 Express each of the following as a percentage. Give suitably rounded figures where necessary.

   a £5 of £20   **b** £4 of £6.60   **c** 241 kg of 520 kg

   d 3 hours of 1 day   **e** 25 minutes of 1 hour   **f** 12 m of 20 m

   g 125 g of 600 g   **h** 12 minutes of 2 hours   **i** 1 week of a year

   j 1 month of 1 year   **k** 25 cm of 55 cm   **l** 105 g of 1 kg

2 Liam went to school with his pocket money of £2.50. He spent 80p at the tuck shop. What percentage of his pocket money had he spent?

3 In Greece, there are 3 654 000 acres of agricultural land. Olives are grown on 237 000 acres of this land. What percentage of the agricultural land is used for olives?

4 During the wet year of 1981, it rained in Manchester on 123 days of the year. What percentage of days were wet?

5 Find, correct to one decimal place, the percentage profit on the following.

Item	Retail price (selling price)	Wholesale price (price the shop paid)
a CD player	£89.50	£60
b TV set	£345.50	£210
c Computer	£829.50	£750

6 Before Anton started to diet, he weighed 95 kg. He now weighs 78 kg. What percentage of his original weight has he lost?

7 In 2004 the Melchester County Council raised £14 870 000 in council tax. In 2005 it raised £15 597 000 in council tax. What was the percentage increase?

8 When Blackburn Rovers won the championship in 1995, they lost only four of their 42 league games. What percentage of games did they *not* lose?

9 In the year 1900 Britain's imports were as follows.

British Commonwealth	£109 530 000
USA	£138 790 000
France	£53 620 000
Other countries	£221 140 000

   a What percentage of the total imports came from each source? Give your answers to 1 decimal place.

   b Add up your answer to part **a**. What do you notice? Explain your answer.

EXERCISE 12F

This exercise includes a mixture of percentage questions, which you should answer without using a calculator.

1 Copy and complete this table.

	Fraction	Decimal	Percentage
a	$\frac{3}{5}$		
b		0.7	
c			55%

2 Work out these amounts.

   a 15% of £68   **b** 12% of 400 kg   **c** 30% of £4.20

3 What percentage is:

   a 28 out of 50   **b** 17 out of 25   **c** 75 out of 200?

4 What is the result if:

   a 240 is increased by 15%   **b** 3600 is decreased by 11%?

5 **a** A paperboy's weekly wage went up from £10 to £12. What was the percentage increase in his wages?

   b The number of houses he has to deliver to increases from 60 to 78. What is the percentage increase in the number of houses he delivers to?

   c The newsagent then increased his new wage of £12 by 10%. What are the boy's wages now?

6 The on-the-road price of a new car was £8000.

   a In the first year it depreciated in value by 20%. What was the value of the car at the end of the first year?

   b In the second year it depreciated by a further 15%. What was the value of the car at the end of the second year?

7 The members of a slimming club had a mean weight of 80 kg before they started dieting. After a month they calculated that they had lost an average of 12% in weight.

   a What was the average weight after the month?

   b One of the members realised she had misread the scale and she was 10 kg heavier than she thought. Which of these statements is true?

      i The mean weight loss will have decreased by more than 12%.

      ii The mean weight loss will have stayed at 12%.

      iii The mean weight loss will have decreased by less than 12%.

      iv There is not enough information to answer the question.

1
 a Write $\frac{1}{4}$ as a percentage.

 b Write 0.23 as a percentage.

 c Write 42% as a fraction. Give your answer in its simplest form.

Edexcel, Question 3, Paper 11A Foundation, January 2004

2
 a This diagram is made from equilateral triangles.

 i What percentage of the diagram is shaded?

 ii What percentage of the diagram is not shaded?

 b Another diagram has 70% shaded. What fraction of the diagram is shaded?
 Simplify your answer.

 c Another diagram has $\frac{3}{5}$ shaded.
 Write $\frac{3}{5}$ as a decimal.

3
 a **i** Write $\frac{7}{16}$ as a decimal.

 ii Write 27% as a decimal.

 b Write these values in order of size, smallest first.

 0.7 $\frac{6}{10}$ 65%   0.095

4
 Mr and Mrs Jones are buying a tumble dryer that normally costs £250. They save 12% in a sale.

 a What is 12% of £250?

 b How much do they pay for the tumble dryer?

5

> Cat facts
> - 40% of people named cats as their favourite pet.
> - 98% of women said they would rather go out with someone who liked cats.
> - About $7\frac{1}{2}$ million families have a cat.
> - $\frac{1}{4}$ of cat owners keep a cat because cats are easy to look after.

 a Write 40% as a fraction. Give your fraction in its simplest form.

 b Write 98% as a decimal.

 c Write $7\frac{1}{2}$ million in figures.

 d Write $\frac{1}{4}$ as a percentage.

 e What percentage of people did *not* name cats as their favourite pet?

Edexcel, Question 7, Paper 1 Foundation, June 2005

6
 Which is the larger amount?

 40% of £30 $\frac{3}{5}$ of £25

7
 Mrs Senior earns £320 per week. She is awarded a pay rise of 4%.

 How much does she earn each week after the pay rise?

8
 Five girls swim a 50 metre race. Their times are shown in the table.

Name	Time (seconds)
Amy	12.8
Joy	14.6
Sophie	13.5
Lydia	13.9
Charlotte	15.8

 a Write down the median time.

 b The five girls swim another 50 metre race. They all reduce their times by 8%.

 i Who won the race?

 ii Who improved her time by the greatest amount of time?

9
 Mr Shaw's bill for new tyres is £120 plus VAT. VAT is charged at $17\frac{1}{2}$%.

 What is his total bill?

10
 Two shops sell DVDs.

HTV Vision	CUS Video
DVDs £9.60 each	**DVD SALE**
Buy 2 DVDs and get a third one FREE	30% OFF normal price of £9.60 each

 Lewis wants to buy three DVDs from one of the above shops. Which shop offers the better value?
 You must show all your working.

11
 Supermarkets often make 'Buy one, get one free' offers. What percentage saving is this?

 10%, 50%, 100% or 200%

12
 There are 75 penguins at a zoo. There are 15 baby penguins.

 What percentage of the penguins are babies?

13 Alistair sells books. He sells each book for £7.60 plus VAT at $17\frac{1}{2}$%.

He sells 1650 books.

Work out how much money Alistair receives.

Edexcel, Question 26, Paper 2 Foundation, June 2005

 14 ABCD is a rectangle with length 35 cm and width 15 cm.

The length of the rectangle is increased by 10%.
The width of the rectangle is increased by 20%.
Find the percentage increase in the area of the rectangle.

  15 In a sale the price of a dress, originally marked as £80, was reduced by 30%.

a What was the sale price of the dress?

b On a special promotion day the shop offered 20% off sale prices.

  i What was the reduced price of the dress after 20% was taken off the sale price?

  ii What percentage was this price of the original £80?

  16 A TV originally cost £300.

In a sale, its price was reduced by 20%, then this sale price was reduced by a further 10%.

Show why this is not a 30% reduction of the original price.

WORKED EXAM QUESTION

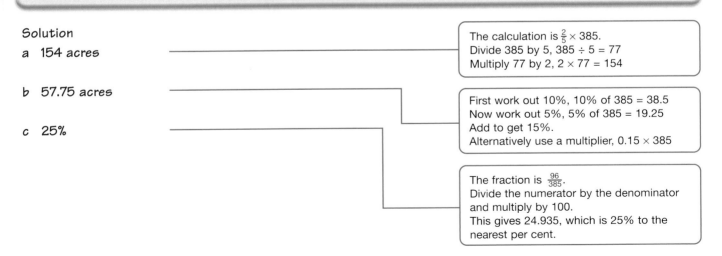

The land area of a farm is 385 acres.

a Two-fifths of the land is used to grow barley. How many acres is this?

b Fifteen per cent of the land is not used. How many acres is this?

c On the farm, 96 acres is pasture. What percentage of the total land is pasture? Give your answer to the nearest 1%.

Solution

a 154 acres

      The calculation is $\frac{2}{5} \times 385$.
      Divide 385 by 5, $385 \div 5 = 77$
      Multiply 77 by 2, $2 \times 77 = 154$

b 57.75 acres

      First work out 10%, 10% of 385 = 38.5
      Now work out 5%, 5% of 385 = 19.25
      Add to get 15%.
      Alternatively use a multiplier, 0.15×385

c 25%

      The fraction is $\frac{96}{385}$.
      Divide the numerator by the denominator and multiply by 100.
      This gives 24.935, which is 25% to the nearest per cent.

GRADE YOURSELF

G Able to find equivalent fractions, decimals and percentages

F Able to find simple percentages of a quantity

E Able to find any percentages of a quantity

D Able to find a new quantity after an increase or decrease by a percentage and find one quantity as a percentage of another

C Able to find a percentage increase

What you should know now

- How to find equivalent percentages, decimals and fractions
- How to calculate percentages, percentage increases and decreases
- How to calculate one quantity as a percentage of another

Equations and inequalities

This chapter will show you ...

- how to solve linear equations with the variable on one side only
- how to solve linear equations with the variable on both sides
- how to solve equations using trial and improvement
- how to rearrange simple formulae
- how to solve simple linear inequalities

Visual overview

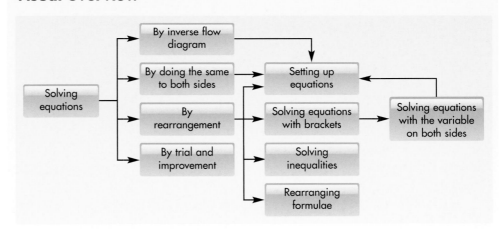

What you should already know

- The basic language of algebra
- How to expand brackets and collect like terms
- That addition and subtraction are opposite (inverse) operations
- That multiplication and division are opposite (inverse) operations

Quick check

1 a Simplify $5x + 3x - 2x$.　　**b** Expand $4(3x - 1)$.

　c Expand and simplify $2(3x - 1) + 3(4x + 3)$.

2 What number can go in the box to make the calculation true?

　a $13 + \square = 9$　　　**b** $4 \times \square = 10$

In this section you will learn how to:

- solve a variety of simple linear equations, such as $3x - 1 = 11$, where the variable only appears on one side
- use inverse operations and inverse flow charts
- solve equations by doing the same on both sides
- deal with negative numbers
- solve equations by rearrangement

Key words

do the same to both sides
equation
inverse flow diagram
inverse operations
rearrangement
solution
variable

A teacher gave these instructions to her class.

What algebraic expression represents the teacher's statement? (See Chapter 7.)

- Think of a number.
- Double it.
- Add 3.

This is what two of her students said.

Can you work out Kim's answer and the number that Freda started with?

Kim's answer will be $2 \times 5 + 3 = 13$.

Freda's answer can be set up as an **equation**.

An equation is formed when an expression is put equal to a number or another expression. You are expected to deal with equations that have only one **variable** or letter.

My final answer was 10.

I chose the number 5.

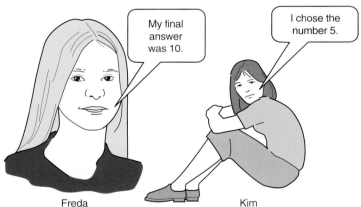

Freda

Kim

The **solution** to an equation is the value of the variable that makes the equation true. For example, the equation for Freda's answer is

$$2x + 3 = 10$$

where x represents Freda's number.

The value of x that makes this true is $x = 3\frac{1}{2}$.

To solve an equation, you have to 'undo' it. That is, you have to reverse the processes that set up the equation in the first place.

Freda did two things. First she multiplied by 2 and then she added 3. The reverse process is first to subtract 3 and then to divide by 2. So, to solve:

$$2x + 3 = 10$$

Subtract 3
$$2x + 3 - 3 = 10 - 3$$

$$2x = 7$$

Divide by 2
$$\frac{2x}{2} = \frac{7}{2}$$

$$x = 3\frac{1}{2}$$

The problem is knowing how an equation is set up in the first place, so that you can undo it in the right order.

There are four ways to solve equations: **inverse operations, inverse flow diagrams, 'doing the same to both sides'** and **rearrangement**. They are all essentially the same. You will have to decide which method you prefer, although you should know how to use all three.

There is one rule about equations that you should *always* follow.

Check that your answer works in the original equation.

For example, to check the answer to Freda's equation, put $x = 3\frac{1}{2}$ into Freda's equation. This gives:

$$2 \times 3\frac{1}{2} + 3 = 7 + 3 = 10$$

which is correct.

Inverse operations

One way to solve equations is to use **inverse operations**. The opposite or inverse operation to addition is subtraction (and vice versa) and the opposite or inverse operation to multiplication is division (and vice versa).

That means you can 'undo' the four basic operations by using the inverse operation.

EXAMPLE 1

Solve these equations.

a $w + 7 = 9$ **b** $x - 8 = 10$ **c** $2y = 8$ **d** $\dfrac{z}{5} = 3$

a The opposite operation to + 7 is − 7, so the solution is 9 − 7 = 2.

Check: 2 + 7 = 9

b The opposite operation to − 8 is + 8, so the solution is 10 + 8 = 18.

Check: 18 − 8 = 10

c 2y means 2 × y. The opposite operation to × 2 is ÷ 2, so the solution is 8 ÷ 2 = 4.

Check: 2 × 4 = 8

d $\dfrac{z}{5}$ means z ÷ 5. The opposite operation to ÷ 5 is × 5, so the solution is 3 × 5 = 15.

Check: 15 ÷ 5 = 3

EXERCISE 13A

Solve the following equations by applying the inverse on the operation on the left-hand side to the right-hand side.

1 $x + 6 = 10$ **2** $w - 5 = 9$

3 $y + 3 = 8$ **4** $p - 9 = 1$

5 $2x = 10$ **6** $3x = 18$

7 $\dfrac{t}{8} = 8$ **8** $4x = 10$

9 $\dfrac{q}{4} = 1$ **10** $x + 9 = 10$

11 $r - 7 = 21$ **12** $\dfrac{s}{6} = 2$

> **HINTS AND TIPS**
>
> Remember to perform the inverse operation on the number on the right-hand side.

Inverse flow diagrams

Another way to solve simple linear equations is to use inverse flow diagrams.

This flow diagram represents the instructions that their teacher gave to Kim and Freda.

The **inverse flow diagram** looks like this.

Running Freda's answer through this gives:

$3\frac{1}{2}$ ← $\div\, 2$ ← 7 ← $-\, 3$ ← 10

So, Freda started with $3\frac{1}{2}$ to get an answer of 10.

EXAMPLE 2

Use an inverse flow diagram to solve the following equation.

$3x - 4 = 11$

Flow diagram:

→ $\times\, 3$ → $-\, 4$ →

Inverse flow diagram:

← $\div\, 3$ ← $+\, 4$ ←

Put through the value on the right-hand side of the equals sign.

5 ← $\div\, 3$ ← 15 ← $+\, 4$ ← 11

So, the answer is $x = 5$.

Checking the answer gives:

$3 \times 5 - 4 = 11$

which is correct.

EXERCISE 13B

Use inverse flow diagrams to solve each of the following equations. Remember to check that each answer works for its original equation.

1 $3x + 5 = 11$

2 $3x - 13 = 26$

3 $3x - 7 = 32$

4 $4y - 19 = 5$

5 $3a + 8 = 11$

6 $2x + 8 = 14$

7 $2y + 6 = 18$

8 $8x + 4 = 12$

9 $2x - 10 = 8$

10 $\dfrac{x}{5} + 2 = 3$

11 $\dfrac{t}{3} - 4 = 2$

12 $\dfrac{y}{4} + 1 = 7$

13 $\dfrac{k}{2} - 6 = 3$

14 $\dfrac{h}{8} - 4 = 1$

15 $\dfrac{w}{6} + 1 = 4$

16 $\dfrac{x}{4} + 5 = 7$

17 $\dfrac{y}{2} - 3 = 5$

18 $\dfrac{f}{5} + 2 = 8$

Doing the same to both sides

You need to know how to solve equations by performing the same operation on both sides of the equals sign.

Mary had two bags of marbles, each of which contained the same number of marbles, and five spare marbles.

She put them on scales and balanced them with 17 single marbles.

How many marbles were there in each bag?

If x is the number of marbles in each bag, then the equation representing Mary's balanced scales is:

$$2x + 5 = 17$$

Take five marbles from each pan:

$$2x + 5 - 5 = 17 - 5$$
$$2x = 12$$

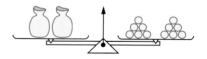

Now halve the number of marbles on each pan.

That is, divide both sides by 2:

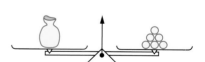

$$\dfrac{2x}{2} = \dfrac{12}{2}$$
$$x = 6$$

Checking the answer gives $2 \times 6 + 5 = 17$, which is correct.

EXAMPLE 3

Solve each of these equations by 'doing the same to both sides'.

a $3x - 5 = 16$

Add 5 to both sides.

$$3x - 5 + 5 = 16 + 5$$

$$3x = 21$$

Divide both sides by 3.

$$\frac{3x}{3} = \frac{21}{3}$$

$$x = 7$$

Checking the answer gives:

$$3 \times 7 - 5 = 16$$

which is correct.

b $\dfrac{x}{2} + 2 = 10$

Subtract 2 from both sides.

$$\frac{x}{2} + 2 - 2 = 10 - 2$$

$$\frac{x}{2} = 8$$

Multiply both sides by 2.

$$\frac{x}{2} \times 2 = 8 \times 2$$

$$x = 16$$

Checking the answer gives:

$$16 \div 2 + 2 = 10$$

which is correct.

Dealing with negative numbers

The solution to an equation may be a negative number. You need to know that when a negative number is multiplied or divided by a positive number, then the answer is also a negative number. For example:

$$-3 \times 4 = -12 \qquad \text{and} \qquad -10 \div 5 = -2$$

Check these on your calculator.

EXERCISE 13C

Solve each of the following equations by 'doing the same to both sides'. Remember to check that each answer works for its original equation.

1 $x + 4 = 60$

2 $3y - 2 = 4$

3 $3x - 7 = 11$

4 $5y + 3 = 18$

5 $7 + 3t = 19$

6 $5 + 4f = 15$

7 $3 + 6k = 24$

8 $4x + 7 = 17$

9 $5m - 3 = 17$

10 $\dfrac{w}{3} - 5 = 2$

11 $\dfrac{x}{8} + 3 = 12$

12 $\dfrac{m}{7} - 3 = 5$

13 $\dfrac{x}{5} + 3 = 3$

14 $\dfrac{h}{7} + 2 = 1$

15 $\dfrac{w}{3} + 10 = 4$

16 $\dfrac{x}{3} - 5 = 7$

17 $\dfrac{y}{2} - 13 = 5$

18 $\dfrac{f}{6} - 2 = 8$

> **HINTS AND TIPS**
>
> Be careful with negative numbers.

ACTIVITY

Balancing with unknowns

Suppose you want to solve an equation such as:

$2x + 3 = x + 4$

You can imagine it as a balancing problem with marbles.

2 bags + 3 marbles = 1 bag + 4 marbles

Take one bag from each side.

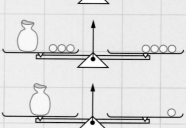

Take three marbles from each side.

There must be one marble in the bag.

This means that $x = 1$.

Checking the answer gives $2 \times 1 + 3 = 1 + 4$, which is correct.

Set up each of the following problems as a 'balancing picture' and solve it by 'doing the same to both sides'. Remember to check that each answer works. The first two problems include the pictures to start you off.

1 $2x + 6 = 3x + 1$

2 $4x + 2 = x + 8$

3 $5x + 1 = 3x + 11$

4 $x + 9 = 2x + 7$ (Some of the marbles could be broken in half!)

5 $3x + 8 = 2x + 10$

6 $5x + 7 = 3x + 21$

7 $2x + 12 = 5x + 6$

8 $3x + 6 = x + 9$

9 Explain why there is no answer to this problem:

$x + 3 = x + 4$

10 One of the bags of marbles on the left-hand pan has had three marbles taken out.

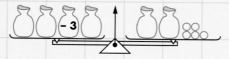

Try to draw the pictures to solve this problem:

$4x - 3 = 2x + 5$

Rearrangement

Solving equations by rearrangement is the most efficient method and the one used throughout the rest of this chapter. The terms of the equation are rearranged until the variable is on its own – usually on the left-hand side of the equals sign.

EXAMPLE 4

Solve $4x + 3 = 23$.

Move the 3 to give: $\qquad\qquad\qquad 4x = 23 - 3 = 20$

Now divide both sides by 4 to give: $\qquad x = \dfrac{20}{4} = 5$

So, the solution is $x = 5$.

EXAMPLE 5

Solve $\dfrac{y - 4}{5} = 3$.

Move the 5 to give: $\qquad\qquad y - 4 = 3 \times 5 = 15$

Now move the 4 to give: $\qquad\; y = 15 + 4 = 19$

So, the solution is $y = 19$.

EXERCISE 13D

Solve each of the following equations. Remember to check that each answer works for its original equation.

1 $2x + 4 = 6$

2 $2t + 7 = 13$

3 $3x + 10 = 16$

4 $4y + 15 = 23$

5 $2x - 8 = 10$

6 $4t - 3 = 17$

7 $5x - 6 = 24$

8 $7 - x = 3$

9 $12 - 3y = 6$

10 $2k + 8 = 4$

11 $\dfrac{x}{3} + 7 = 15$

12 $\dfrac{t}{5} + 3 = 5$

13 $\dfrac{w}{3} - 5 = 2$

14 $\dfrac{x}{8} + 3 = 12$

15 $\dfrac{m}{7} - 3 = 5$

16 $\dfrac{k + 1}{2} = 3$

17 $\dfrac{h - 4}{8} = 3$

18 $\dfrac{w + 1}{6} = 1$

19 $\dfrac{x + 5}{4} = 10$

20 $\dfrac{y - 3}{6} = 5$

21 $\dfrac{f + 2}{5} = 5$

> **HINTS AND TIPS**
>
> When a variable changes sides of the equals sign, it also changes signs, that is, plus becomes minus and vice versa, multiply becomes divide and vice versa. This is sometimes called 'Change sides, change signs'.

Solving equations with brackets

In this section you will learn how to:

- solve equations that include brackets

When an equation contains brackets, you must first multiply out the brackets and then solve the equation by using one of the previous methods.

EXAMPLE 6

Solve $5(x + 3) = 25$.

First multiply out the brackets: $5x + 15 = 25$

Rearrange. $\quad 5x = 25 - 15 = 10$

Divide by 5. $\quad \dfrac{5x}{5} = \dfrac{10}{5}$

$\quad x = 2$

EXAMPLE 7

Solve $3(2x - 7) = 15$.

Multiply out the brackets: $6x - 21 = 15$

Add 21 to both sides. $\quad 6x = 36$

Divide both sides by 6. $\quad x = 6$

EXERCISE 13E

Solve each of the following equations. Some of the answers may be decimals or negative numbers. Remember to check that each answer works for its original equation. Use your calculator if necessary.

1 $2(x + 5) = 16$

2 $5(x - 3) = 20$

3 $3(t + 1) = 18$

4 $4(2x + 5) = 44$

5 $2(3y - 5) = 14$

6 $5(4x + 3) = 135$

7 $4(3t - 2) = 88$

8 $6(2t + 5) = 42$

9 $2(3x + 1) = 11$

10 $4(5y - 2) = 42$

11 $6(3k + 5) = 39$

12 $5(2x + 3) = 27$

13 $5(2x - 1) = -45$

14 $7(3y + 5) = -7$

HINTS AND TIPS

Once the brackets have been expanded the equations are the same sort as those you have already been dealing with. Remember to multiply everything inside the brackets with what is outside.

D

Equations with the letter on both sides

In this section you will learn how to:

- solve equations where the variable appears on both sides of the equation

When a letter appears on both sides of an equation, it is best to use the 'do the same to both sides' method of solution and collect all the terms containing the letter on the left-hand side of the equation. If there are more of the letter on the right-hand side, it is easier to turn the equation round. When an equation contains brackets, they must be multiplied out first.

EXAMPLE 8

Solve $5x + 4 = 3x + 10$.

There are more xs on the left-hand side, so leave the equation as it is.

Subtract $3x$ from both sides. $2x + 4 = 10$

Subtract 4 from both sides. $2x = 6$

Divide both sides by 2. $x = 3$

EXAMPLE 9

Solve $2x + 3 = 6x - 5$.

There are more xs on the right-hand side, so turn the equation round.

$$6x - 5 = 2x + 3$$

Subtract $2x$ from both sides. $4x - 5 = 3$

Add 5 to both sides. $4x = 8$

Divide both sides by 4. $x = 2$

EXAMPLE 10

Solve $3(2x + 5) + x = 2(2 - x) + 2$.

Multiply out both brackets. $6x + 15 + x = 4 - 2x + 2$

Simplify both sides. $7x + 15 = 6 - 2x$

There are more xs on the left-hand side, so leave the equation as it is.

Add $2x$ to both sides. $9x + 15 = 6$

Subtract 15 from both sides. $9x = -9$

Divide both sides by 9. $x = -1$

EXERCISE 13F

Solve each of the following equations.

1 $2x + 3 = x + 5$

2 $5y + 4 = 3y + 6$

3 $4a - 3 = 3a + 4$

4 $5t + 3 = 2t + 15$

5 $7p - 5 = 3p + 3$

6 $6k + 5 = 2k + 1$

7 $2t - 7 = 4t - 3$

8 $2p - 1 = 9 - 3p$

9 $2(d + 3) = d + 12$

10 $5(x - 2) = 3(x + 4)$

11 $3(2y + 3) = 5(2y + 1)$

12 $3(h - 6) = 2(5 - 2h)$

13 $4(3b - 1) + 6 = 5(2b + 4)$

14 $2(5c + 2) - 2c = 3(2c + 3) + 7$

> **HINTS AND TIPS**
>
> Remember the rule 'Change sides, change signs'. Show all your working on this type of question. Rearrange before you simplify. If you try to rearrange and simplify at the same time, you will probably get it wrong.

13.4 Setting up equations

In this section you will learn how to:

- set up equations from given information and then use the methods already seen to solve them

Equations are used to represent situations, so that you can solve real-life problems.

EXAMPLE 11

A milkman sets off from the dairy with eight crates of milk each containing b bottles. He delivers 92 bottles to a large factory and finds that he has exactly 100 bottles left on his milk float. How many bottles were in each crate?

The equation is:

$8b - 92 = 100$

$8b = 192$ (Add 92 to both sides.)

$b = 24$ (Divide both sides by 8.)

EXAMPLE 12

The rectangle shown has a perimeter of 40 cm.
Find the value of x.
The perimeter of the rectangle is:

$3x + 1 + x + 3 + 3x + 1 + x + 3 = 40$

This simplifies to $8x + 8 = 40$.

Subtract 8. $8x = 32$

Divide by 8. $x = 4$

$3x + 1$

$x + 3$

EXERCISE 13G

Set up an equation to represent each situation described below. Then solve the equation. Remember to check each answer.

1 A man buys a daily paper from Monday to Saturday for *d* pence. On Sunday he buys his paper for £1. His weekly paper bill is £4.30.
What is the price of his daily paper?

2 The diagram shows a rectangle.

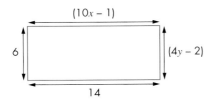

a What is the value of *x*?

b What is the value of *y*?

3 In this rectangle, the length is 3 cm more than the width. The perimeter is 12 cm.

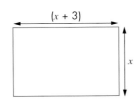

a What is the value of *x*?

b What is the area of the rectangle?

4 Mary has two bags, each of which contains the same number of sweets. She eats four sweets. She then finds that she has 30 sweets left. How many sweets were there in each bag to start with?

5 A boy is *Y* years old. His father is 25 years older than he is. The sum of their ages is 31. How old is the boy?

6 Another boy is *X* years old. His sister is twice as old as he is. The sum of their ages is 27. How old is the boy?

7 The diagram shows a square.
Find *x* if the perimeter is 44 cm.

$(4x - 1)$

8 Max thought of a number. He then multiplied his number by 3. He added 4 to the answer. He then doubled that answer to get a final value of 38. What number did he start with?

9 The angles of a triangle are $2x$, $x + 5°$ and $x + 35°$.

a Write down an equation to show this.

b Solve your equation to find the value of *x*.

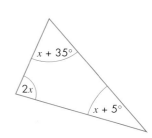

Trial and improvement

In this section you will learn how to:

- use the method of trial and improvement to estimate the answer to equations that do not have exact solutions

Key words

comment
decimal place
guess
trial and improvement

Certain equations cannot be solved exactly. However, a close enough solution to such an equation can be found by the **trial-and-improvement** method. (Sometimes wrongly called the trial-and-error method.)

The idea is to keep trying different values in the equation to take it closer and closer to the 'true' solution. This step-by-step process is continued until a value is found that gives a solution that is close enough to the accuracy required.

The trial-and-improvement method is the way in which computers are programmed to solve equations.

EXAMPLE 13

Solve the equation $x^3 + x = 105$, giving the solution correct to one **decimal place**.

Step 1 You must find the two consecutive whole numbers between which x lies. You do this by intelligent guessing.

Try $x = 5$: $125 + 5 = 130$ Too high – next trial needs to be much smaller.

Try $x = 4$: $64 + 4 = 68$ Too low.

So you now know that the solution lies between $x = 4$ and $x = 5$.

Step 2 You must find the two consecutive one-decimal-place numbers between which x lies. Try 4.5, which is halfway between 4 and 5.

This gives $91.125 + 4.5 = 95.625$ Too small.

Now attempt to improve this by trying 4.6.

This gives $97.336 + 4.6 = 101.936$ Still too small.

Try 4.7 which gives 108.523.   This is too high, so the solution is between 4.6 and 4.7.

It looks as though 4.7 is closer but there is a very important final step.

Step 3 Now try the value that is halfway between the two one-decimal-place values. In this case 4.65.

This gives 105.194 625.

This means that 4.6 is nearer the actual solution than 4.7 is, so never assume that the one-decimal-place number that gives the closest value to the solution is the answer.

The diagram on the right shows why this is.

The approximate answer is $x = 4.6$ to 1 decimal place.

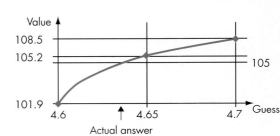

The best way to answer this type of question is to set up a table to show working. There will be three columns: **guess** (the trial); the equation to be solved; and a **comment** whether the value of the equation is too high or too low.

Guess	$x^3 + x$	Comment
4	68	Too low
5	130	Too high
4.5	95.625	Too low
4.6	101.936	Too low
4.7	108.523	Too high
4.65	105.194 625	Too high

EXERCISE 13H

1 Find the two consecutive *whole numbers* between which the solution to each of the following equations lies.

a $x^2 + x = 24$ **b** $x^3 + 2x = 80$ **c** $x^3 - x = 20$

2 Copy and complete the table by using trial and improvement to find an approximate solution to:

$$x^3 + 2x = 50$$

Give your answer correct to 1 decimal place.

Guess	$x^3 + 2x$	Comment
3	33	Too low
4	72	Too high

3 Copy and complete the table by using trial and improvement to find an approximate solution to:

$$x^3 - 3x = 40$$

Give your answer correct to 1 decimal place.

Guess	$x^3 - 3x$	Comment
4	52	Too high

4 Use trial and improvement to find an approximate solution to:

$$2x^3 + x = 35$$

Give your answer correct to 1 decimal place.

You are given that the solution lies between 2 and 3.

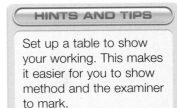

HINTS AND TIPS

Set up a table to show your working. This makes it easier for you to show method and the examiner to mark.

5 Use trial and improvement to find an exact solution to:

$$4x^2 + 2x = 12$$

Do not use a calculator.

6 Find a solution to each of the following equations, correct to 1 decimal place.

a $2x^3 + 3x = 35$ **b** $3x^3 - 4x = 52$ **c** $2x^3 + 5x = 79$

C

7 A rectangle has an area of 100 cm². Its length is 5 cm longer than its width.

 a Show that, if x is the width, then $x^2 + 5x = 100$.

 b Find, correct to 1 decimal place, the dimensions of the rectangle.

8 Use trial and improvement to find a solution to the equation $x^2 + x = 40$.

13.6 Rearranging formulae

In this section you will learn how to:
- rearrange formulae, using the same methods as for solving equations

Key words
expression
rearrange
subject
transpose
variable

The **subject** of a formula is the **variable** (letter) in the formula that stands on its own, usually on the left-hand side of the 'equals' sign. For example, x is the subject of each of the following.

$$x = 5t + 4 \qquad x = 4(2y - 7) \qquad x = \frac{1}{t}$$

If you need to change the existing subject to a different variable, you have to **rearrange** (**transpose**) the formula to get that variable on the left-hand side.

You do this by using the same rule as that for solving equations, that is, move the terms concerned from one side of the 'equals' sign to the other.

The main difference is that when you solve an equation each step gives a numerical value. When you rearrange a formula each step gives an algebraic **expression**.

EXAMPLE 14

Make m the subject of $T = m - 3$.

Move the 3 away from the m. $\qquad T + 3 = m$

Reverse the formula. $\qquad\qquad m = T + 3$

EXAMPLE 15

From the formula $P = 4t$, express t in terms of P.

(This is another common way of asking you to make t the subject.)

Divide both sides by 4. $\qquad \dfrac{P}{4} = \dfrac{4t}{4}$

Reverse the formula. $\qquad t = \dfrac{P}{4}$

EXAMPLE 16

From the formula $C = 2m + 3$, make m the subject.

Move the 3 away from the $2m$. $\quad C - 3 = 2m$

Divide both sides by 2. $\quad \dfrac{C - 3}{2} = \dfrac{2m}{2}$

Reverse the formula. $\quad m = \dfrac{C - 3}{2}$

EXERCISE 13I

1 $T = 3k$ Make k the subject.

2 $P = m + 7$ Make m the subject.

3 $X = y - 1$ Express y in terms of X.

4 $Q = \dfrac{p}{3}$ Express p in terms of Q.

5 $p = m + t$ **a** Make m the subject.

                  b Make t the subject.

6 $t = 2k + 7$ Express k in terms of t.

7 $g = \dfrac{m}{v}$ Make m the subject.

8 $t = m^2$ Make m the subject.

9 $C = 2\pi r$ Make r the subject.

10 $A = bh$ Make b the subject.

11 $P = 2l + 2w$ Make l the subject.

12 $m = p^2 + 2$ Make p the subject.

> **HINTS AND TIPS**
>
> Remember about inverse operations and the rule 'Change sides, change signs'.

13.7 Solving linear inequalities

In this section you will learn how to:
- solve a simple linear inequality

Key words
integer
linear inequality
number line

Inequalities behave similarly to equations, which you have already met. In the case of **linear inequalities**, you can use the same rules to solve them as you use for linear equations. There are four inequality signs, $<$ which means 'less than', $>$ which means 'greater than', $\leqslant$ which means 'less than or equal to' and $\geqslant$ which means 'greater than or equal to'.

EXAMPLE 17

Solve $2x + 3 < 14$.

This is rewritten as:

$$2x < 14 - 3$$

that is $2x < 11$.

Divide both sides by 2.　　　$\dfrac{2x}{2} < \dfrac{11}{2}$

$$\Rightarrow \quad x < 5.5$$

This means that x can take any value below 5.5 but it *cannot* take the value 5.5.

Note: The inequality sign given in the problem is the sign to give in the answer.

EXAMPLE 18

Solve $\dfrac{x}{2} + 4 \geqslant 13$.

Solve just like an equation but leave the inequality sign in place of the equals sign.

Subtract 4 from both sides.　　$\dfrac{x}{2} \geqslant 9$

Multiply both sides by 2.　　　$x \geqslant 18$

This means that x can take any value above 18 and including 18.

EXERCISE 13J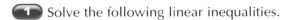

1 Solve the following linear inequalities.

    a $x + 4 < 7$ **b** $t - 3 > 5$ **c** $p + 2 \geqslant 12$

    d $2x - 3 < 7$ **e** $4y + 5 \leqslant 17$ **f** $3t - 4 > 11$

    g $\dfrac{x}{2} + 4 < 7$ **h** $\dfrac{y}{5} + 3 \leqslant 6$ **i** $\dfrac{t}{3} - 2 \geqslant 4$

    j $3(x - 2) < 15$ **k** $5(2x + 1) \leqslant 35$ **l** $2(4t - 3) \geqslant 34$

2 Write down the largest value of x that satisfies each of the following.

    a $x - 3 \leqslant 5$, where x is a positive **integer**.

    b $x + 2 < 9$, where x is a positive, even integer.

    c $3x - 11 < 40$, where x is a square number.

    d $5x - 8 \leqslant 15$, where x is a positive, odd number.

    e $2x + 1 < 19$, where x is a positive, prime number.

3 Write down the smallest value of x that satisfies each of the following.

a $x - 2 \geqslant 9$, where x is a positive integer.

b $x - 2 > 13$, where x is a positive, even integer.

c $2x - 11 \geqslant 19$, where x is a square number.

d $3x + 7 \geqslant 15$, where x is a positive, odd number.

e $4x - 1 > 23$, where x is a positive, prime number.

The number line

The solution to a linear inequality can be shown on the **number line** by using the following conventions.

Below are five examples.

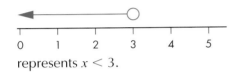

represents $x < 3$.

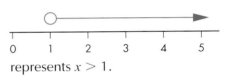

represents $x > 1$.

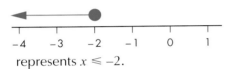

represents $x \leqslant -2$.

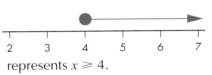

represents $x \geqslant 4$.

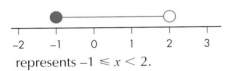

represents $-1 \leqslant x < 2$.

EXAMPLE 19

a Write down the inequality shown by this diagram.

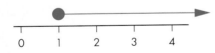

b i Solve the inequality $2x + 3 < 11$.   **ii** Mark the solution to **b** on a number line.

c Write down the integers that satisfy both the inequality in **a** and the inequality in **b**.

a The inequality shown is $x \geqslant 1$.

b i $2x + 3 < 11 \Rightarrow 2x < 8 \Rightarrow x < 4$

ii

c The integers that satisfy both inequalities are 1, 2 and 3.

EXERCISE 13K

1 Write down the inequality that is represented by each diagram below.

a

b

c
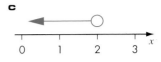

d

e
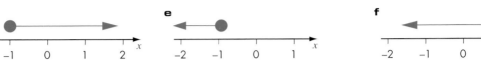

f
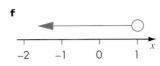

g

h
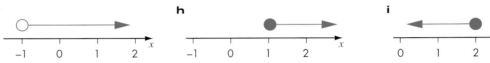

i

j

k
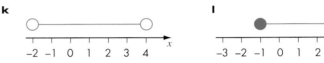

l

2 Draw diagrams to illustrate the following.

a $x \leqslant 3$ **b** $x > -2$ **c** $x \geqslant 0$ **d** $x < 5$

e $x \geqslant -1$ **f** $2 < x \leqslant 5$ **g** $-1 \leqslant x \leqslant 3$ **h** $-3 < x < 4$

i $-4 \leqslant x \leqslant 4$ **j** $3 \leqslant x < 7$

3 Solve the following inequalities and illustrate their solutions on number lines.

a $x + 4 \geqslant 8$ **b** $x + 5 < 3$ **c** $x - 1 \leqslant 2$ **d** $x - 4 > -1$

e $2x > 8$ **f** $3x \leqslant 15$ **g** $4x < 10$ **h** $2x \geqslant 9$

i $\dfrac{x}{2} \leqslant 5$ **j** $\dfrac{x}{4} > 3$ **k** $\dfrac{3x}{4} \geqslant 9$ **l** $\dfrac{2x}{5} < 10$

4 Solve the following equations and illustrate the solutions to **a**, **b**, **c** and **d** on number lines.

a $2x + 3 \leqslant 7$ **b** $4x - 2 \geqslant 12$ **c** $3x - 1 > 14$ **d** $2x + 5 < 3$

e $2x - 5 < 3$ **f** $5x + 1 \geqslant 11$ **g** $3x + 7 > 4$ **h** $2x - 3 \geqslant 4$

i $\dfrac{x}{3} + 1 > 6$ **j** $\dfrac{x}{4} - 3 \leqslant 3$ **k** $\dfrac{x}{2} + 3 < 9$ **l** $\dfrac{x}{7} - 1 \geqslant 9$

5 Solve the following equations and illustrate the solutions to **a**, **b**, **c** and **d** on number lines.

a $2(4x + 3) < 18$ **b** $\dfrac{x}{2} + 3 \leqslant 2$ **c** $\dfrac{x}{5} - 2 > 8$ **d** $\dfrac{x}{3} + 5 \geqslant 3$

e $3(x + 4) > 9$ **f** $2(x - 1) \leqslant 7$ **g** $5(x + 3) \geqslant 10$ **h** $2(x - 7) < 2$

i $\dfrac{x + 2}{3} > 4$ **j** $\dfrac{x - 5}{4} \leqslant 1$ **k** $\dfrac{x + 1}{5} \geqslant 2$ **l** $\dfrac{x - 1}{4} < 3$

1 Solve these equations.

a $4x = 20$

b $y + 5 = 14$

c $8t - 3 = 13$

d $4(m - 5) = 16$

2 Solve these equations.

a $5x - 1 = 9$

b $3 + x = 9$

c $4x + 3 = 2x + 13$

3 Solve these equations.

a $5x + 3 = 38$

b $4(x - 3) = 16$

c $\dfrac{x + 5}{3} = 9$

4

Jason: My answer is 3.

Teacher: Think of a number double it and subtract 7.

Zara: The number I thought of was 15.

a What answer did Zara get?

b What was the number Jason thought of?

5 An orange costs z pence. A lemon costs 4 pence more than an orange.

a Write down an expression, in terms of z, for the cost of one lemon.

b Write down an expression, in terms of z, for the total cost of three oranges and one lemon.

c The total cost of three oranges and one lemon is 60 pence.

Form an equation in terms of z and solve it to find the cost of one orange.

6 a Solve these equations.

i $2x = 9$

ii $3x - 8 = 13$

iii $6x + 9 = x + 24$

b Simplify these expressions.

i $5q + 6q + 2q$

ii $5n + 4p + 2n - p$

7 The length of a rectangle is twice its width.

The area of the rectangle is 128 cm^2.

Show that the length of the rectangle is 16 cm.

8 In the table below, the letters a, b, c and d represent different numbers. The total of each row is given at the side of the table.

a	a	a	a	20
a	b	b	a	24
c	c	c	d	11
d	d	b	c	14

Find the values of a, b, c and d.

9 a Write down an expression for the cost, in pence, of x buns at 30p each and four tarts at 40p each.

b The total cost of x buns and four tarts is £3.10. Find the number of buns sold.

10 Solve these equations.

a $5x - 4 = 11$ **b** $3(m + 7) = 27$

c $8k + 3 = 33 - 2k$

11 Solve these equations.

a $5x + 4 = 9$

b $9p + 7 = 6p + 16$

c $\dfrac{11 - t}{4} = 7$

12 Solve these equations.

a $4x + 3 = 13$

b $12x + 1 = 4x + 5$

13 The lengths of the sides of a triangle are x cm, $(x + 2)$ cm and $(x - 1)$ cm.

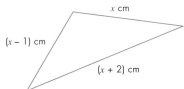

a Write an expression, in terms of x, for the perimeter of this triangle. Give your answer in its simplest form.

b The perimeter is 22 cm.
Write down an equation in x and use it to find the value of x.

14 The width of a rectangle is x centimetres. The length of the rectangle is $(x + 4)$ centimetres.

x + 4

x

a Find an expression, in terms of x, for the perimeter of the rectangle. Give your expression in its simplest form.

The perimeter of the rectangle is 54 centimetres.

b Work out the length of the rectangle.

Edexcel, Question 5, Paper 17 Intermediate, June 2005

 15 Solve the equation $5x + 6 = 6 - x$.

 16 ABC is a triangle with angles, given in degrees, of x, $x + 40°$ and $x + 80°$.

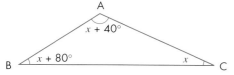

A

$x + 40°$

$x + 80°$

B $\qquad$ x $\qquad$ C

a Write down an expression, in terms of x, for the sum of the angles in the triangle.

b Calculate the value of x.

  17 a Solve $\quad 20y - 16 = 18y - 9$

b Solve $\quad \dfrac{40 - x}{3} = 4 + x$

Edexcel, Question 13, Paper 4 Intermediate, June 2004

 18 You are given that $y = 12 + 3x$.

a When $x = -4$, work out the value of y.

b When $y = 0$, work out the value of x.

c Make x the subject of the formula.

  19 Make x the subject of the formula:

$5x + 7 = 6y$

Simplify your answer as much as possible.

 20 Make m the subject of the formula:

$p = \dfrac{m + 1}{4}$

 21 Parveen is using trial and improvement to find a solution to the equation:

$x^2 + 9x = 40$

The table shows her first two tries.

x	$x^2 + 9x = 40$	Comment
3	36	Too low
4	52	Too high

Continue the table to find a solution to the equation. Give your answer correct to one decimal place.

  22 ABC is a triangle with sides, given in centimetres, of x, $2x + 1$ and $3x - 3$.

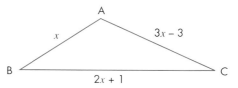

A

x $\qquad$ $3x - 3$

B $\qquad$ $2x + 1$ $\qquad$ C

The perimeter of the triangle is 22 cm. Find the value of x.

 23 a Rearrange the formula:

$T = 5p$

to make p the subject.

b Rearrange the formula:

$V = 5t^2$

to make t the subject.

 24 Solve the equation:

$3(x + 4) = 8 - 2x$

  25 a Solve $5 - 3x = 2(x + 1)$

b $-3 \leqslant y < 3$

y is an integer. Write down all the possible values of y.

Edexcel, Question 10, Paper 16 Intermediate, June 2005

WORKED EXAM QUESTIONS

1 The angles of a quadrilateral are 83°, $x°$, $4x°$ and 97°.

   a Write down an equation in x.

   b Use your equation to find the largest angle in the quadrilateral.

Solution

1   a $5x + 180 = 360$

     b   144°

> You should know that the angles in a quadrilateral add up to 360°. This means that:
> $x + 4x + 83 + 97 = 360$
> This would get the marks for part (a) but you will need to simplify this equation. You should always try to simplify expressions whenever you can.

> Solving the equation gives:
> subtracting 180 $5x = 360 - 180 = 180$
> dividing by 5 $x = 36$
> Do not stop at this point as the question asks for the largest angle. This is the angle $4x°$, which is $4 \times 36 = 144°$.

2 Mark is x years old.

  Nell is eight years older than Mark.

  Oliver is twice as old as Nell.

   a Write down expressions in x for the ages of Nell and Oliver.

   b Show that the total of their ages is given by the expression $4(x + 6)$.

   c Given that their total age is 44, find Mark's age.

Solution

2   a   Nell: $x + 8$

        Oliver: $2(x + 8)$

    b $x + x + 8 + 2(x + 8)$

        $= 2x + 8 + 2x + 16$

        $= 4x + 24$

        $= 4(x + 6)$

    c $4(x + 6) = 44$

        $4x + 24 = 44$

        $4x = 20$

         $x = 5$

      Mark is five years old.

> '8 years older' means an addition, so Nell's age is $x + 8$.
> 'Twice as' means multiply. Use brackets around Nell's age, as $2x + 8$ is wrong.

> Write down the total of all the ages.
> Expand the brackets and collect terms.
> Either expand $4(x + 6)$ or factorise $4x + 24$.

> Set up the equation and expand the brackets.
> Subtract 24, then divide by 4.

GRADE YOURSELF

F Able to solve equations such as $4x = 12$ and $x - 8 = 3$

E Able to solve equations such as $3x + 2 = 7$ or $\frac{x}{3} - 7 = 1$

D Able to solve equations such as $\frac{x - 2}{3} = 6$ or $3x + 7 = x - 6$

D Able to set up simple equations from given information

C Able to solve equations such as $3(x - 4) = 5x + 8$

C Able to solve inequalities such as $3x + 2 < 5$

C Able to solve equations by trial and improvement

C Able to rearrange simple formulae

What you should know now

- How to solve a variety of linear equations using rearrangement or 'doing the same thing to both sides'

- How to solve equations using trial and improvement

- How to rearrange simple formulae

- How to solve simple inequalities

Quick check

1 24   **2** 21   **3** 40   **4** 18   **5** 42

6 27   **7** 30   **8** 6   **9** 12   **10** 5

11 10   **12** 8   **13** 5   **14** 7   **15** 4

16 80   **17** 900   **18** 30   **19** 1400

20 170

Exercise 1A

1 a 45   **b** 43   **c** 40   **d** 45   **e** 45   **f** 36
   g 43   **h** 42   **i** 41
2 a 0, 4, 8   **b** 6, 2, 9   **c** 1, 0, 6   **d** 9, 1, 7, 6
   e 4, 9, 0, 10, 3, 8   **f** 6, 5, 7, 18, 8, 17, 45
   g 8, 6, 12, 1, 7, 22   **h** 1, 8, 0, 13, 5, 19, 43
   i 1, 6, 5, 0, 7, 3, 7, 14, 11 or 1, 6, 5, 7, 14, 3, 0, 7, 11

Exercise 1B

1 a 20   **b** 21   **c** 24   **d** 15   **e** 16   **f** 12
   g 10   **h** 42   **i** 24   **j** 18   **k** 30   **l** 28
   m 18   **n** 56   **o** 25   **p** 45   **q** 27   **r** 30
   s 49   **t** 24   **u** 36   **v** 35   **w** 32   **x** 36
   y 48
2 a 5   **b** 4   **c** 6   **d** 6   **e** 5   **f** 4   **g** 7
   h 6   **i** 2   **j** 3   **k** 7   **l** 8   **m** 9   **n** 5
   o 8   **p** 9   **q** 4   **r** 7   **s** 7   **t** 9   **u** 5
   v 4   **w** 5   **x** 7   **y** 6
3 a 12   **b** 15   **c** 21   **d** 13   **e** 8   **f** 7
   g 14   **h** 3   **i** 30   **j** 6   **k** 35   **l** 5
   m 16   **n** 7   **o** 16   **p** 15   **q** 27   **r** 6
   s 15   **t** 24   **u** 40   **v** 6   **w** 17   **x** 72
   y 46
4 a 30   **b** 50   **c** 80   **d** 100   **e** 120
   f 180   **g** 240   **h** 400   **i** 700   **j** 900
   k 1000   **l** 1400   **m** 2400   **n** 7200
   o 10 000   **p** 2   **q** 7   **r** 9   **s** 17
   t 30   **u** 3   **v** 8   **w** 12   **x** 29
   y 50

Exercise 1C

1 a 11   **b** 6   **c** 10   **d** 12   **e** 11   **f** 13
   g 11   **h** 12   **i** 12   **j** 4   **k** 13   **l** 3
2 a 16   **b** 2   **c** 10   **d** 10   **e** 6   **f** 18
   g 6   **h** 15   **i** 9   **j** 12   **k** 3   **l** 8
3 b $3 + (2 \times 4) = 11$ **c** $(9 \div 3) - 2 = 1$
   d $9 - (4 \div 2) = 7$ **e** $(5 \times 2) + 3 = 13$
   f $5 + (2 \times 3) = 11$ **g** $(10 \div 5) - 2 = 0$
   h $10 - (4 \div 2) = 8$ **i** $(4 \times 6) - 7 = 17$
   j $7 + (4 \times 6) = 31$ **k** $(6 \div 3) + 7 = 9$
   l $7 + (6 \div 2) = 10$
4 a 38   **b** 48   **c** 3   **d** 2   **e** 5   **f** 14
   g 10   **h** 2   **i** 5   **j** 19   **k** 15   **l** 2
   m 20   **n** 19   **o** 54   **p** 7   **q** 2   **r** 7
   s 7   **t** 38   **u** 42   **v** 10   **w** 2   **x** 10
   y 10   **z** 24

5 a (4 + 1)   **b** No brackets needed
   c (2 + 1)   **d** No brackets needed
   e (4 + 4)   **f** (16 − 4)
   g No brackets needed   **h** No brackets needed
   i (20 − 10)   **j** No brackets needed
   k (5 + 5)   **l** (4 + 2)
   m (15 − 5)   **n** (7 − 2)   **o** (3 + 3)
   p No brackets needed   **q** No brackets needed
   r (8 − 2)
6 a 8   **b** 6   **c** 6   **d** 13   **e** 11   **f** 9
   g 12   **h** 8   **i** 15   **j** 16   **k** 1   **l** 7
7 a $2 \times 3 + 5$ **b** $2 \times (3 + 5)$ **c** $2 + 3 \times 5$
   d $5 - (3 - 2)$ and $(5 + 3) \div 2$ **e** $5 \times 3 - 2$
   f $5 \times 3 \times 2$

Exercise 1D

1 a 40   **b** 5 units   **c** 100   **d** 90   **e** 80
   f 9 units   **g** 80   **h** 500   **i** 0   **j** 5000
   k 0   **l** 4 units   **m** 300   **n** 90   **o** 80 000
2 a Forty-three, two hundred
   b One hundred and thirty-six; four thousand and ninety-nine
   c Two hundred and seventy-one; ten thousand, seven hundred and forty-four
3 a Five million, six hundred thousand
   b Four million, seventy-five thousand, two hundred
   c Three million, seven thousand, nine hundred and fifty
   d Two million, seven hundred and eighty-two
4 a 8 200 058   **b** 9 406 107   **c** 1 000 502   **d** 2 076 040
5 a 9, 15, 21, 23, 48, 54, 56, 85
   b 25, 62, 86, 151, 219, 310, 400, 501
   c 97, 357, 368, 740, 888, 2053, 4366
6 a 95, 89, 73, 52, 34, 25, 23, 7
   b 700, 401, 174, 117, 80, 65, 18, 2
   c 6227, 3928, 2034, 762, 480, 395, 89, 59
7 a Larger   **b** Larger   **c** Smaller   **d** Larger
   e Larger   **f** Smaller   **g** Larger   **h** Smaller
   i Smaller
8 a 368, 386, 638, 683, 836, 863   **b** 368   **c** 863
9 408, 480, 804, 840
10 33, 35, 38, 53, 55, 58, 83, 85, 88

Exercise 1E

1 a 20   **b** 60   **c** 80   **d** 50   **e** 100
   f 20   **g** 90   **h** 70   **i** 10   **j** 30
   k 30   **l** 50   **m** 80   **n** 50   **o** 90
   p 40   **q** 70   **r** 20   **s** 100   **t** 110
2 a 200   **b** 600   **c** 800   **d** 500   **e** 1000
   f 100   **g** 600   **h** 400   **i** 1000   **j** 1100
   k 300   **l** 500   **m** 800   **n** 500   **o** 900
   p 400   **q** 700   **r** 800   **s** 1000   **t** 1100
3 a 1   **b** 2   **c** 1   **d** 1   **e** 3   **f** 2
   g 3   **h** 2   **i** 1   **j** 1   **k** 3   **l** 2
   m 74   **n** 126   **o** 184
4 a 2000   **b** 6000   **c** 8000   **d** 5000
   e 10 000   **f** 1000   **g** 6000   **h** 3000
   i 9000   **j** 2000   **k** 3000   **l** 5000
   m 8000   **n** 5000   **o** 9000   **p** 4000

q 7000   **r** 8000   **s** 1000   **t** 2000

5 a 230   **b** 570   **c** 720   **d** 520   **e** 910
  f 230   **g** 880   **h** 630   **i** 110   **j** 300
  k 280   **l** 540   **m** 770   **n** 500   **o** 940
  p 380   **q** 630   **r** 350   **s** 1010   **t** 1070

6 a True   **b** False   **c** True
  d True   **e** True   **f** False

7 a Man Utd v West Brom   **b** Blackburn v Fulham
  c 40 000, 19 000, 42 000, 26 000, 40 000, 68 000, 35 000, 25 000, 20 000
  d 39 600, 19 000, 42 100, 26 100, 40 400, 67 800, 34 800, 25 500, 20 200

8 a 35 min   **b** 55 min   **c** 15 min   **d** 50 min
  e 10 min   **f** 15 min   **g** 45 min   **h** 35 min
  i 5 min   **j** 0 min

Exercise 1F

1 a 713   **b** 151   **c** 6381   **d** 968   **e** 622
  f 1315   **g** 8260   **h** 818   **i** 451   **j** 852

2 a 646   **b** 826   **c** 3818   **d** 755   **e** 2596
  f 891   **g** 350   **h** 2766   **i** 8858   **j** 841
  k 6831   **l** 7016   **m** 1003   **n** 4450
  o 9944

3 a 450   **b** 563   **c** 482   **d** 414   **e** 285
  f 486   **g** 244   **h** 284   **i** 333   **j** 216
  k 2892   **l** 4417   **m** 3767   **n** 4087
  o 1828

4 a 128   **b** 29   **c** 334   **d** 178   **e** 277
  f 285   **g** 335   **h** 399   **i** 4032   **j** 4765
  k 3795   **l** 5437

5 a 6, 7   **b** 4, 7   **c** 4, 8   **d** 4, 7, 9
  e 6, 7, 9   **f** 2, 7, 6   **g** 6, 6, 2   **h** 4, 5, 9
  i 4, 8, 8   **j** 4, 4, 9, 8

6 a 5, 3   **b** 8, 3   **c** 5, 8   **d** 5, 4, 8
  e 6, 5, 7   **f** 2, 1, 1   **g** 2, 7, 7   **h** 5, 5, 6
  i 8, 8, 3   **j** 1, 8, 8, 9

Exercise 1G

1 a 56   **b** 65   **c** 51   **d** 38   **e** 108
  f 115   **g** 204   **h** 294   **i** 212   **j** 425
  k 150   **l** 800   **m** 960   **n** 1360   **o** 1518

2 a 294   **b** 370   **c** 288   **d** 832   **e** 2163
  f 2520   **g** 1644   **h** 3215   **i** 3000   **j** 2652
  k 3696   **l** 1880   **m** 54 387
  n 21 935   **o** 48 888

3 a 219   **b** 317   **c** 315   **d** 106   **e** 99
  f 121   **g** 252   **h** 141   **i** 144   **j** 86
  k 63   **l** 2909   **m** 416   **n** 251   **o** 1284

4 a 119   **b** 96   **c** 144   **d** 210   **e** 210

5 a 13   **b** 37 weeks   **c** 43 m
  d 36   **e** 45

Really Useful Maths!: Paradise in Pembrokeshire

Totals: £64, £70, £36, £58, £65, £118, £38, £46, £99

Cost of holiday (£): Activities, 594.00; Cottage, 550.00; Petrol, 54.00; Total, 1198

ANSWERS TO CHAPTER 2

Quick check

1 8   **2** 15   **3** 10   **4** 18   **5** 14

6 20   **7** 24   **8** 24   **9** 18   **10** 21

11 5   **12** 6   **13** 8   **14** 4   **15** 10

16 3   **17** 5   **18** 3   **19** 2   **20** 4

Exercise 2A

1 a $\frac{1}{4}$ **b** $\frac{1}{3}$ **c** $\frac{5}{8}$ **d** $\frac{7}{12}$ **e** $\frac{4}{9}$ **f** $\frac{3}{10}$ **g** $\frac{3}{8}$
  h $\frac{15}{16}$ **i** $\frac{5}{12}$ **j** $\frac{7}{18}$ **k** $\frac{4}{8}=\frac{1}{2}$ **l** $\frac{4}{12}=\frac{1}{3}$
  m $\frac{6}{9}=\frac{2}{3}$ **n** $\frac{6}{10}=\frac{3}{5}$ **o** $\frac{4}{8}=\frac{1}{2}$ **p** $\frac{5}{64}$

Exercise 2B

1 a $\frac{3}{4}$ **b** $\frac{4}{8}=\frac{1}{2}$ **c** $\frac{3}{5}$ **d** $\frac{8}{10}=\frac{4}{5}$ **e** $\frac{2}{3}$ **f** $\frac{5}{7}$
  g $\frac{7}{9}$ **h** $\frac{5}{6}$ **i** $\frac{4}{5}$ **j** $\frac{7}{8}$ **k** $\frac{5}{10}=\frac{1}{2}$ **l** $\frac{5}{7}$ **m** $\frac{4}{5}$
  n $\frac{5}{6}$ **o** $\frac{5}{9}$ **p** $\frac{7}{11}$

2 a $\frac{2}{4}=\frac{1}{2}$ **b** $\frac{3}{5}$ **c** $\frac{3}{8}$ **d** $\frac{3}{10}$ **e** $\frac{1}{3}$ **f** $\frac{4}{6}=\frac{2}{3}$

g $\frac{3}{7}$ **h** $\frac{5}{9}$ **i** $\frac{1}{5}$ **j** $\frac{3}{7}$ **k** $\frac{3}{9}=\frac{1}{3}$ **l** $\frac{6}{10}=\frac{3}{5}$
  m $\frac{3}{6}=\frac{1}{2}$ **n** $\frac{2}{8}=\frac{1}{4}$ **o** $\frac{2}{11}$ **p** $\frac{4}{10}=\frac{2}{5}$

3 a   **b**   **c i** $\frac{3}{4}$ **ii** $\frac{1}{4}$

4 a   **b**

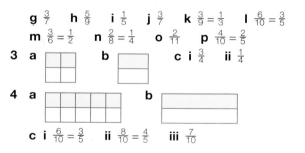

  c i $\frac{6}{10}=\frac{3}{5}$ **ii** $\frac{8}{10}=\frac{4}{5}$ **iii** $\frac{7}{10}$

Exercise 2C

1 a $\frac{4}{24}$ **b** $\frac{8}{24}$ **c** $\frac{3}{24}$ **d** $\frac{16}{24}$ **e** $\frac{20}{24}$ **f** $\frac{18}{24}$
  g $\frac{9}{24}$ **h** $\frac{15}{24}$ **i** $\frac{21}{24}$ **j** $\frac{12}{24}$

2 a $\frac{11}{24}$ **b** $\frac{9}{24}$ **c** $\frac{7}{24}$ **d** $\frac{19}{24}$ **e** $\frac{23}{24}$ **f** $\frac{23}{24}$
  g $\frac{21}{24}$ **h** $\frac{22}{24}$ **i** $\frac{19}{24}$ **j** $\frac{23}{24}$

3 a $\frac{5}{20}$ **b** $\frac{4}{20}$ **c** $\frac{15}{20}$ **d** $\frac{16}{20}$ **e** $\frac{2}{20}$ **f** $\frac{10}{20}$
  g $\frac{12}{20}$ **h** $\frac{8}{20}$ **i** $\frac{14}{20}$ **j** $\frac{6}{20}$

4 a $\frac{9}{20}$ **b** $\frac{14}{20}$ **c** $\frac{11}{20}$ **d** $\frac{19}{20}$ **e** $\frac{19}{20}$

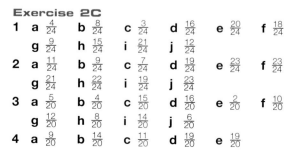

Exercise 2D

1 a $\frac{8}{20}$ **b** $\frac{3}{12}$ **c** $\frac{15}{40}$ **d** $\frac{12}{15}$ **e** $\frac{15}{18}$ **f** $\frac{12}{28}$

g $\times 2, \frac{6}{20}$ **h** $\times 3, \frac{3}{9}$ **i** $\times 4, \frac{12}{20}$ **j** $\times 6, \frac{12}{18}$

k $\times 3, \frac{9}{12}$ **l** $\times 5, \frac{25}{40}$ **m** $\times 2, \frac{14}{20}$ **n** $\times 4, \frac{4}{24}$

o $\times 5, \frac{15}{40}$

2 a $\frac{1}{2} = \frac{2}{4} = \frac{3}{6} = \frac{4}{8} = \frac{5}{10} = \frac{6}{12}$

b $\frac{1}{3} = \frac{2}{6} = \frac{3}{9} = \frac{4}{12} = \frac{5}{15} = \frac{6}{18}$

c $\frac{3}{4} = \frac{6}{8} = \frac{9}{12} = \frac{12}{16} = \frac{15}{20} = \frac{18}{24}$

d $\frac{2}{5} = \frac{4}{10} = \frac{6}{15} = \frac{8}{20} = \frac{10}{25} = \frac{12}{30}$

e $\frac{3}{7} = \frac{6}{14} = \frac{9}{21} = \frac{12}{28} = \frac{15}{35} = \frac{18}{42}$

3 a $\frac{2}{3}$ **b** $\frac{4}{5}$ **c** $\frac{5}{7}$ **d** $\div 6, \frac{2}{3}$ **e** $\frac{3}{5}$ **f** $\div 3, \frac{7}{10}$

4 a $\frac{2}{3}$ **b** $\frac{1}{3}$ **c** $\frac{2}{3}$ **d** $\frac{3}{4}$ **e** $\frac{1}{3}$ **f** $\frac{1}{2}$ **g** $\frac{7}{8}$

h $\frac{4}{5}$ **i** $\frac{1}{2}$ **j** $\frac{1}{4}$ **k** $\frac{4}{5}$ **l** $\frac{5}{7}$ **m** $\frac{5}{7}$ **n** $\frac{2}{3}$

o $\frac{2}{5}$ **p** $\frac{2}{5}$ **q** $\frac{1}{3}$ **r** $\frac{7}{10}$ **s** $\frac{1}{4}$ **t** $\frac{3}{2} = 1\frac{1}{2}$

u $\frac{2}{3}$ **v** $\frac{2}{3}$ **w** $\frac{3}{4}$ **x** $\frac{3}{2} = 1\frac{1}{2}$ **y** $\frac{7}{2} = 3\frac{1}{2}$

5 a $\frac{1}{2}, \frac{2}{3}, \frac{5}{6}$ **b** $\frac{1}{2}, \frac{5}{8}, \frac{3}{4}$ **c** $\frac{2}{5}, \frac{1}{2}, \frac{7}{10}$ **d** $\frac{7}{12}, \frac{2}{3}, \frac{3}{4}$

e $\frac{1}{6}, \frac{1}{4}, \frac{1}{3}$ **f** $\frac{3}{4}, \frac{4}{5}, \frac{9}{10}$ **g** $\frac{7}{10}, \frac{4}{5}, \frac{5}{6}$ **h** $\frac{3}{10}, \frac{1}{3}, \frac{2}{5}$

Exercise 2E

1 $2\frac{1}{3}$ **2** $2\frac{2}{3}$ **3** $2\frac{1}{4}$ **4** $1\frac{3}{7}$ **5** $2\frac{2}{5}$ **6** $1\frac{2}{5}$

7 $2\frac{2}{5}$ **8** $3\frac{3}{4}$ **9** $3\frac{1}{3}$ **10** $2\frac{1}{7}$ **11** $2\frac{5}{6}$ **12** $3\frac{3}{5}$

13 $4\frac{3}{4}$ **14** $3\frac{1}{7}$ **15** $1\frac{3}{11}$ **16** $1\frac{1}{11}$ **17** $5\frac{3}{5}$ **18** $2\frac{5}{5}$

19 $5\frac{5}{7}$ **20** $8\frac{2}{5}$ **21** $2\frac{1}{10}$ **22** $2\frac{1}{2}$ **23** $1\frac{2}{3}$ **24** $3\frac{1}{8}$

25 $2\frac{3}{10}$ **26** $2\frac{1}{11}$ **27** $7\frac{3}{5}$ **28** $5\frac{3}{7}$ **29** 5 **30** 2

31 $\frac{10}{3}$ **32** $\frac{35}{6}$ **33** $\frac{9}{5}$ **34** $\frac{37}{7}$ **35** $\frac{41}{10}$ **36** $\frac{17}{2}$

37 $\frac{5}{2}$ **38** $\frac{13}{4}$ **39** $\frac{43}{6}$ **40** $\frac{29}{8}$ **41** $\frac{19}{3}$ **42** $\frac{89}{9}$

43 $\frac{59}{5}$ **44** $\frac{16}{6}$ **45** $\frac{35}{8}$ **46** $\frac{28}{9}$ **47** $\frac{26}{5}$ **48** $\frac{11}{4}$

49 $\frac{30}{7}$ **50** $\frac{49}{6}$ **51** $\frac{26}{9}$ **52** $\frac{37}{6}$ **53** $\frac{61}{5}$ **54** $\frac{13}{4}$

55 $\frac{71}{10}$ **56** $\frac{73}{9}$ **57** $\frac{61}{8}$ **58** $\frac{21}{2}$ **59** $\frac{17}{16}$ **60** $\frac{19}{4}$

Exercise 2F

1 a $\frac{6}{8} = \frac{3}{4}$ **b** $\frac{4}{10} = \frac{2}{5}$ **c** $\frac{6}{9} = \frac{2}{3}$ **d** $\frac{3}{4}$ **e** $\frac{6}{10} = \frac{3}{5}$

f $\frac{6}{12} = \frac{1}{2}$ **g** $\frac{8}{16} = \frac{1}{2}$ **h** $\frac{10}{16} = \frac{5}{8}$

2 a $\frac{12}{10} = \frac{6}{5} = 1\frac{1}{5}$ **b** $\frac{9}{8} = 1\frac{1}{8}$ **c** $\frac{9}{8} = 1\frac{1}{8}$ **d** $\frac{13}{8} = 1\frac{5}{8}$

e $\frac{11}{8} = 1\frac{3}{8}$ **f** $\frac{7}{6} = 1\frac{1}{6}$ **g** $\frac{9}{6} = 1\frac{3}{6} = 1\frac{1}{2}$ **h** $\frac{5}{4} = 1\frac{1}{4}$

3 a $\frac{10}{8} = \frac{5}{4} = 1\frac{1}{4}$ **b** $\frac{6}{4} = \frac{3}{2} = 1\frac{1}{2}$ **c** $\frac{5}{5} = 1$

d $\frac{16}{10} = \frac{8}{5} = 1\frac{3}{5}$ **e** $\frac{10}{8} = \frac{5}{4} = 1\frac{1}{4}$ **f** $\frac{22}{16} = \frac{11}{8} = 1\frac{3}{8}$

g $\frac{16}{12} = \frac{4}{3} = 1\frac{1}{3}$ **h** $\frac{18}{16} = \frac{9}{8} = 1\frac{1}{8}$ **i** $1\frac{3}{4}$ **j** $3\frac{1}{4}$

k $6\frac{1}{4}$ **l** $3\frac{5}{8}$

4 a $\frac{4}{8} = \frac{1}{2}$ **b** $\frac{6}{10} = \frac{3}{5}$ **c** $\frac{1}{4}$ **d** $\frac{3}{8}$ **e** $\frac{1}{4}$ **f** $\frac{3}{8}$

g $\frac{4}{10} = \frac{2}{5}$ **h** $\frac{5}{16}$ **i** $\frac{1}{4}$ **j** $1\frac{2}{3}$ **k** $2\frac{1}{4}$ **l** $2\frac{1}{8}$

Exercise 2G

1 $\frac{1}{8}$ **2 a** $\frac{1}{4}$ **b** $\frac{3}{8}$ **c** Ayesha **3** $\frac{4}{6} = \frac{2}{3}$

4 $\frac{3}{8}$ **5** $\frac{2}{5}$ **6** $\frac{3}{8}$ **7** $\frac{4}{11}$ **8** $\frac{1}{6}$ **9** $\frac{5}{8}$

Exercise 2H

1 a 18 **b** 10 **c** 18 **d** 28 **e** 15 **f** 18

g 48 **h** 45

2 a £1800 **b** 128 g **c** 160 kg **d** £116

e 65 litres **f** 90 min **g** 292 d **h** 21 h

i 18 h **j** 2370 miles

3 a $\frac{5}{8}$ of 40 = 25 **b** $\frac{3}{4}$ of 280 = 210

c $\frac{4}{5}$ of 70 = 56 **d** $\frac{5}{6}$ of 72 = 60

e $\frac{3}{5}$ of 95 = 57 **f** $\frac{3}{4}$ of 340 = 255

4 £6080 **5** £31 500 **6** 23 000 **7** 52 kg

8 a 856 **b** 187 675

9 a £50 **b** £550

10 a 180 g **b** 900 g

11 a £120 **b** £240

12 £6400

Exercise 2I

1 $\frac{1}{6}$ **2** $\frac{1}{20}$ **3** $\frac{2}{9}$ **4** $\frac{1}{6}$ **5** $\frac{1}{4}$ **6** $\frac{2}{5}$ **7** $\frac{1}{2}$

8 $\frac{1}{2}$ **9** $\frac{3}{14}$ **10** $\frac{35}{48}$ **11** $\frac{8}{15}$ **12** $\frac{21}{32}$

Exercise 2J

1 a $\frac{1}{3}$ **b** $\frac{1}{5}$ **c** $\frac{2}{5}$ **d** $\frac{5}{24}$ **e** $\frac{2}{5}$ **f** $\frac{1}{6}$ **g** $\frac{2}{7}$

h $\frac{1}{3}$

2 $\frac{3}{5}$ **3** $\frac{12}{31}$ **4** $\frac{7}{12}$

Exercise 2K

1 a 0.5 **b** $0.\dot{3}$ **c** 0.25 **d** 0.2 **e** $0.1\dot{6}$

f $0.\dot{1}4285\dot{7}$ **g** 0.125 **h** $0.\dot{1}$ **i** 0.1

j $0.\dot{0}7692\dot{3}$

2 a i $0.\dot{5}7142\dot{8}$ **ii** $0.\dot{7}1428\dot{5}$ **iii** $0.\dot{8}5714\dot{2}$

b The recurring digits are all in the same sequence but they start in a different place each time.

3 $0.\dot{1}, 0.\dot{2}, 0.\dot{3}, 0.\dot{4}, 0.\dot{5}, 0.\dot{6}, 0.\dot{7}, 0.\dot{8}$

The recurring digit is the numerator of the fraction.

4 $0.\dot{0}\dot{9}, 0.\dot{1}\dot{8}, 0.\dot{2}\dot{7}, 0.\dot{3}\dot{6}, 0.\dot{4}\dot{5}, 0.\dot{5}\dot{4}, 0.\dot{6}\dot{3}, 0.\dot{7}\dot{2},$
$0.\dot{8}\dot{1}, 0.\dot{9}\dot{0}$

The recurring digits follow the nine times table.

5 $\frac{9}{22} = 0.4\dot{0}\dot{9}, \frac{3}{7} = 0.\dot{4}2857\dot{1}, \frac{16}{37} = 0.\dot{4}3\dot{2}, \frac{4}{9} = 0.\dot{4},$
$\frac{5}{11} = 0.\dot{4}\dot{5}, \frac{6}{13} = 0.\dot{4}6153\dot{8}$

6 $\frac{7}{24} = \frac{35}{120}, \frac{3}{10} = \frac{36}{120}, \frac{19}{60} = \frac{38}{120}, \frac{2}{5} = \frac{48}{120}, \frac{5}{12} = \frac{50}{120}$

7 a $\frac{1}{8}$ **b** $\frac{17}{50}$ **c** $\frac{29}{40}$ **d** $\frac{5}{16}$ **e** $\frac{89}{100}$ **f** $\frac{1}{20}$

g $2\frac{7}{20}$ **h** $\frac{7}{32}$

8 a $0.08\dot{3}$ **b** 0.0625 **c** 0.05 **d** 0.04

e 0.02

9 a $\frac{4}{3} = 1\frac{1}{3}$ **b** $\frac{6}{5} = 1\frac{1}{5}$ **c** $\frac{5}{2} = 2\frac{1}{2}$ **d** $\frac{10}{7} = 1\frac{3}{7}$

e $\frac{20}{11} = 1\frac{9}{11}$ **f** $\frac{15}{4} = 3\frac{3}{4}$

10 a $0.75, 1.\dot{3}$ **b** $0.8\dot{3}, 1.2$ **c** $0.4, 2.5$

d $0.7, 1.\dot{4}2857\dot{1}$ **e** $0.55, 1.8\dot{1}$ **f** 3.75

11 The answer is always 1.

Quick check

1 0, 1, 2, 4, 5, 8, 9, 17, 19 51, 92

2 10, 11, 14,

3 0, 24, 32,

4 12, 56, 87, 136, 288

5 0, $\frac{1}{2}$, 5, 50, 87, 100

Exercise 3A

1 –£5 **2** –£9 **3** Profit **4** –200 m **5** –50 m **6** Above **7** –3 h **8** –5 h **9** After **10** –2 °C **11** –8 °C **12** Above **13** –70 km **14** –200 km **15** North **16** +5 m **17** –5 mph **18** –2

Exercise 3B

1 Many different answers to each part
2 Many different answers to each part
3 **a** Is smaller than **b** Is bigger than **c** Is smaller than **d** Is smaller than **e** Is bigger than **f** Is smaller than **g** Is smaller than **h** Is bigger than **i** Is bigger than **j** Is smaller than **k** Is smaller than **l** Is bigger than
4 **a** Is smaller than **b** Is smaller than **c** Is smaller than **d** Is bigger than **e** Is smaller than **f** Is smaller than
5 **a** < **b** > **c** < **d** < **e** < **f** > **g** < **h** > **i** > **j** > **k** < **l** < **m** > **n** > **o** < **p** >
6 a

| –5 | –4 | –3 | –2 | –1 | 0 | 1 | 2 | 3 | 4 | 5 |

b

| –25 | –20 | –15 | –10 | –5 | 0 | 5 | 10 | 15 | 20 | 25 |

c

| –10 | –8 | –6 | –4 | –2 | 0 | 2 | 4 | 6 | 8 | 10 |

d

| –50 | –40 | –30 | –20 | –10 | 0 | 10 | 20 | 30 | 40 | 50 |

e

| –15 | –12 | –9 | –6 | –3 | 0 | 3 | 6 | 9 | 12 | 15 |

f

| –20 | –16 | –12 | –8 | –4 | 0 | 4 | 8 | 12 | 16 | 20 |

g

| $-2\frac{1}{2}$ | –2 | $-1\frac{1}{2}$ | –1 | $-\frac{1}{2}$ | 0 | $\frac{1}{2}$ | 1 | $1\frac{1}{2}$ | 2 | $2\frac{1}{2}$ |

h

| –100 | –80 | –60 | –40 | –20 | 0 | 20 | 40 | 60 | 80 | 100 |

i

| –250 | –200 | –150 | –100 | –50 | 0 | 50 | 100 | 150 | 200 | 250 |

Exercise 3C

1 **a** –2° **b** –3° **c** –2° **d** –3° **e** –2° **f** –3° **g** 3 **h** 3 **i** –1 **j** –1 **k** 2 **l** –3 **m** –4 **n** –6 **o** –6 **p** –1 **q** –5 **r** –4 **s** 4 **t** –1 **u** –5 **v** –4 **w** –5 **x** –5
2 **a** –4 **b** –4 **c** –10 **d** 2 **e** 8 **f** –5 **g** 2 **h** 5 **i** –7 **j** –12 **k** 13 **l** 25 **m** –32 **n** –30 **o** –5 **p** –8 **q** –12 **r** 10 **s** –36 **t** –14 **u** 41 **v** 12 **w** –40 **x** –101
3 **a** 6 **b** –5 **c** 6 **d** –1 **e** –2 **f** –6 **g** –6 **h** –2 **i** 3 **j** 0 **k** –7 **l** –6 **m** 8 **n** 1 **o** –9 **p** –9 **q** –5 **r** –80 **s** –7 **t** –1 **u** –47

Exercise 3D

1 **a** 6 **b** 7 **c** 8 **d** 6 **e** 8 **f** 10 **g** 2 **h** –3 **i** 1 **j** 2 **k** –1 **l** –7 **m** 2 **n** –3 **o** 1 **p** –5 **q** 3 **r** –4 **s** –3 **t** –8 **u** –10 **v** –9 **w** –4 **x** –9
2 **a** –8 **b** –10 **c** –11 **d** –3 **e** 2 **f** –5 **g** 1 **h** 4 **i** 7 **j** –8 **k** –5 **l** –11 **m** 11 **n** 6 **o** 8 **p** 8 **q** –2 **r** –1 **s** –9 **t** –5 **u** 5 **v** –9 **w** 8 **x** 0
3 **a** 3 °C **b** 0 °C **c** –3 °C **d** –5 °C **e** –11 °C
4 **a** 10 degrees Celsius **b** 7 degrees Celsius **c** 9 degrees Celsius
5 –9, –6, –5, –1, 1, 2, 3, 8
6 **a** –3 **b** –4 **c** –2 **d** –7 **e** –14 **f** –6 **g** –12 **h** –10 **i** 4 **j** –4 **k** 14 **l** 11 **m** –4 **n** –1 **o** –10 **p** –5 **q** –3 **r** 5 **s** –4 **t** –8
7 **a** 2 **b** –3 **c** –5 **d** –7 **e** –10 **f** –20
8 **a** 2 **b** 4 **c** –1 **d** –5 **e** –11 **f** 8
9 **a** 13 **b** 2 **c** 5 **d** 4 **e** 11 **f** –2
10 **a** –10 **b** –5 **c** –2 **d** 4 **e** 7 **f** –4
13 **a** –5 **b** 6 **c** 0 **d** 2 **e** 13 **f** 0 **g** –6 **h** –2 **i** 212 **j** 5 **k** 3 **l** 3 **m** –67 **n** 7 **o** 25
14 **a** –1, 0, 1, 2, 3 **b** –6, –5, –4, –3, –2 **c** –3, –2, –1, 0, 1 **d** –8, –7, –6, –5, –4 **e** –9, –8, –7, –6, –5 **f** 3, 4, 5, 6, 7 **g** –12, –11, –10, –9. –8 **h** –16, –15, –14, –13, –12 **i** –2, –1, 0, 1, 2, 3; –4, –3, –2, –1, 0, 1 **j** –12, –11, –10, –9, –8, –7; –14, –13, –12, –11, –10, –9 **k** –2, –1, 0, 1, 2, 3; 0, 1, 2, 3, 4, 5 **l** –8, –7, –6, –5, –4, –3, –2; –5, –4, –3, –2, –1, 0, 1 **m** –10, –9, –8, –7, –6, –5, –4; –1, 0, 1, 2, 3, 4, 5 **n** 3, 4, 5, 6, 7, 8, 9; –5, –4, –3, –2, –1, 0, 1
15 **a** –4 **b** 3 **c** 4 **d** –6 **e** 7 **f** 2 **g** 7 **h** –6 **i** –7 **j** 0 **k** 0 **l** –6 **m** –7 **n** –9 **o** 4 **p** 0 **q** 5 **r** 0 **s** 10 **t** –5 **u** 3 **v** –3 **w** –9 **x** 0 **y** –3 **z** –3

16 a +6 + 5 = 11 **b** +6 + −9 = −3
 c +6 − −9 = 15 **d** +6 − 5 = 1
17 a +5 + +7 − −9 = +21 **b** +5 + −9 − +7 = −11
 c +7 + −7, +4 + −4

Exercise 3E

1

−1	−9	−2
−5	−4	−3
−6	1	−7

−12

2

1	−4	3
2	0	−2
−3	4	−1

0

3

0	−14	−1
−6	−5	−4
−9	4	−10

−15

4

2	−12	1
−4	−3	−2
−7	6	−8

−9

5

−3	−6	−9
−12	−6	0
−3	−6	−9

−18

6

−2	−18	−1
−6	−7	−8
−13	4	−12

−21

7

−4	−12	−5
−8	−7	−6
−9	−2	−10

−21

8

2	1	−3
−5	0	5
3	−1	−2

0

9

−2	−10	−3
−6	−5	−4
−7	0	−8

−15

10

−8	−1	−3	−14
−8	−9	−7	−2
−11	−6	−4	−5
1	−10	−12	−5

−26

11

−7	5	2	−16
−6	−8	−5	3
−11	−3	0	−2
8	−10	−13	−1

−16

Quick check

1 a 6 **b** 12 **c** 15 **d** 18 **e** 21 **f** 24

2 a 8 **b** 16 **c** 20 **d** 24 **e** 28 **f** 32

3 a 10 **b** 45 **c** 25 **d** 30 **e** 35 **f** 40

4 a 12 **b** 54 **c** 64 **d** 36 **e** 63 **f** 48

5 a 14 **b** 63 **c** 72 **d** 42 **e** 49 **f** 56

Exercise 4A

1 a 3, 6, 9, 12, 15 **b** 7, 14, 21, 28, 35
 c 9, 18, 27, 36, 45 **d** 11, 22, 33, 44, 55
 e 16, 32, 48, 64, 80
2 a 254, 108, 68, 162, 98, 812, 102, 270
 b 111, 255, 108, 162, 711, 615, 102, 75, 270
 c 255, 615, 75, 270
 d 108, 162, 711, 270
3 a 72, 132, 216, 312, 168, 144
 b 161, 91, 168, 294
 c 72, 102, 132, 78, 216, 312, 168, 144, 294
4 a 98 **b** 99 **c** 96 **d** 95 **e** 98 **f** 96
5 a 1002 **b** 1008 **c** 1008

Exercise 4B

1 a 1, 2, 5, 10 **b** 1, 2, 4, 7, 14, 28
 c 1, 2, 3, 6, 9, 18 **d** 1, 17
 e 1, 5, 25 **f** 1, 2, 4, 5, 8, 10, 20, 40
 g 1, 2, 3, 5, 6, 10, 15, 30 **h** 1, 3, 5, 9, 15, 45
 i 1, 2, 3, 4, 6, 8, 12, 24 **j** 1, 2, 4, 8, 16
2 a 1, 2, 3, 4, 5, 6, 8, 10, 12, 15, 20, 24, 30, 40, 60, 120
 b 1, 2, 3, 5, 6, 10, 15, 25, 30, 50, 75, 150
 c 1, 2, 3, 4, 6, 8, 9, 12, 16, 18, 24, 36, 48, 72, 144

d 1, 2, 3, 4, 5, 6, 9, 10, 12, 15, 18, 20, 30, 36, 45, 60, 90, 180
e 1, 13, 169
f 1, 2, 3, 4, 6, 9, 12, 18, 27, 36, 54, 108
g 1, 2, 4, 7, 14, 28, 49, 98, 196
h 1, 3, 9, 17, 51, 153
i 1, 2, 3, 6, 9, 11, 18, 22, 33, 66, 99, 198 **j** 1, 199
3 a 55 **b** 67 **c** 29 **d** 39 **e** 65 **f** 80
 g 80 **h** 70 **i** 81 **j** 50
4 a 2 **b** 2 **c** 3 **d** 5 **e** 3 **f** 3
 g 7 **h** 5 **i** 10 **j** 11

Exercise 4C

1 36, 49, 64, 81, 100, 121, 144, 169, 196, 225, 256, 289, 324, 361, 400
2 4, 9, 16, 25, 36, 49
3 a 3 **b** 5 **c** 7 **d** Odd numbers
4 a 50, 65, 82 **b** 98, 128, 162 **c** 51, 66, 83
 d 48, 63, 80 **e** 149, 164, 181
5 a 529 **b** 3249 **c** 5929 **d** 15 129
 e 23 104 **f** 10.24 **g** 90.25 **h** 566.44
 i 16 **j** 144
6 a 25, 169, 625, 1681, 3721
 b Answers in each row are the same.

Exercise 4D

1 a 6, 12, 18, 24, 30 **b** 13, 26, 39, 52, 65
 c 8, 16, 24, 32, 40 **d** 20, 40, 60, 80, 100
 e 18, 36, 54, 72, 90
2 a 12, 24, 36 **b** 20, 40, 60 **c** 15, 30, 45
 d 18, 36, 54 **e** 35, 70, 105
3 a 1, 2, 3, 4, 6, 12 **b** 1, 2, 4, 5, 10, 20
 c 1, 3, 9 **d** 1, 2, 4, 8, 16, 32
 e 1, 2, 3, 4, 6, 8, 12, 24 **f** 1, 2, 19, 38

g 1, 13   **h** 1, 2, 3, 6, 7, 14, 21, 42
i 1, 3, 5, 9, 15, 45   **j** 1, 2, 3, 4, 6, 9, 12, 18, 36
4 13 is a prime number.
5 Square numbers
6 2, 3, 5, 7, 11, 13, 17, 19
7 1, 4, 9, 16, 25, 36, 49, 64, 81, 100
8 4 packs of sausages, 5 packs of buns
9 24 seconds
10 30 seconds
11 12 minutes; Debbie: 3 and Fred: 4
12 a 12   **b** 9   **c** 6   **d** 13   **e** 15   **f** 14
g 16   **h** 10   **i** 18   **j** 17   **k** 8   **l** 21
13 $1 + 3 + 5 + 7 + 9 = 25$
$1 + 3 + 5 + 7 + 9 + 11 = 36$
$1 + 3 + 5 + 7 + 9 + 11 + 13 = 49$
$1 + 3 + 5 + 7 + 9 + 11 + 13 + 15 = 64$
14 b 21, 28, 36, 45, 55

Exercise 4E

1 a 2   **b** 5   **c** 7   **d** 1   **e** 9   **f** 10
g 8   **h** 3   **i** 6   **j** 4   **k** 11   **l** 12
m 20   **n** 30   **o** 13
2 a 5   **b** 6   **c** 10   **d** 7   **e** 8   **f** 4
g 3   **h** 9   **i** 1   **j** 12
3 a 81   **b** 40   **c** 100   **d** 14   **e** 36   **f** 15
g 49   **h** 12   **i** 25   **j** 21   **k** 121   **l** 16
m 64   **n** 17   **o** 441
4 a 24   **b** 31   **c** 45   **d** 40   **e** 67   **f** 101
g 3.6   **h** 6.5   **i** 13.9   **j** 22.2

Exercise 4F

1 a 27   **b** 125   **c** 216   **d** 1728   **e** 16
f 256   **g** 625   **h** 32   **i** 2187   **j** 1024
2 a 100   **b** 1000   **c** 10 000   **d** 100 000
e 1 000 000
f The power is the same as the number of zeros.
g i 100 000 000   **ii** 10 000 000 000
iii 1 000 000 000 000 000
3 a 2^4 **b** 3^5 **c** 7^2 **d** 5^3 **e** 10^7 **f** 6^4
g 4^4 **h** 1^7 **i** 0.5^4 **j** 100^3
4 a $3 \times 3 \times 3 \times 3$ **b** $9 \times 9 \times 9$ **c** 6×6
d $10 \times 10 \times 10 \times 10 \times 10$
e $2 \times 2 \times 2 \times 2 \times 2 \times 2 \times 2 \times 2 \times 2 \times 2$
f $8 \times 8 \times 8 \times 8 \times 8 \times 8$ **g** $0.1 \times 0.1 \times 0.1$
h 2.5×2.5 **i** $0.7 \times 0.7 \times 0.7$ **j** 1000×1000
5 a 16   **b** 243   **c** 49   **d** 125
e 10 000 000   **f** 1296   **g** 256   **h** 1
i 0.0625   **j** 1 000 000
6 a 81   **b** 729   **c** 36   **d** 100 000
e 1024   **f** 262 144   **g** 0.001   **h** 6.25
i 0.343   **j** 1 000 000
7 10^6
8 10^6
9 4, 8, 16, 32, 64, 128, 256, 512
10 0.001, 0.01, 0.1, 1, 10, 100, 1000, 10 000, 100 000, 1 000 000, 10 000 000, 100 000 000

Exercise 4G

1 a 31   **b** 310   **c** 3100   **d** 31 000

2 a 65   **b** 650   **c** 6500   **d** 65 000
3 Factors of 10 are the same, e.g. $100 = 10^2$
4 a 7.3×10 **b** 7.3×10^2 **c** 7.3×10^3 **d** 7.3×10^5
5 a 0.31   **b** 0.031   **c** 0.0031   **d** 0.000 31
6 a 0.65   **b** 0.065   **c** 0.0065   **d** 0.000 65
7 Factors of 10 are the same, e.g. $1000 = 10^3$
8 a $7.3 \div 10$ **b** $7.3 \div 10^2$ **c** $7.3 \div 10^3$
d $7.3 \div 10^5$
9 a 250   **b** 34.5   **c** 4670   **d** 346   **e** 207.89
f 56 780   **g** 89 700   **h** 865   **i** 10 050
j 999 000   **k** 23 456   **l** 98 765.4
10 a 0.025   **b** 0.345   **c** 0.004 67   **d** 3.46
e 0.207 89   **f** 0.056 78   **g** 0.0246   **h** 0.000 865
i 1.005   **j** 0.000 000 999   **k** 20.367   **l** 7.643
11 a 60 000   **b** 120 000   **c** 10 000   **d** 200 000
e 28 000   **f** 900   **g** 400   **h** 8000   **i** 160 000
12 a 20   **b** 2   **c** 1   **d** 16   **e** 150   **f** 12
g 15   **h** 40   **i** 5   **j** 40   **k** 320
13 i a 2.3×10^7 **b** 3.4×10^{-2} **c** 6.3×10^{10}
d 1.6×10^{-3} **e** 5.5×10^{-4} **f** 1.2×10^{14}
ii a 23 000 000   **b** 0.034   **c** 63 000 000 000
d 0.0016   **e** 0.00055   **f** 120 000 000 000 000
14 a 51 000 000 000   **b** 8160 000 000 000
c 5 333 33.3333   **d** 1500 000.000

Exercise 4H

1 a $84 = 2 \times 2 \times 3 \times 7$
b $100 = 2 \times 2 \times 5 \times 5$
c $180 = 2 \times 2 \times 3 \times 3 \times 5$
d $220 = 2 \times 2 \times 5 \times 11$
e $280 = 2 \times 2 \times 2 \times 5 \times 7$
f $128 = 2 \times 2 \times 2 \times 2 \times 2 \times 2 \times 2$
g $50 = 2 \times 5 \times 5$
h $1000 = 2 \times 2 \times 2 \times 5 \times 5 \times 5$
i $576 = 2 \times 2 \times 2 \times 2 \times 2 \times 2 \times 3 \times 3$
j $650 = 2 \times 5 \times 5 \times 13$
2 a $2^2 \times 3 \times 7$ **b** $2^2 \times 5^2$ **c** $2^2 \times 3^2 \times 5$
d $2^2 \times 5 \times 11$ **e** $2^3 \times 5 \times 7$ **f** 2^7 **g** 2×5^2
h $2^3 \times 5^3$ **i** $2^6 \times 3^2$ **j** $2 \times 5^2 \times 13$
3 1, 2, 3, 2^2, 5, 2×3, 7, 2^3, 3^2, 2×5, 11, $2^2 \times 3$, 13, 2×7, 3×5, 2^4, 17, 2×3^2, 19, $2^2 \times 5$, 3×7, 2×11, 23, $2^3 \times 3$, 5^2, 2×13, 3^3, $2^2 \times 7$, 29, $2 \times 3 \times 5$, 31, 2^5, 3×11, 2×17, 5×7, $2^2 \times 3^2$, 37, 2×19, 3×13, $2^3 \times 5$, 41, $2 \times 3 \times 7$, 43, $2^2 \times 11$, $3^2 \times 5$, 2×23, 47, $2^4 \times 3$, 7^2, 2×5^2
4 a Each is double the previous number.
b 64, 128
c 81, 243
d 256, 1024, 4096
e 3, 3^2, 3^3, 3^4, 3^5, 3^6, …; 4, 4^2, 4^3, 4^4, 4^5, …

Exercise 4I

1 a 20   **b** 56   **c** 6   **d** 28   **e** 10   **f** 15
g 24   **h** 30
2 It is their product.
3 a 8   **b** 18   **c** 12   **d** 30
4 No. Because the numbers in each part have common factors.

5 **a** 168 **b** 105 **c** 84 **d** 168 **e** 96
f 54 **g** 75 **h** 144
6 **a** 8 **b** 7 **c** 4 **d** 14 **e** 4 **f** 9
g 5 **h** 4 **i** 3 **j** 16 **k** 5 **l** 9
7 **a i** no **ii** yes **iii** yes **iv** no
b i no **ii** no **iii** yes **iv** no

Exercise 4J
1 **a** 5^4 **b** 5^{10} **c** 5^5 **d** 5^3 **e** 5^{15} **f** 5^9
g 5^6 **h** 5^9 **i** 5^8
2 **a** 6^3 **b** 6^5 **c** 6^1 **d** 6^0 **e** 6^1 **f** 6^3
g 6^2 **h** 6^1 **i** 6^2
3 **a** x^8 **b** x^9 **c** x^8 **d** x^5 **e** x^{12} **f** x^{13}
g x^{11} **h** x^{10} **i** x^{16}
4 **a** x^4 **b** x^5 **c** x^3 **d** x^3 **e** x^6 **f** x^5
g x^2 **h** x^6 **i** x^9

ANSWERS TO CHAPTER 5

Quick check

20 cm, 16 cm^2

Exercise 5A
1 10 cm
2 8 cm
3 14 cm
4 12 cm
5 16 cm
6 6 cm
7 10 cm
8 12 cm
9 12 cm
10 14 cm
11 12 cm
12 12 cm

Exercise 5B
1 **a** 10 cm^2 **b** 11 cm^2
c 13 cm^2 **d** 12 cm^2 (estimates only)

Exercise 5C
1 35 cm^2, 24 cm
2 33 cm^2, 28 cm
3 45 cm^2, 36 cm
4 70 cm^2, 34 cm
5 56 cm^2, 30 cm
6 10 cm^2, 14 cm
7 53.3 cm^2, 29.4 cm
8 84.96 cm^2, 38 cm
9 **a** 20 cm, 21 cm^2 **b** 18 cm, 20 cm^2
c 2 cm, 8 cm^2 **d** 3 cm, 15 cm^2
e 3 mm, 18 mm **f** 4 mm, 22 mm
g 5 m, 10 m^2 **h** 7 m, 24 m
10 **a** 390 m **b** 6750 m^2
11 **a** 920 m **b** 1 h 52 min
12 £839.40 **13** 40 cm
14 **a** 100 mm^2
b i 300 mm^2 **ii** 500 mm^2 **iii** 630 mm^2
15 **a** 10 000 cm^2
b i 20 000 cm^2 **ii** 40 000 cm^2 **iii** 56 000 cm^2

Exercise 5D
1 30 cm^2
2 40 cm^2
3 51 cm^2
4 35 cm^2

5 43 cm^2
6 51 cm^2
7 48 cm^2
8 33 cm^2
9 24 m^2

Exercise 5E
1 **a** 6 cm^2, 12 cm **b** 120 cm^2, 60 cm
c 30 cm^2, 30 cm
2 40 cm^2
3 84 m^2
4 **a** 21 cm^2 **b** 55 cm^2 **c** 165 cm^2

Exercise 5F
1 **a** 21 cm^2 **b** 12 cm^2 **c** 14 cm^2
d 55 cm^2 **e** 90 cm^2 **f** 140 cm^2
2 **a** 28 cm^2 **b** 8 cm **c** 4 cm
d 3 cm **e** 7 cm **f** 44 cm^2
3 **a** 40 cm^2 **b** 65 m^2 **c** 80 cm^2
4 **a** 65 cm^2 **b** 50 m^2
5 For example: height 10 cm, base 10 cm; height 5 cm, base 20 cm; height 25 cm, base 4 cm; height 50 cm, base 2 cm

Exercise 5G
1 96 cm^2
2 70 cm^2
3 20 cm^2
4 125 cm^2
5 10 cm^2
6 112 m^2

Exercise 5H
1 **a** 30 cm^2 **b** 77 cm^2 **c** 24 cm^2 **d** 42 cm^2
e 40 cm^2 **f** 6 cm **g** 3 cm
2 **a** 27.5 cm, 36.25 cm^2 **b** 33.4 cm, 61.2 cm^2
c 38.6 m, 88.2 m^2
3 Any pair of lengths that add up to 10 cm
For example: 1 cm, 9 cm; 2 cm, 8 cm; 3 cm, 7 cm; 4 cm, 6 cm; 4.5 cm, 5.5 cm
4 Shape c. Its area is 25.5 cm^2
5 Shape a. Its area is 28 cm^2

Exercise 5I

1 $P = 2a + 2b$

2 $P = a + b + c + d$

3 $P = 4x$

4 $P = p + 2q$

5 $P = 4x + 4y$

6 $P = a + 3b$

7 $P = 5x + 2y + 2z$

8 $P = 2\pi r$

9 $P = 2h + (2 + \pi)r$

Exercise 5J

1 $A = a^2 + ab$

2 $A = \frac{1}{2}bh$

3 $A = bh$

4 $\frac{1}{2}(a + b)h$

5 $A = \pi r^2$

6 $A = 2ad - a^2$

7 $A = \frac{1}{2}bh + \frac{1}{2}bw$

8 $A = 2rh + \pi r^2$

9 $A = \pi d^2 + \frac{1}{2}dh$

Exercise 5K

1 $V = abc$

2 $V = p^3$

3 $V = 6p^3$

4 $V = \pi r^2 h$

5 $V = \frac{1}{2}bhw$

6 $V = \frac{1}{2}bhl$

Exercise 5L

1 **a** A **b** L **c** L **d** A **e** V **f** V **g** V

h A **i** L **j** V **k** A **l** L **m** V **n** A

o V **p** A **q** V **r** A **s** A **t** A **u** L

v A **w** A **x** A **y** V **z** V

2 **a** C **b** I **c** C **d** I **e** C **f** I **g** C

h I **i** C **j** I **k** C **l** C **m** C **n** C

o C **p** I

Really Useful Maths!: A new floor

Room	Floor area (m^2)	Edging needed (m)
Hall	14	18
Bathroom	9	12
Total	23	30

Room	Floor area (m^2)	Edging needed (m)
Lounge	57	32
Sitting room	30	22
Kitchen/diner	50	32
Conservatory	12	14
Total	149	100

	Number of packs	Price per pack	Total cost
Beech flooring	12	£32	£384
Beech edging	3	£18	£54
Oak flooring	75	£38	£2850
Oak edging	9	£22	£198
		Total	£3486

cost after VAT £4096.05

Quick check

a

Size	Tally	Frequency
8	⊬⊬⊬ ⊬⊬⊬ ⊬⊬⊬ I	16
10	⊬⊬⊬ ⊬⊬⊬ II	12
12	⊬⊬⊬ ⊬⊬⊬ II	12
14	⊬⊬⊬ I	6
16	IIII	4

b Size 8

Exercise 6A

1 a

Goals	0	1	2	3
Frequency	6	8	4	2

b 1 goal   **c** 22

2 a

Temperature (°C)	14–16	17–19	20–22	23–25	26–28
Frequency	5	10	8	5	2

b 17–19 °C

c Getting warmer in the first half and then getting cooler towards the end.

3 a Observation   **b** Sampling   **c** Observation   **d** Sampling   **e** Observation   **f** Experiment

4 a

Score	1	2	3	4	5	6
Frequency	5	6	6	6	3	4

b 30   **c** Yes, frequencies are similar

5 a

Height (cm)	151–155	156–160	161–165	166–170	171–175	176–180	181–185	186–190
Frequency	2	5	5	7	5	4	3	1

b 166 – 170 cm

Exercise 6B

1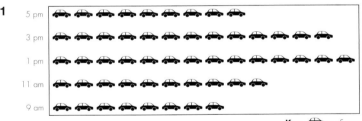

Key 🚗 = 5 cars

2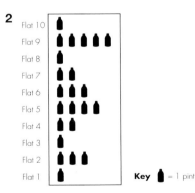

Key 🍶 = 1 pint

3 a May 9 h, Jun 11 h, Jul 12 h, Aug 11 h, Sep 10 h   **b** July   **c** Visual impact, easy to understand
4 a Simon   **b** £165   **c** Difficult to show fractions of a symbol

Exercise 6C

1 a Swimming   **b** 74   **c** For example: limited facilities   **d** No. It may not include people who are not fit

2 a

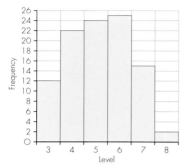

b $\frac{40}{100} = \frac{2}{5}$

c Easier to read the exact frequency

3 a

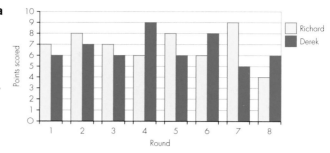

b Richard got more points overall, but Derek was more consistent.

4 a

Time (min)	1–10	11–20	21–30	31–40	41–50	51–60
Frequency	4	7	5	5	7	2

b

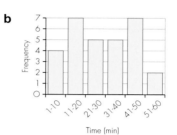

c Some live close to the school. Some live a good distance away and probably travel to school by bus

5 a

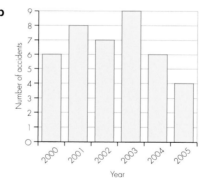

Key 🚚 = 1 accident

b

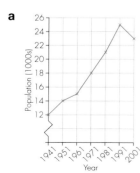

c Use the pictogram because an appropriate symbol makes more impact

Exercise 6D

1 a Tuesday, 52p   **b** 2p   **c** Friday   **d** £90

2 a

b about 16 500
c 1981 and 1991
d No; do not know the reason why the population started to decrease after 1991

3 a

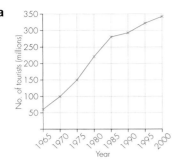

b Between 178 and 180 million
c 1975 and 1980

d Increasing; better communications, cheaper air travel, more advertising, better living standards

4 a

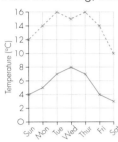

b 7 °C and 10 °C

---- Maximum temperature
—— Minimum temperature

Exercise 6E
1 a 17 s   **b** 22 s   **c** 21 s
2 a 57   **b** 55   **c** 56   **d** 48
   e Boys, because their marks are higher
3 a 2   8   9
      3   4   5   6   8   8   9
      4   1   1   3   3   3   8   8
   Key 4 | 3 represents 43 cm
   b 48 cm   **c** 43 cm   **d** 20 cm
4 a 0   2   8   9   9   9
      1   2   3   7   7   8
      2   0   1   2   3
   Key 1 | 2 represents 12 messages
   b 23   **c** 9

ANSWERS TO CHAPTER 7

Quick check

1 a 8   **b** 3

2 14

3 a $(2 + 3 + 5) \times 4$ **b** $2 + (3 + 5) \times 4$

Exercise 7A
1 a $2 + x$ **b** $x - 6$ **c** $k + x$ **d** $x - t$
   e $x + 3$ **f** $d + m$ **g** $b - y$ **h** $p + t + w$
   i $8x$ **j** hj **k** $x \div 4$ or $\dfrac{x}{4}$ **l** $2 \div x$ or $\dfrac{2}{x}$
   m $y \div t$ or $\dfrac{y}{t}$ **n** wt **o** a^2 **p** g^2
2 a i $P = 4, A = 1$ **ii** $P = 4x, A = x^2$
      iii $P = 12, A = 9$ **iv** $P = 4t, A = t^2$
   b i $P = 4s$ cm   **ii** $A = s^2$ cm^2
3 a $x + 3$ yr   **b** $x - 4$ yr
4 $F = 2C + 30$
5 Rule **c**
6 a $C = 100M$ **b** $N = 12F$ **c** $W = 4C$
   d $H = P$
7 a $3n$ **b** $3n + 3$ **c** $n + 1$ **d** $n - 1$
8 Rob: $2n$, Tom: $n + 2$, Vic: $n - 3$, Wes: $2n + 3$
9 a $P = 8n, A = 9n^2$ **b** $P = 24n, A = 36n^2$
10 a £4   **b** £$(10 - x)$ **c** £$(y - x)$ **d** £$2x$
11 a 75p   **b** $15x$ p   **c** $4A$ p   **d** Ay p
12 £$(A - B)$

13 £$A \div 5$ or $\dfrac{£A}{5}$
14 Dad: $(72 + x)$ yr, me: $(T + x)$ yr
15 a $T \div 2$ or $\dfrac{T}{2}$ **b** $T \div 2 + 4$ or $\dfrac{T}{2} + 4$
   c $T - x$
16 a $8x$ **b** $12m$ **c** $18t$
17 Andrea: $3n - 3$, Bert: $3n - 1$, Colin: $3n - 6$ or $3(n - 2)$, Davina: 0, Emma: $3n - n = 2n$, Florinda: $3n - 3m$

Exercise 7B
1 $6t$ **2** $12y$ **3** $15y$ **4** $8w$ **5** $3t^2$
6 $5b^2$ **7** $2w^2$ **8** $15y^2$ **9** $8p^2$ **10** $6t^2$
11 $12m^2$ **12** $15t^2$ **13** $2mt$ **14** $3wy$ **15** $5qt$
16 $6mn$ **17** $6qt$ **18** $12fg$ **19** $10hk$ **20** $21pr$
21 y^3 **22** t^3 **23** $3m^3$ **24** $4t^3$ **25** $6n^3$
26 $20r^3$ **27** t^4 **28** h^5 **29** $12n^5$ **30** $10t^7$
31 $6a^7$ **32** $4k^7$ **33** t^3 **34** $6y^2$ **35** $12d^3$
36 $15p^6$ **37** $3mp^2$ **38** $6t^2y$ **39** $6m^2n$ **40** $8m^2p^2$

Exercise 7C
1 a £t **b** £$(4t + 3)$
2 a $10x + 2y$ **b** $7x + y$ **c** $6x + y$
3 a $5a$ **b** $6c$ **c** $9e$ **d** $6f$ **e** $3g$
   f $4i$ **g** $4j$ **h** $3q$ **i** 0   **j** $-w$
   k $6x^2$ **l** $5y^2$ **m** 0
4 a $7x$ **b** $6y$ **c** $3t$ **d** $-3t$ **e** $-5x$
   f $-5k$ **g** $2m^2$ **h** 0   **i** f^2
5 a $7x + 5$ **b** $5x + 6$ **c** $5p$ **d** $5x + 6$
   e $5p + t + 5$ **f** $8w - 5k$ **g** c

h $8k - 6y + 10$

6 a $2c + 3d$ **b** $5d + 2e$ **c** $f + 3g + 4h$
d $2i + 3k$ **e** $2k + 9p$ **f** $3k + 2m + 5p$
g $7m - 7n$ **h** $6n - 3p$ **i** $6u - 3v$
j $2v$ **k** $2w - 3y$ **l** $11x^2 - 5y$
m $-y^2 - 2z$ **n** $x^2 - z^2$

7 a $8x + 6$ **b** $3x + 16$ **c** $2x + 2y + 8$

Exercise 7D

1 $6 + 2m$ **2** $10 + 5l$ **3** $12 - 3y$
4 $20 + 8k$ **5** $6 - 12f$ **6** $10 - 6w$
7 $3g + 3h$ **8** $10k + 15m$ **9** $12d - 8n$
10 $t^2 + 3t$ **11** $m^2 + 5m$ **12** $k^2 - 3k$
13 $3g^2 + 2g$ **14** $5y^2 - y$ **15** $5p - 3p^2$
16 $3m^2 + 12m$ **17** $4t^2 - 4t$ **18** $8k - 2k^2$
19 $8g^2 + 20g$ **20** $15h^2 - 10h$ **21** $15t - 12t^2$
22 $6d^2 + 12de$ **23** $6y^2 + 8ky$ **24** $15m^2 - 10mp$
25 $y^3 + 5y$ **26** $h^4 + 7h$ **27** $k^3 - 5k$
28 $3t^3 + 12t$ **29** $4h^4 - 4h$ **30** $5g^4 - 10g$
31 $12m^3 + 4m^2$ **32** $10k^4 + 5k^3$ **33** $15d^3 - 3d^4$
34 $6w^3 + 3tw$ **35** $15a^3 - 10ab$ **36** $12p^4 - 15mp$
37 $5m^2 + 4m^3$ **38** $t^4 + 2t^4$ **39** $5g^2t - 4g^4$
40 $15t^3 + 3mt^2$ **41** $12h^3 + 8gh^2$ **42** $8m^3 + 2m^4$

Exercise 7E

1 a $7t$ **b** $9m$ **c** $3y$ **d** $9d$ **e** $3e$ **f** $2g$
    g $3p$ **h** $2t$ **i** $5t^2$ **j** $4y^2$ **k** $5ab$ **l** $3a^2d$
2 a $22 + 5t$ **b** $21 + 19k$ **c** $10 + 16m$
    d $16 + 17y$ **e** $22 + 2f$ **f** $14 + 3g$
    g $10 + 11t$ **h** $22 + 4w$
3 a $2 + 2h$ **b** $9g + 5$ **c** $6y + 11$ **d** $7t - 4$
    e $17k + 16$ **f** $6e + 20$ **g** $7m + 4$ **h** $3t + 10$
4 a $4m + 3p + 2mp$ **b** $3k + 4h + 5hk$
    c $3n + 2t + 7nt$ **d** $3p + 7q + 6pq$
    e $6h + 6j + 13hj$ **f** $6t + 8y + 21ty$
    g $24p + 12r + 13pr$ **h** $20k - 6m + 19km$
5 a $13t + 9t^2$ **b** $5y + 13y^2$ **c** $18w + 5w^2$
    d $14p + 23p^2$ **e** $7m + 4m^2$ **f** $22d - 9d^2$
    g $10e^2 - 6e$ **h** $14k^2 - 3kp$
6 a $17ab + 12ac + 6bc$ **b** $18wy + 6ty - 8tw$
    c $16gh - 2gk - 10hk$ **d** $10ht - 3hp - 12pt$
    e $ab - 2ac + 6bc$ **f** $12pq + 2qw - 10pw$
    g $14mn - 15mp - 6np$ **h** $8r^3 - 6r^2$

Exercise 7F

1 $6(m + 2t)$ **2** $3(3t + p)$ **3** $4(2m + 3k)$

4 $4(r + 2t)$ **5** $m(n + 3)$ **6** $g(5g + 3)$
7 $2(2w - 3t)$ **8** $2(4p - 3k)$ **9** $2(8h - 5k)$
10 $2m(p + k)$ **11** $2b(2c + k)$ **12** $2a(3b + 2c)$
13 $y(3y + 2)$ **14** $t(4t - 3)$ **15** $2d(2d - 1)$
16 $3m(m - p)$ **17** $3p(2p + 3t)$ **18** $2p(4t + 3m)$
19 $4b(2a - c)$ **20** $4a(3a - 2b)$ **21** $3t(3m - 2p)$
22 $4at(4t + 3)$ **23** $5bc(b - 2)$ **24** $2b(4ac + 3ed)$
25 $2(2a^2 + 3a + 4)$ **26** $3b(2a + 3c + d)$
27 $t(5t + 4 + a)$ **28** $3mt(2t - 1 + 3m)$
29 $2ab(4b + 1 - 2a)$ **30** $5pt(2t + 3 + p)$
31 Not possible   **32** $m(5 + 2p)$ **33** $t(t - 7)$
34 Not possible   **35** $2m(2m - 3p)$ **36** Not possible
37 $a(4a - 5b)$ **38** Not possible   **39** $b(5a - 3bc)$

Exercise 7G

1 $x^2 + 5x + 6$ **2** $t^2 + 7t + 12$ **3** $w^2 + 4w + 3$
4 $m^2 + 6m + 5$ **5** $k^2 + 8k + 15$ **6** $a^2 + 5a + 4$
7 $x^2 + 2x - 8$ **8** $t^2 + 2t - 15$ **9** $w^2 + 2w - 3$
10 $f^2 - f - 6$ **11** $g^2 - 3g - 4$ **12** $y^2 + y - 12$
13 $x^2 + x - 12$ **14** $p^2 - p - 2$ **15** $k^2 - 2k - 8$
16 $y^2 + 3y - 10$ **17** $a^2 + 2a - 3$ **18** $t^2 + t - 12$
19 $x^2 - 5x + 4$ **20** $r^2 - 5r + 6$ **21** $m^2 - 4m + 3$
22 $g^2 - 6g + 8$ **23** $h^2 - 8h + 15$ **24** $n^2 - 2n + 1$
25 $x^2 + 10x + 25$ **26** $t^2 + 12t + 36$ **27** $15 - 2b - b^2$
28 $y^2 - 6y + 5$ **29** $p^2 - 8p + 16$ **30** $k^2 - 4k + 4$
31 $x^2 - 9$ **32** $t^2 - 25$ **33** $m^2 - 16$
34 $t^2 - 4$ **35** $y^2 - 64$ **36** $p^2 - 1$
37 $25 - x^2$ **38** $49 - g^2$ **39** $x^2 - 36$

Exercise 7H

1 a 8   **b** 17   **c** 32   **2 a** 3   **b** 11   **c** 43
3 a 9   **b** 15   **c** 29   **4 a** 9   **b** 5   **c** −1
5 a 13   **b** 33   **c** 78   **6 a** 10   **b** 13   **c** 58
7 a 32   **b** 64   **c** 160   **8 a** 6.5   **b** 0.5   **c** −2.5
9 a 2   **b** 8   **c** −10   **10 a** 3   **b** 2.5   **c** −5
11 a 6   **b** 3   **c** 2   **12 a** 12   **b** 8   **c** $1\frac{1}{2}$

Exercise 7I

1 a 11   **b** 17   **c** 13   **2 a** 7   **b** 14   **c** −2
3 a 7   **b** 32   **c** −3   **4 a** 27   **b** 5   **c** 0
5 a 75   **b** 8   **c** −6   **6 a** 900   **b** 180   **c** 0
7 a 5   **b** 8   **c** 1   **8 a** 4.4   **b** 2.6   **c** −1.4

Really Useful Maths!: Walking holiday

Day	Distance (km)	Height climbed (m)	Time (minutes)	Time (hours and minutes)	Start time	Time allowed for breaks	Finish time
1	16	250	265	4 h 25 min	10.00 am	2 hours	4.25 pm
2	18	0	270	4 h 30 min	10.00 am	1 1/2 hours	4.00 pm
3	11	340	199	3 h 19 min	9.30 am	2 1/2 hours	3.19 pm
4	13	100	205	3 h 25 min	10.30 am	2 1/2 hours	4.25 pm
5	14	110	221	3 h 41 min	10.30 am	2 1/2 hours	4.41 pm

Quick check

1 6, 12, 18, 24, 30

2 8, 16, 24, 32, 40

3 15

4 20

5 12

6 **a** $\frac{4}{5}$ **b** $\frac{1}{4}$ **c** $\frac{1}{4}$ **d** $\frac{8}{25}$ **e** $\frac{9}{25}$ **f** $\frac{2}{3}$ **g** $\frac{8}{25}$

Exercise 8A

1 12 138 **2** 45 612 **3** 29 988 **4** 20 654
5 51 732 **6** 25 012 **7** 19 359 **8** 12 673
9 19 943 **10** 26 235 **11** 31 535 **12** 78 399
13 17 238 **14** 43 740 **15** 66 065 **16** 103 320
17 140 224 **18** 92 851 **19** 520 585 **20** 78 660

EExercise 8B

1 25 **2** 15 **3** 37 **4** 43 **5** 27 **6** 48
7 53 **8** 52 **9** 32 **10** 57 **11** 37 rem 15
12 25 rem 5 **13** 34 rem 11 **14** 54 rem 9
15 36 rem 11 **16** 17 rem 4 **17** 23
18 61 rem 14 **19** 42 **20** 27 rem 2

Exercise 8C

1 6000 **2** 312 **3** 68 **4** 38
5 57 600 m or 57.6 km **6** 60 200 **7** 5819 litres
8 £302.40 **9** 33 **10** 34 h **11** £1.75
12 £136.80

Exercise 8D

1 **a** 4.8 **b** 3.8 **c** 2.2 **d** 8.3 **e** 3.7
f 46.9 **g** 23.9 **h** 9.5 **i** 11.1 **j** 33.5
k 7.1 **l** 46.8 **m** 0.1 **n** 0.1 **o** 0.6
p 65.0 **q** 213.9 **r** 76.1 **s** 455.2 **t** 51.0
2 **a** 5.78 **b** 2.36 **c** 0.98 **d** 33.09 **e** 6.01
f 23.57 **g** 91.79 **h** 8.00 **i** 2.31 **j** 23.92
k 6.00 **l** 1.01 **m** 3.51 **n** 96.51 **o** 0.01
p 0.07 **q** 7.81 **r** 569.90 **s** 300.00 **t** 0.01
3 **a** 4.6 **b** 0.08 **c** 45.716 **d** 94.85
e 602.1 **f** 671.76 **g** 7.1 **h** 6.904
i 13.78 **j** 0.1 **k** 4.002 **l** 60.0
m 11.99 **n** 899.996 **o** 0.1 **p** 0.01
q 6.1 **r** 78.393 **s** 200.00 **t** 5.1
4 **a** 9 **b** 9 **c** 3 **d** 7 **e** 3
f 8 **g** 3 **h** 8 **i** 6 **j** 4
k 7 **l** 2 **m** 47 **n** 23 **o** 96
p 33 **q** 154 **r** 343 **s** 704 **t** 910

Exercise 8E

1 **a** 49.8 **b** 21.3 **c** 48.3 **d** 33.3 **e** 5.99
f 8.08 **g** 90.2 **h** 21.2 **i** 12.15 **j** 13.08
k 13.26 **l** 24.36

2 **a** 1.4 **b** 1.8 **c** 4.8 **d** 3.8 **e** 3.75
f 5.9 **g** 3.7 **h** 3.77 **i** 3.7 **j** 1.4
k 11.8 **l** 15.3
3 **a** 30.7 **b** 6.6 **c** 3.8 **d** 16.7 **e** 11.8
f 30.2 **g** 43.3 **h** 6.73 **i** 37.95 **j** 4.7
k 3.8 **l** 210.5

Exercise 8F

1 **a** 7.2 **b** 7.6 **c** 18.8 **d** 37.1 **e** 32.5
f 28.8 **g** 10.0 **h** 55.2 **i** 61.5 **j** 170.8
k 81.6 **l** 96.5
2 **a** 9.36 **b** 10.35 **c** 25.85 **d** 12.78 **e** 1.82
f 3.28 **g** 2.80 **h** 5.52 **i** 42.21 **j** 56.16
k 7.65 **l** 48.96
3 **a** 1.8 **b** 1.4 **c** 1.4 **d** 1.2 **e** 2.13
f 0.69 **g** 2.79 **h** 1.21 **i** 1.89 **j** 1.81
k 0.33 **l** 1.9
4 **a** 1.75 **b** 1.28 **c** 1.85 **d** 3.65 **e** 1.66
f 1.45 **g** 1.42 **h** 1.15 **i** 3.35 **j** 0.98
k 2.3 **l** 1.46
5 **a** 1.89 **b** 1.51 **c** 0.264 **d** 4.265 **e** 1.224
f 0.182 **g** 0.093 **h** 2.042 **i** 1.908 **j** 2.8
k 4.25 **l** 18.5
6 Pack of 8 at £0.625 each
7 £49.90
8 Yes. She only needed 8 paving stones.

Exercise 8G

1 **a** 89.28 **b** 298.39 **c** 66.04 **d** 167.98
e 2352.0 **f** 322.4 **g** 1117.8 **h** 4471.5
i 464.94 **j** 25.55 **k** 1047.2 **l** 1890.5
2 **a** £224.10 **b** £223.75 **c** £29.90
3 £54.20
4 £120.75

Exercise 8H

1 **a** 0.48 **b** 2.92 **c** 1.12 **d** 0.12
e 0.028 **f** 0.09 **g** 0.192 **h** 3.0264
i 7.134 **j** 50.96 **k** 3.0625 **l** 46.512
2 **a** 35, 35.04, 0.04 **b** 16, 18.24, 2.24
c 60, 59.67, 0.33 **d** 180, 172.86, 7.14
e 12, 12.18, 0.18 **f** 24, 26.016, 2.016
g 40, 40.664, 0.664 **h** 140, 140.58, 0.58

Exercise 8I

1 **a** $\frac{7}{10}$ **b** $\frac{2}{5}$ **c** $\frac{1}{2}$ **d** $\frac{3}{100}$ **e** $\frac{3}{50}$ **f** $\frac{13}{100}$
g $\frac{1}{4}$ **h** $\frac{19}{50}$ **i** $\frac{11}{20}$ **j** $\frac{16}{25}$
2 **a** 0.5 **b** 0.75 **c** 0.6 **d** 0.9
e 0.333 **f** 0.625 **g** 0.667 **h** 0.35
i 0.636 **j** 0.444
3 **a** 0.3, $\frac{1}{2}$, 0.6 **b** 0.3, $\frac{2}{5}$, 0.8 **c** 0.15, $\frac{1}{4}$, 0.35
d $\frac{7}{10}$, 0.71, 0.72 **e** 0.7, $\frac{3}{4}$, 0.8 **f** $\frac{1}{20}$, 0.08, 0.1
g 0.4, $\frac{1}{2}$, 0.55 **h** 1.2, 1.23, $1\frac{1}{4}$

Exercise 8J

1 a $\frac{8}{15}$ b $\frac{7}{12}$ c $\frac{3}{10}$ d $\frac{11}{12}$ e $\frac{7}{8}$ f $\frac{1}{2}$

   g $\frac{1}{6}$ h $\frac{1}{20}$ i $\frac{1}{10}$ j $\frac{1}{8}$ k $\frac{1}{12}$ l $\frac{1}{3}$

   m $\frac{1}{6}$ n $\frac{7}{9}$ o $\frac{5}{8}$ p $\frac{3}{8}$ q $\frac{1}{15}$ r $1\frac{13}{24}$

   s $\frac{59}{80}$ t $\frac{22}{63}$ u $\frac{37}{54}$

2 a $3\frac{5}{14}$ b $10\frac{3}{5}$ c $2\frac{1}{6}$ d $3\frac{31}{45}$ e $4\frac{47}{60}$ f $\frac{41}{72}$

   g $\frac{29}{48}$ h $1\frac{43}{48}$ i $1\frac{109}{120}$ j $1\frac{23}{30}$ k $1\frac{31}{84}$

3 $\frac{1}{20}$ **4** $\frac{1}{6}$ **5** $\frac{13}{15}$ **6** $\frac{1}{3}$ **7** $\frac{3}{8}$

Exercise 8K

1 a $\frac{1}{6}$ b $\frac{1}{10}$ c $\frac{3}{8}$ d $\frac{3}{14}$ e $\frac{8}{15}$ f $\frac{1}{5}$

   g $\frac{2}{7}$ h $\frac{3}{10}$ i $\frac{3}{32}$ j $\frac{1}{2}$ k $\frac{2}{5}$ l $\frac{3}{8}$

   m $\frac{7}{20}$ n $\frac{16}{45}$ o $\frac{3}{5}$ p $\frac{5}{8}$

2 3 km   **3** $\frac{1}{12}$

4 $\frac{3}{8}$ **5** 21

6 260   **7** £51

8 18

9 a $\frac{5}{12}$ b $2\frac{1}{12}$ c $6\frac{1}{4}$ d $2\frac{11}{12}$ e $3\frac{9}{10}$ f $3\frac{1}{3}$

   g $12\frac{1}{2}$ h 30

10 $\frac{2}{5}$ of $6\frac{1}{2} = 2\frac{3}{5}$ **11** £5

12 Three-quarters of 68 = 51

13 7 min   **14** £10.40   **15** £30

Exercise 8L

1 a $\frac{3}{4}$ b $1\frac{2}{5}$ c $1\frac{1}{15}$ d $1\frac{1}{14}$ e 4   f 4

   g 5   h $1\frac{5}{7}$ i $\frac{4}{9}$ j $1\frac{3}{5}$

2 18   **3** 40   **4**   15   **5** 16

6 a $2\frac{2}{15}$ b 38   c $1\frac{7}{8}$ d $\frac{9}{32}$ e $\frac{1}{16}$ f $\frac{256}{625}$

Exercise 8M

1 a −15   b −14   c −24   d 6   e 14
   f 2   g −2   h −8   i −4   j 3
   k −24   l −10   m −18   n 16   o 36
   p −4   q −12   r −4   s 7   t 25
   u 18   v −8   w −45   x 3   y −40

2 a −9   b 16   c −3   d −32   e 18
   f 18   g 6   h −4   i 20   j 16
   k 8   l −48   m 13   n −13   o −8
   p 0   q 16   r −42   s 6   t 1
   u −14   v 6   w −4   x 7   y 0

3 a −2   b 30   c 15   d −27   e −7

4 a 4   b −9   c −3   d 6   e −4

5 a −9   b 3   c 1

6 a 16   b −2   c −12

7 a 24   b 6   c −4   d −2

8 For example: $1 \times (-12)$, -1×12, $2 \times (-6)$, $6 \times (-2)$, $3 \times (-4)$, $4 \times (-3)$

9 For example: $4 \div (-1)$, $8 \div (-2)$, $12 \div (-3)$, $16 \div (-4)$, $20 \div (-5)$, $24 \div (-6)$

10 a 21   b −4   c 2   d −16   e 2
   f −5   g −35   h −17   i −12   j 6
   k 45   l −2   m 0   n −1   o −7
   p −36   q 9   r 32   s 0   t −65

Exercise 8N

1 a 50 000   b 60 000   c 30 000   d 90 000
   e 90 000   f 50   g 90   h 30
   i 100   j 200   k 0.5   l 0.3
   m 0.006   n 0.05   o 0.0009   p 10
   q 90   r 90   s 200   t 1000

2 a 65, 74   b 95, 149   c 950, 1499

3 Elsecar 750, 849; Hoyland 950, 1499;
   Barnsley 150 000, 249 999

4 a 60 000   b 27 000   c 80 000   d 30 000
   e 10 000   f 6000   g 1000   h 800
   i 100   j 600   k 2   l 4
   m 3   n 8   o 40   p 0.8
   q 0.5   r 0.07   s 1   t 0.01

Exercise 8P

1 a 35 000   b 15 000   c 960   d 12 000
   e 1000   f 4000   g 4   h 20
   i 1200

2 a £3000   b £2000   c £1500   d £700

3 a £15 000   b £18 000   c £18 000

4 8

5 £21 000

6 a 14   b 10   c 3 or 4   d $\frac{1}{2}$
   e 6   f 400   g 2   h 20

7 a 40   b 10   c £70

8 1000 or 1200

9 a 28   b 120   c 1440

10 400

11 a 3 kg   b 200

12 a i 850 grams   ii 750 grams
   b i 133   ii 117

Exercise 8Q

1 a 1.7 m   b 6 min   c 240 g
   d 80 °C   e 35 000   f 16 miles
   g 284 519   h 14 m^2

2 82 °F, 5.3 km, 110 min, 43 000 people, 6.2 s, 67th, 1788, 15, 5 s

Really Useful Maths!: The gym

Person	Weight category	Calories in breakfast	Minutes exercising
Dave	Overweight	833	119
Pete	OK	308.6	35
Andy	OK	297	38
Sue	Overweight	685.2	115
Sally	Underweight	440	55
Lynn	OK	607	68

Quick check

1 a $\frac{3}{5}$　　**b** $\frac{1}{5}$　　**c** $\frac{1}{3}$　　**d** $\frac{16}{25}$　　**e** $\frac{2}{5}$

　f $\frac{3}{4}$　　**g** $\frac{1}{3}$

2 a £12　　**b** £66　　**c** 175 litres　　**d** 15 kg
　e 40 m　　**f** £35　　**g** 135 g　　**h** 1.05 litres

Exercise 9A

1 a 1 : 3　　**b** 3 : 4　　**c** 2 : 3　　**d** 2 : 3　　**e** 2 : 5
　f 2 : 5　　**g** 5 : 8　　**h** 25 : 6　　**i** 3 : 2　　**j** 8 : 3
　k 7 : 3　　**l** 5 : 2　　**m** 1 : 6　　**n** 3 : 8　　**o** 5 : 3
　p 4 : 5
2 a 1 : 3　　**b** 3 : 2　　**c** 5 : 12　　**d** 8 : 1
　e 17 : 15　　**f** 25 : 7　　**g** 4 : 1　　**h** 5 : 6
　i 1 : 24　　**j** 48 : 1　　**k** 5 : 2　　**l** 3 : 14
　m 2 : 1　　**n** 3 : 10　　**o** 31 : 200　　**p** 5 : 8
3 $\frac{7}{10}$
4 $\frac{10}{25} = \frac{2}{5}$
5 a $\frac{2}{5}$　　**b** $\frac{3}{5}$
6 a $\frac{7}{10}$　　**b** $\frac{3}{10}$　　**7**　Amy $\frac{3}{5}$, Katie $\frac{2}{5}$
8 Fruit crush $\frac{5}{32}$, lemonade $\frac{27}{32}$
9 a $\frac{2}{9}$　　**b** $\frac{1}{3}$　　**c** twice as many
10 a $\frac{1}{2}$　　**b** $\frac{7}{20}$　　**c** $\frac{3}{20}$
11 James $\frac{1}{2}$　　John $\frac{3}{10}$　　Joseph $\frac{1}{5}$
12 sugar $\frac{5}{22}$, flour $\frac{3}{11}$, margarine $\frac{2}{11}$, fruit $\frac{7}{22}$

Exercise 9B

1 a 160 g, 240 g　　**b** 80 kg, 200 kg　　**c** 150, 350
　d 950 m, 50 m　　**e** 175 min, 125 min
　f £20, £30, £50　　**g** £36, £60, £144
　h 50 g, 250 g, 300 g　　**i** £1.40, £2, £1.60
　j 120 kg, 72 kg, 8 kg
2 a 160　　**b** 37.5%
3 a 28.6%　　**b** 250 kg
4 a 21　　**b** 94.1%
5 a Mott: no, Wright: yes, Brennan: no, Smith: no, Kaye:
　　yes
　b For example: W26, H30; W31, H38; W33, H37
6 a 1 : 400 000　　**b** 1 : 125 000　　**c** 1 : 250 000
　d 1 : 25 000　　**e** 1 : 20 000　　**f** 1 : 40 000
　g 1 : 62 500　　**h** 1 : 10 000　　**i** 1 : 60 000
7 a 1 : 1 000 000　　**b** 47 km　　**c** 8 mm
8 a 1 : 250 000　　**b** 2 km　　**c** 4.8 cm
9 a 1 : 20 000　　**b** 0.54 km　　**c** 40 cm
10 a 1 : 1.6　　**b** 1 : 3.25　　**c** 1 : 1.125　　**d** 1 : 1.44
　e 1 : 5.4　　**f** 1 : 1.5　　**g** 1 : 4.8　　**h** 1 : 42
　i 1 : 1.25

Exercise 9C

1 a 3 : 2　　**b** 32　　**c** 80
2 a 100　　**b** 160

3 0.4 litres　　**4** 102　　**5** 1000 g　　**6** 10 125
7 5.5 litres
8 a 14 min　　**b** 75 min (= $1\frac{1}{4}$ h)
9 11 pages
10 Kevin £2040, John £2720
11 a 160 cans　　**b** 48 cans
12 lemonade 20 litres, ginger 0.5 litres
13 a $\frac{7}{50}$　　**b** 75

Exercise 9D

1 18 mph
2 280 miles
3 52.5 mph
4 11.50 am
5 500 s
6 a 75 mph　　**b** 6.5 h　　**c** 175 miles
　d 240 km　　**e** 64 km/h　　**f** 325 km
　g 4.3 h (4 h 18 min)
7 a 120 km　　**b** 48 km/h
8 a 30 min　　**b** 6 mph
9 a 7.75 h　　**b** 52.9 mph
10 a 2.25 h　　**b** 99 miles
11 a 1.25 h　　**b** 1 h 15 min
12 a 48 mph　　**b** 6 h 40 min
13 a 10 m/s　　**b** 3.3 m/s　　**c** 16.7 m/s
　d 41.7 m/s　　**e** 20.8 m/s
14 a 90 km/h　　**b** 43.2 km/h　　**c** 14.4 km/h
　d 108 km/h　　**e** 1.8 km/h
15 a 64.8 km/h　　**b** 28 s　　**c** 8.07
16 a 6.7 m/s　　**b** 66 km　　**c** 5 minutes
　d 133.3 metres

Exercise 9E

1 60 g　　**2** £5.22　　**3** 45　　**4** £6.72
5 a £312.50　　**b** 8
6 a 56 litres　　**b** 350 miles
7 a 300 kg　　**b** 9 weeks
8 40 s
9 a i 100 g, 200 g, 250 g, 150 g
　　ii 150 g, 300 g, 375 g, 225 g
　　iii 250 g, 500 g, 625 g, 375 g
　b 24

Exercise 9F

1 a Large jar　　**b** 600 g tin　　**c** 5 kg bag
　d 75 ml tube　　**e** Large box　　**f** Large box
　g 400 ml bottle
2 a £5.11　　**b** Large tin
3 a 95p　　**b** Family size
4 Bashir's
5 Mary
6 Kelly

Really Useful Maths!: Party time!

Marinated mushrooms (serves 6)
mushrooms	675 g
wine vinegar	45 ml
olive oil	135 ml

Leek and macaroni bake (serves 6)
macaroni	195 g
butter	75 g
leeks	405 g
flour	45 g
milk	900 ml
cheese	270 g
breadcrumbs	30 g

Crème caramel (serves 6)
sugar	180 g
eggs	6
milk	0.9 litres or 900 ml

There are four possible seating plans:
Bob, Elizabeth, Frank, Alison, Derek, Claire;
Bob, Elizabeth, Derek, Alison, Frank, Claire;
Bob, Claire, Frank, Alison, Derek, Elizabeth;
Bob, Claire, Derek, Alison, Frank, Elizabeth

They will need two bottles of wine.

ANSWERS TO CHAPTER 10

Quick check

a cube **b** cuboid **c** square-based pyramid **d** triangular prism **e** cylinder **f** cone
g sphere

Exercise 10A

1
a **b** **c** **d** **e** **f** **g**

2 a i 5 **ii** 6 **iii** 8 **b** 10 **3 a** **b** **c**

4 a **b** **c** **d** **e** **f**

5 2, 1, 1, 2, 0 **6 a**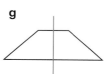

7 a 1 **b** 5 **c** 1 **d** 6
8 c Infinite number

Exercise 10B

1 a 4 **b** 2 **c** 2 **d** 3 **e** 6
2 a 4 **b** 5 **c** 6 **d** 4 **e** 6
3 a 2 **b** 2 **c** 2 **d** 2 **e** 2

4 a 4 **b** 3 **c** 8 **d** 2 **e** 4 **f** 2
5 A, B, C, D, E, F, G, J, K, L, M, P, Q, R, T, U, V, W, Y
6 Infinite number

Exercise 10C

1 a 9 **b** 4 **c** 4
3 a Sphere **b**

Cylinder   Cone

4 a 3 **b** 1 **c** 1 **d** 1 **e** Infinite **f** 1

ANSWERS TO CHAPTER 11

Quick check

a 7 **b** 6 **c** 8 **d** 90

Exercise 11A

1 a 4 **b** 48 **c** −1 **d** $\frac{1}{4}$ **e** no mode **f** 3.21
2 a red **b** sun **c** β **d** ✶
3 a 32 **b** 6 **c** no
  d no; boys generally take larger shoe sizes
4 a 5
  b no; more than half the form got a higher mark
5 a

Frequency chart with bars:
0–4: 9, 5–9: 12, 10–14: 14, 15–19: 11, 20–24: 10, 25–29: 8, 30–34: 4, 35–39: 2

  b 70 **c** 24
  d cannot tell; know only that 9 households had between 0 and 4 e-mails **e** 10–14
6 The mode will be the most popular item or brand sold in a shop.
7 a 28 **b i** brown **ii** blue **iii** brown
  c Both pupils had blue eyes.

Exercise 11B

1 a 5 **b** 33 **c** $7\frac{1}{2}$ **d** 24 **e** $8\frac{1}{2}$ **f** 0 **g** 5.25
2 a £2.20 **b** £2.25
  c median, because it is the central value
3 a 5 **b i** 15 **ii** 215 **iii** 10 **iv** 10
4 a 13, Ella **b** 162 cm, Pat **c** 40 kg, Elisa
  d Ella, because she is closest to the 3 medians
5 a 12 **b** 13
6 a 21 **b** 16 **d** 15
7 Answers will vary
8 a 22 s **b** 25 s
9 a 56 **b** 48 **c** 49 **d** 45.5
  e Girls have higher average but boys have highest score
10 12, 14, 14, 16, 20, 22, 24
11 53

Exercise 11C

1 a 6 **b** 24 **c** 45 **d** 1.57 **e** 2
2 a 55.1 **b** 324.7 **c** 58.5 **d** 44.9 **e** 2.3
3 a 61 **b** 60 **c** 59 **d** Brian **e** 2
4 42 min
5 a £200 **b** £260 **c** £278
  d median, because the extreme value of £480 is not taken into account
6 a 35 **b** 36
7 a 6
  b 16; all the numbers and the mean are 10 more than those in part **a**
  c i 56 **ii** 106 **iii** 7
8 24

Exercise 11D

1 a 7 **b** 26 **c** 5 **d** 2.4 **e** 7
2 a 5°, 3°, 2°, 7°, 3°
  b variable weather over England
3 a £31, £28, £33 **b** £8, £14, £4
  c not particularly consistent
4 a 82 and 83 **b** 20 and 12
  c Fay, because her scores are more consistent
5 a 5 min and 4 min **b** 9 min and 13 min
  c number 50, because times are more consistent

Exercise 11E

1 a 29 **b** 28 **c** 27.1 **d** 14
2 a i Mode 3, median 4, mean 5 **ii** 6, 7, $7\frac{1}{2}$ **iii** 4, 6, 8
  b i Mean: balanced data
    ii Mode: 6 appears five times
    iii Median: 28 is an extreme value
3 a Mode 73, median 76, mean 80
  b The mean, because it is the highest average
4 a 150 **b** 20
5 a i 6 **ii** 16 **iii** 26 **iv** 56 **v** 96
  b units are the same
  c i 136 **ii** 576 **iii** 435 **iv** 856
  d i 5.6 **ii** 15.6 **iii** 25.6 **iv** 55.6 **v** 95.6
6 a Mean **b** Median **c** Mode **d** Median
  e Mode **f** Mean
7 No. Mode is 31, median is 31, and mean is $31\frac{1}{2}$
8 a i £18 000 **ii** £24 000 **iii** £23 778
  b i The 6% rise, because it gives a greater increase in salary for the higher paid employees

ii 6% increase: £19 080, £25 440, £25 205; +£1500:
£19 500, £25 500, £25 278

9 a Median **b** Mode **c** Mean

10 11.6 **11** 42.7

3 a 2.2, 1.7, 1.3 **b** Better dental care
4 a 0 **b** 0.96
5 a 7 **b** 6.5 **c** 6.5
6 a 1 **b** 1 **c** 0.98
7 a Roger 5, Brian 4 **b** Roger 3, Brian 8
c Roger 5, Brian 4 **d** Roger 5.4, Brian 4.5
e Roger, because he has the smaller range
f Brian, because he has the better mean

Exercise 11F

1 a i 7 **ii** 6 **iii** 6.4 **b i** 4 **ii** 4 **iii** 3.7
c i 8 **ii** 8.5 **iii** 8.2 **d i** 0 **ii** 0 **iii** 0.3
2 a 668 **b** 1.9 **c** 0 **d** 328

Exercise 11G

1 a i $30 < x \le 40$ **ii** 29.5 **b i** $0 < y \le 100$ **ii** 158.3 **c i** $5 < z \le 10$ **ii** 9.43 **d i** 7–9 **ii** 8.4
2 a $100 < w \le 120$ g **b** 10 860 **c** 108.6 g
3 a 207 **b** 19–22 cm **c** 20.3 cm
4 a 160 **b** 52.6 min **c** modal group **d** 65%
5 a $175 < h \le 200$ **b** 31% **c** 193.25 **d** No
6 Average price increases: Soundbuy 17.7p, Springfields 18.7p, Setco 18.2p
7 a Yes average distance is 11.7 miles per day.
b Because shorter runs will be completed faster, which will affect the average.
c Yes because the shortest could be 1 mile and the longest 25 miles.

Exercise 11H

1 a 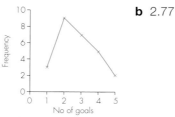 **b** 1.72 **2 a** **b** 2.77

3 a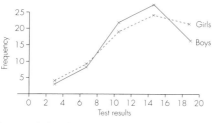

b boys 12.9, girls 13.1

4 a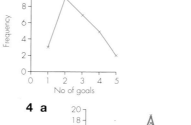

b Mon 28.4, Tue 20.9, Wed 21.3
c There are more people on a Monday as they became ill over the weekend.

5 a i 17, 13, 6, 3, 1 **ii** £1.45
b i 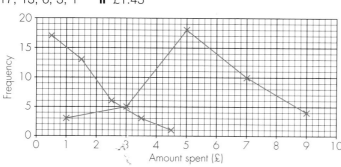 **ii** £5.35

c There is a much higher mean, first group of people just want a paper or a few sweets. Later, people are buying food for the day.

Really Useful Maths!: A pint of milk please

Monthly milk production in thousands of litres		
	2004	**2005**
mean	62	72
median	63	71
mode	64	62
range	24	24

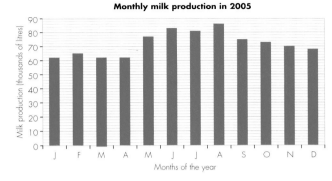

Milk production compared to rainfall: as the rainfall decreases, the milk production increases, and as the rainfall increases the milk production decreases. Milk production compared to sunshine: as the sunshine increases, the milk production increases, and as the sunshine decreases, the milk production decreases.

ANSWERS TO CHAPTER 12

Quick check

1 a $\frac{3}{8}$ **b** $\frac{4}{9}$ **c** $\frac{7}{12}$ **d** $\frac{3}{5}$

2 a 18   **b** 20   **c** 19   **d** 27

3 a 1200   **b** 0.34   **c** 23   **d** 0.047

Exercise 12A

1 a $\frac{2}{25}$ **b** $\frac{1}{2}$ **c** $\frac{1}{4}$ **d** $\frac{7}{20}$ **e** $\frac{9}{10}$ **f** $\frac{3}{4}$

2 a 0.27   **b** 0.85   **c** 0.13   **d** 0.06   **e** 0.8   **f** 0.32

3 a $\frac{3}{25}$ **b** $\frac{2}{5}$ **c** $\frac{9}{20}$ **d** $\frac{17}{25}$ **e** $\frac{1}{4}$ **f** $\frac{5}{8}$

4 a 29%   **b** 55%   **c** 3%   **d** 16%   **e** 60%   **f** 125%

5 a 28%   **b** 30%   **c** 95%   **d** 34%   **e** 27.5%   **f** 87.5%

6 a 0.6   **b** 0.075   **c** 0.76   **d** 0.3125   **e** 0.05   **f** 0.125

7 150   **8** none   **9** 20

10 a 77%   **b** 39%   **c** 63%

11 27%   **12** 61.5%

13 a 50%   **b** 20%   **c** 80%

14 a 87.5%, 75%, 62.5%, 50%, 25%
  b 12.5%, 12.5%, 12.5%, 12.5%, 25%

15 a 20%   **b** 25%   **c** 75%   **d** 45%   **e** 14%
  f 50%   **g** 60%   **h** 17.5%   **i** 55%   **j** 130%

16 a 33.3%   **b** 16.7%   **c** 66.7%   **d** 83.3%   **e** 28.6%
  f 78.3%   **g** 68.9%   **h** 88.9%   **i** 81.1%   **j** 20.9%

17 a 7%   **b** 80%   **c** 66%   **d** 25%   **e** 54.5%
  f 82%   **g** 30%   **h** 89.1%   **i** 120%   **j** 278%

18 a $\frac{3}{5}$ **b** 0.6   **c** 60%

19 63%, 83%, 39%, 62%, 77%

20 a 80%   **b** 20%

21 6.7%

22 25.5%

23 34%, 0.34, $\frac{17}{50}$; 85%, 0.85, $\frac{17}{20}$; 7.5%, 0.075, $\frac{3}{40}$

24 a 0.3, 0.35, 0.75, 0.8   **b** 10%, 0.15, $\frac{1}{5}$, $\frac{1}{2}$
  c $\frac{1}{4}$, 26%, 0.275, 30%   **d** 3%, 0.32, $\frac{3}{8}$, $\frac{3}{4}$
  e 45%, $\frac{1}{2}$, 0.55, 0.6   **f** 9%, $\frac{1}{10}$, 0.111, $\frac{1}{8}$
  g 0.23, $\frac{1}{4}$, 0.275, 28%   **h** 8%, $\frac{1}{8}$, 0.8, 0.88
  i 0.3, 0.325, $\frac{1}{3}$, 35%   **j** $\frac{1}{5}$, 0.35, 50%, $\frac{3}{5}$

Exercise 12B

1 a 0.88   **b** 0.3   **c** 0.25   **d** 0.08   **e** 1.15

2 a 78%   **b** 40%   **c** 75%   **d** 5%   **e** 110%

3 a £45   **b** £6.30   **c** 128.8 kg   **d** 1.125 kg
  e 1.08 h   **f** 37.8 cm   **g** £0.12   **h** 2.94 m
  i £7.60   **j** 33.88 min   **k** 136 kg   **l** £162

4 96   **5** £1205   **6 a** 86%   **b** 215

7 8520   **8** 287

9 Each team: 22 500, referees: 750, other teams: 7500, FA: 15 000, celebrities: 6750

10 114

11 Mon: 816, Tue: 833, Wed: 850, Thu: 799, Fri: 748

12 Lead 150 g, tin 87.5 g, bismuth 12.5 g

13 a £3.25   **b** 2.21 kg   **c** £562.80   **d** £6.51
  e 42.93 m   **f** £24

14 480 cm^3 nitrogen, 120 cm^3 oxygen

15 13   **16** £270

Exercise 12C

1 a 1.1   **b** 1.03   **c** 1.2   **d** 1.07   **e** 1.12

2 a £62.40   **b** 12.96 kg   **c** 472.5 g   **d** 599.5 m
  e £38.08   **f** £90   **g** 391 kg   **h** 824.1 cm
  i 253.5 g   **j** £143.50   **k** 736 m   **l** £30.24

3 £29 425

4 1 690 200

5 a Bob: £17 325, Anne: £18 165, Jean: £20 475, Brian: £26 565
  b No

6 £411.95   **7** 193 800   **8** 575 g   **9** 918

10 60

11 TV: £287.88, microwave: £84.60, CD: £135.13, stereo: £34.66

Exercise 12D

1 a 0.92   **b** 0.85   **c** 0.75   **d** 0.91   **e** 0.88

2 a £9.40   **b** 23 kg   **c** 212.4 g   **d** 339.5 m
  e £4.90   **f** 39.6 m   **g** 731 m   **h** 83.52 g
  i 360 cm   **j** 117 min   **k** 81.7 kg   **l** £37.70
3 £5525
4 a 52.8 kg   **b** 66 kg   **c** 45.76 kg
5 Mr Speed: £176, Mrs Speed: £297.50,
  James: £341, John: £562.50
6 448
7 705
8 £18 975
9 a 66.5 mph   **b** 73.5 mph
10 £16.72, £22.88   **11** 524.8 units
12 TV £222.31, DVD player £169.20

Exercise 12E
1 a 25%   **b** 60.6%   **c** 46.3%   **d** 12.5%

e 41.7%   **f** 60%   **g** 20.8%   **h** 10%
  i 1.9%   **j** 8.3%   **k** 45.5%   **l** 10.5%
2 32%   **3** 6.5%   **4** 33.7%
5 a 49.2%   **b** 64.5%   **c** 10.6%
6 17.9%   **7** 4.9%   **8** 90.5%
9 a Brit Com: 20.9%, USA: 26.5%, France: 10.3%, Other
  42.3%
  b total 100%, all imports

Exercise 12F
1 a 0.6, 60%   **b** $\frac{7}{10}$, 70%   **c** $\frac{11}{20}$, 0.55
2 a £10.20   **b** 48   **c** £1.26
3 a 56%   **b** 68%   **c** 37.5%
4 a 276   **b** 3204
5 a 20%   **b** 30%   **c** £13.20
6 a £6400   **b** £5440
7 a 70.4 kg   **b** iii

ANSWERS TO CHAPTER 13

Quick check

1 a $6x$ **b** $12x - 4$ **c** $18x + 7$

2 a -4 **b** 2.5

Exercise 13A
1 $x = 4$ **2** $w = 14$ **3** $y = 5$
4 $p = 10$ **5** $x = 5$ **6** $x = 6$
7 $z = 24$ **8** $x = 2.5$ **9** $q = 4$
10 $x = 1$ **11** $r = 28$ **12** $s = 12$

Exercise 13B
1 $\leftarrow \div 3 \leftarrow -5 \leftarrow$, $x = 2$
2 $\leftarrow \div 3 \leftarrow + 13 \leftarrow$, $x = 13$
3 $\leftarrow \div 3 \leftarrow + 7 \leftarrow$, $x = 13$
4 $\leftarrow \div 4 \leftarrow + 19 \leftarrow$, $y = 6$
5 $\leftarrow \div 3 \leftarrow -8$, $a = 1$
6 $\leftarrow \div 2 \leftarrow -8 \leftarrow$, $x = 3$
7 $\leftarrow \div 2 \leftarrow -6 \leftarrow$, $y = 6$
8 $\leftarrow \div 8 \leftarrow -4 \leftarrow$, $x = 1$
9 $\leftarrow \div 2 \leftarrow + 10 \leftarrow$, $x = 9$
10 $\leftarrow \times 5 \leftarrow -2 \leftarrow$, $x = 5$
11 $\leftarrow \times 3 \leftarrow + 4 \leftarrow$, $t = 18$
12 $\leftarrow \times 4 \leftarrow -1 \leftarrow$, $y = 24$
13 $\leftarrow \times 2 \leftarrow + 6 \leftarrow$, $k = 18$
14 $\leftarrow \times 8 \leftarrow + 4 \leftarrow$, $h = 40$
15 $\leftarrow \times 6 \leftarrow -1 \leftarrow$, $w = 18$
16 $\leftarrow \times 4 \leftarrow -5 \leftarrow$, $x = 8$
17 $\leftarrow \times 2 \leftarrow + 3 \leftarrow$, $y = 16$
18 $\leftarrow \times 5 \leftarrow -2 \leftarrow$, $f = 30$

Exercise 13C
1 56   **2** 2   **3** 6   **4** 3   **5** 4   **6** $2\frac{1}{2}$ **7** $3\frac{1}{2}$
8 $2\frac{1}{2}$ **9** 4   **10** 21   **11** 72   **12** 56   **13** 0
14 -7 **15** -18 **16** 36   **17** 36   **18** 60

Exercise 13D
1 1   **2** 3   **3** 2   **4** 2   **5** 9   **6** 5   **7** 6
8 4   **9** 2   **10** -2 **11** 24   **12** 10   **13** 21   **14** 72   **15** 56   **16** 5   **17** 28   **18** 5   **19** 35   **20** 33
21 23

Exercise 13E
1 3   **2** 7   **3** 5   **4** 3   **5** 4   **6** 6   **7** 8
8 1   **9** 1.5   **10** 2.5   **11** 0.5   **12** 1.2
13 -4 **14** -2

Exercise 13F
1 2   **2** 1   **3** 7   **4** 4   **5** 2   **6** -1 **7** -2 **8** 2
9 6   **10** 11   **11** 1   **12** 4   **13** 9   **14** 6

Exercise 13G
1 55p   **2**   **a** 1.5   **b** 2
3 a 1.5 cm   **b** 6.75 cm^2 **4** 17   **5** 3 yr   **6** 9 yr
7 3 cm   **8** 5   **9**   **a** $4x + 40 = 180$ **b** $x = 35°$

Exercise 13H
1 a 4 and 5   **b** 4 and 5   **c** 2 and 3
2 $x = 3.5$
3 $x = 3.7$
4 $x = 2.5$
5 $x = 1.5$
6 a $x = 2.4$ **b** $x = 2.8$ **c** $x = 3.2$
7 $x = 7.8$ cm, 12.8 cm
8 $x = 5.8$

Exercise 13I
1 $k = \dfrac{T}{3}$ **2** $m = P - 7$ **3** $y = X + 1$ **4** $p = 3Q$

5 a $m = p - t$ **b** $t = p - m$

6 $k = \dfrac{t - 7}{2}$

7 $m = gv$ **8** $m = \sqrt{t}$

9 $r = \dfrac{C}{2\pi}$ **10** $b = \dfrac{A}{h}$

11 $l = \dfrac{P - 2w}{2}$ **12** $p = \sqrt{m - 2}$

Exercise 13J

1 a $x < 5$ **b** $t > 8$ **c** $p \geqslant 10$ **d** $x < 5$
  e $y \leqslant 3$ **f** $t > 5$ **g** $x < 6$ **h** $y \leqslant 15$
  i $t \geqslant 18$ **j** $x < 7$ **k** $x \leqslant 3$ **l** $t \geqslant 5$
2 a 8   **b** 6   **c** 16   **d** 3   **e** 7
3 a 11   **b** 16   **c** 16   **d** 3   **e** 7

Exercise 13K

1 a $x > 1$ **b** $x \leqslant 3$ **c** $x < 2$ **d** $x \geqslant -1$
  e $x \leqslant -1$ **f** $x < 1$ **g** $x > -1$ **h** $x \geqslant 1$
  i $x \leqslant 2$ **j** $1 < x \leqslant 4$ **k** $-2 < x < 4$
  l $-1 \leqslant x \leqslant 3$

2 a    **b**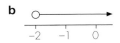

  c 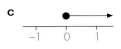   **d**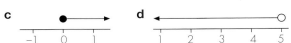

  e    **f**

  g

  h    **i** 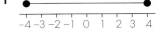   **j**

3 a $x \geqslant 4$ **b** $x < -2$ **c** $x \leqslant 3$

  d $x > 3$ **e** $x > 4$ **f** $x \leqslant 5$

  g $x < 2.5$ **h** $x \geqslant 4.5$ **i** $x \leqslant 10$

  j $x > 12$ **k** $x \geqslant 12$ **l** $x < 25$

      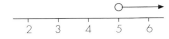

4 a $x \leqslant 2$ **b** $x \geqslant 3\frac{1}{2}$ **c** $x > 5$

  d $x < -1$ **e** $x < 4$ **f** $x \geqslant 2$

   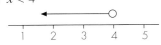

g $x \geqslant -1$

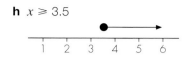

h $x \geqslant 3.5$

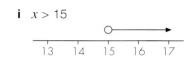

i $x > 15$

j $x \leqslant 24$

k $x < 12$

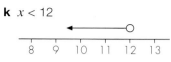

l $x \geqslant 70$

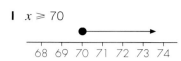

5 a $x < 1\frac{1}{2}$

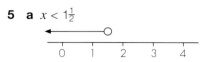

b $x \leqslant -2$

c $x > 50$

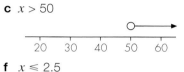

d $x \geqslant -6$

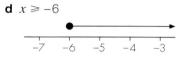

e $x > -1$

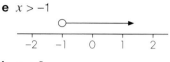

f $x \leqslant 2.5$

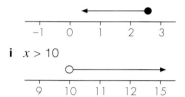

g $x \geqslant -1$

h $x < 8$

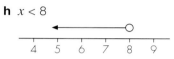

i $x > 10$

j $x \leqslant 9$

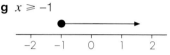

k $x \geqslant 9$

l $x < 13$

Index

NEW TESTAMENT SURVEY

NEW TESTAMENT SURVEY

REVISED EDITION

By
KEVIN CONNER & KEN MALMIN

Distributed By:
Bible Temple Publications
7545 N.E. Glisan Street
Portland, Oregon 97213

ISBN 0-914-936-12-3
PRINTED IN U.S.A.

INTRODUCTION

It is of utmost importance that the Bible student obtain a good grasp of the Bible as a whole. However, in order to do so he must first gain an understanding of each book that makes up The Book. This text has been designed to be of help in this process of understanding the parts and relating them to the whole.

The format of this book is quite simple. It is designed to give a patterned glimpse of each book of the New Testament. This has been done by applying these ten points to each book: (1) Titles, (2) Author, (3) Date, (4) Key Words and Phrases, (5) Key Verses, (6) Purpose, (7) Message, (8) Outline, (9) Summary, and (10) Christ Seen. The following is an explanation of each of the ten points.

1. TITLES:

Under this heading you will find basically three things: First, the meaning of the title of the book is given (e.g. Matthew means "gift of God"). Next, alternate titles are listed when significant. Last, a distinct title has been suggested for each book. This title is meant to both describe the content of the book and to distinguish it from the other books of the Bible (e.g. Matthew is called The Book of The King because it presents Jesus as the Kingly Messiah and deals with things pertaining to the Kingdom of Heaven, a key word).

2. AUTHOR:

Under this heading is listed the author of the book. In cases where the book does not name its author, the most probable author from our point of view has been given. You will also find a brief point or two distinguishing the author and pointing out any other books written by him.

3. DATE:

Under this heading you will find under the historical books first a reference to the number of years that pass during the accounts given in the book. Then for every book an approximate date has been given as to when the book was written. Also on the Pauline Epistles information has been given to relate those epistles to the book of Acts. (There are many differences of opinion concerning the dates when the New Testament books were written. Thus, the dates listed in this text are conservative estimates.)

4. KEY WORDS AND PHRASES:

Under this heading you will find words and phrases that are keys to understanding the book at hand. These have been chosen on the basis of frequency of usage, relation to the subject of the book, and frequency of usage in relation to usage in other books of the Bible. These tabulations are based upon the King James Version unless otherwise noted. These words can be used for good word/theme studies in their respective books.

5. KEY VERSES:

Under this heading you will find verses that express the main subject, theme, or message of the book.

6. PURPOSE:

Under this heading you will find statements that answer the question, "Why was this book written?". These lend insight into the importance of each book. It must be considered that there are many different types of reasons why a book is written (e.g. for historical, instructional, prophetical, etc. reasons). Those thought most important have been included.

7. MESSAGE:

Under this heading you will find, with some exceptions, the statements of principle that are taught by each book as a whole or at least by a major portion of it. Of these sort of statements there could be no end but once again only those felt most significant have been included.

8. OUTLINE:

Under this heading you will find a brief, condensed outline of each book showing its structure and arrangement.

9. SUMMARY:

Under this heading you will find a paragraph description of the book, pointing out its subject and its relation to other books of the Bible, as well as other facts of interest concerning the book or its author.

10. CHRIST SEEN:

Under this heading you will find a brief description of some ways in which Christ can be seen in the book, sometimes accompanied by Scripture references supporting them.

Any correspondence concerning this text may be directed to:

Ken Malmin
Portland Bible College
9201 N.E. Fremont
Portland, Oregon 97220
U.S.A.

THE BOOKS OF THE NEW TESTAMENT

		The Book Of:
1.	MATTHEW	The King
2.	MARK	The Servant
3.	LUKE	The Perfect Man
4.	JOHN	The Son of God
5.	ACTS	The Holy Spirit
6.	ROMANS	Justification
7.	I CORINTHIANS	N.T. Church Order
8.	II CORINTHIANS	Apostolic Qualification
9.	GALATIANS	Christian Liberty
10.	EPHESIANS	The Church
11.	PHILIPPIANS	Joy and Rejoicing
12.	COLOSSIANS	The Head of The Body
13.	I THESSALONIANS	The Second Coming of Christ In Coming
14.	II THESSALONIANS	The Second Coming of Christ In Judgment
15.	I TIMOTHY	The Minister--Qualifications
16.	II TIMOTHY	The Minister--Doctrine
17.	TITUS	The Minister--Godliness
18.	PHILEMON	Reconciliation
19.	HEBREWS	Christ's Priesthood
20.	JAMES	Faith and Works
21.	I PETER	Suffering and Glory
22.	II PETER	True Knowledge
23.	I JOHN	Love
24.	II JOHN	Truth--Doctrinal
25.	III JOHN	Truth--Practical
26.	JUDE	The Apostates
27.	REVELATION	Ultimates

THE BOOKS OF THE NEW TESTAMENT

NEW TESTAMENT HISTORY 5	HISTORIC FOUNDATIONS 5	MATTHEW MARK LUKE JOHN ACTS
DOCTRINAL EPISTLES 22	CHRISTIAN CHURCH EPISTLES 9	ROMANS I CORINTHIANS II CORINTHIANS GALATIANS EPHESIANS PHILIPPIANS COLOSSIANS I THESSALONIANS II THESSALONIANS
	PASTORAL & PERSONAL EPISTLES 4	I TIMOTHY II TIMOTHY TITUS PHILEMON
	HEBREW CHRISTIAN EPISTLES 9	HEBREWS JAMES I PETER II PETER I JOHN II JOHN III JOHN JUDE REVELATION

MATTHEW

1. **TITLES**

   A. Matthew = gift of God; Levi = joined
   B. The Gospel According to Matthew
   C. The Book of The King

2. **AUTHOR:**

   Written by Matthew, a tax collector, who was called by Christ to be one of the twelve apostles.

3. **DATE:**

   A. Covers approximately 34 years from Christ's birth to His Ascension.
   B. Probably written between 52 and 68 A.D. before the fall of Jerusalem.

4. **KEY WORDS:**

   A. Kingdom (of heaven) -- 56
   B. Just, Right (eous, ness) (same Greek word) -------------------- 25
   C. Fulfill (ed) --- 18

   KEY PHRASES:

   A. Son of Man -- 32
   B. Father in heaven, heavenly Father -------------------------------- 20
   C. Which was spoken --- 13
   D. Son of David --- 9

5. **KEY VERSES:**   1:1; 5:17, 18; 24:14

6. **PURPOSE:**

   A. To show the Jews, by prophecy and fulfillment, that Jesus of Nazareth was the promised Kingly Messiah.
   B. To show the Jews' rejection of their King and His Kingdom.
   C. To give a preview of the events of this present age from Christ's Ascension to His Second Coming

7. **MESSAGE:**

   A. The Kingdom of heaven is not a materialistic kingdom governed by worldy principles neither is it a nationalistic kingdom confined to this earth.
   B. The Kingdom of God is a spiritual kingdom of heavenly character, nature, and order. It refers specifically to where the rule and reign of God is made effective by submission to the spiritual principles of the King.

8. **OUTLINE:**

   I.   Preparation of the King . . . . Ch. 1 - 4
   II. Presentation of the Kingdom . . . . Ch. 5 - 10
   III. Preaching of the Kingdom . . . . Ch. 11 - 25
   IV. Passion of the King . . . . Ch. 26 - 28

9. **SUMMARY:**

   The distinctive characteristic of Matthew's Gospel is its appeal to the Jewish mind. It was probably originally written in Hebrew and contains many more Old Testament quotations than the other Gospels. It was thus meant to convince the Jews that Jesus of Nazareth was their promised Messiah. It presents the King and His Kingdom. Because of their nationalistic and materialistic concept of the Kingdom they rejected the King. Thus the Kingdom was taken from them and it became the ministry of the church (only mentioned in Matthew's Gospel) to preach the Gospel of the Kingdom to all the world.

10. **CHRIST SEEN:**

   Christ is seen as the King (2:2), the Lawgiver (Is. 33:22; Mt. 5-7), the Anointed (3:16, 17). The Son of David (1:1), and the Fulfillment of the Law and the Prophets (5:17).

MARK

1. **TITLES:**

   A. Mark = polite, shining (John Mark)
   B. The Gospel According to Mark
   C. The Book of <u>The Servant</u>

2. **AUTHOR:**

   Written by <u>John Mark</u>, who was a cousin of Barnabas and a companion of Peter. Many conclude that Mark was actually writing the "Gospel according to <u>Peter</u>."

3. **DATE:**

   A. Covers approximately 4 years from John's ministry to the beginning of the ministry of the early church.
   B. Probably written between 55 and 68 A.D.

4. **KEY WORDS**

   A. Straightway, Immediately, Forthwith,
      Anon, As Soon (same Greek word) --------------------------------- 42
   B. Multitude, People, Press (same Greek word) ------------------ 38
   C. Gospel ('s) --- 8

5. **KEY VERSE:** 10:45

6. **PURPOSE:**

   A. To present Jesus of Nazareth as the perfect and faithful <u>Servant</u> of Jehovah.
   B. To show to the Romans that Jesus was the <u>Servant</u> acting under the authority of Jehovah, giving <u>immediate</u> and full obedience to all commandments.

7. **MESSAGE:**

   A. The way to be great in the Kingdom of God is to be <u>servant</u> of all.
   B. He that humbleth himself under the hand of God shall be exalted in due time (1 Peter 5:6).

8. **OUTLINE:**

   I.   The <u>Separation</u> of the Servant . . . . 1:1 - 13
   II.   The <u>Service</u> of the Servant . . . . 1:14 - 8:30
   III. The <u>Sacrifice</u> of the Servant . . . . 8:31 - 15:47
   IV.   The <u>Session</u> of the Servant . . . . 16:1 - 20

9. **SUMMARY:**

   The distinctive characteristic of Mark's Gospel is its appeal to the Roman mind. It was probably written in Rome and contains more Latinisms than the other Gospels. Jewish customs, places, coins, and Aramaic expressions are explained, which would be necessary in order for the Roman mind to comprehend them. Mark's Gospel presents the <u>Servant</u> - Son as a man of action, of <u>deeds</u> more than <u>words,</u> recording more miracles than any other Gospel. It opens with the presentation of the <u>Servant</u> and closes with the <u>Servant</u> being made Lord (Mk. 16:19; Phil. 2:6 - 11; Acts 2:36).

10. **CHRIST SEEN:**

    Christ is seen as the <u>Son of God</u> (1:1) who became the <u>Son of Man</u> (10:45), the <u>Sent-One</u> (9:37), and the suffering <u>Servant</u> who after giving his life a ransom for many became the exalted <u>Lord</u> (16:19).

LUKE

1. **TITLES**
   A. Luke = Luminous
   B. The Gospel According to Luke
   C. The Book of The Perfect Man

2. **AUTHOR:**

   Written by Luke, a physician, who was not one of the twelve apostles but was a companion of Paul. He also wrote the book of Acts.

3. **DATE:**
   A. Covers approximately 35 years from the birth of John the Baptist to the Ascension.
   B. Probably written between 58 and 60 A.D.

4. **KEY WORDS:**
   A. Son --- 145
   B. Kingdom (of God) ---------------------------------- 45
   C. Preach, Publish, Proclaim, Show, Bring ------------- 20 (3 Greek words)
   D. Spirit, Holy Ghost ------------------------------------ 17

   KEY PHRASE:
   A. Son of Man -- 25

5. **KEY VERSES:** 4:18, 19; 19:10

6. **PURPOSE:**
   A. To present Jesus of Nazareth as the anointed perfect man, who after a perfect ministry provided a perfect salvation for sinful humanity.
   B. To show to the Greeks that Jesus was God's ideal man, the only Saviour.

7. **MESSAGE:**
   A. All preaching of the Gospel must be done in the power of the Holy Spirit.
   B. God's ideal for man is to be perfected even as His own Son.

8. **OUTLINE:**
   I. The Preparation for/of the Son of Man . . . . . . 1:1 - 4:15
   II. The Ministry of the Son of Man . . . . 4:16 - 21:38
   III. The Suffering of the Son of Man . . . . 22:1 - 23:56
   IV. The Exaltation of the Son of Man . . . . 24:1 - 53

9. **SUMMARY:**

   The distinctive characteristic of Luke's Gospel is its appeal to the Greek mind. While the Romans had exalted strength of action, the Greeks had exalted wisdom of thought. Thus Luke records more of the parables of Jesus than the other Gospel writers. The portrait Luke draws of Jesus is that of the perfect man, the wisdom of God, the one who more than meets the highest ideals of the Greeks. Luke also shows Christ's relationship to the Holy Spirit. It opens with His being born of the Spirit, continues with His ministry by the power of the Spirit, and closes with His promise of the outpoured Spirit.

10. **CHRIST SEEN:**

    Christ is seen as the perfect Son of Man, the Anointed Preacher, and the Saviour of lost humanity (4:18, 19; 19:10).

JOHN

1. **TITLES:**
   A. John = beloved
   B. The Gospel According to John
   C. The Book of The Son of God

2. **AUTHOR:**
   Written by John, a fisherman, who was one of the twelve apostles. He also wrote three epistles and The Revelation.

3. **DATE:**
   A. Covers approximately 4 years from John the Baptist's ministry to just before the Ascension.
   B. Probably written between 85 and 95 A.D.

4. **KEY WORDS:**

A.	Father (God)	122	G.	True, Truth	47
B.	Believe (ed, est, eth, ing)	101	H.	Witness (two Greek words)	47
C.	World	80	I.	Son (Christ)	43
D.	Jew (s, s')	70	J.	Abide (Greek word)	41
E.	Love (ed, edst, est, eth)	57	K.	Verily, Verily	25
F.	Life, Live	52	L.	Light	24

5. **KEY VERSES:** 3:16; 20:31

6. **PURPOSE:**
   A. To present Jesus Christ as the only-begotten Son of God, and to show His relationship with the Father.
   B. To show to the whole world that Jesus was sent by God the Father into the world that the world, through Him, might be saved.
   C. To show that in Jesus, God was manifested.
   D. To give a Divine interpretation of the person of Jesus Christ as to His Deity and Humanity, thus refuting prevalent heresies.

7. **MESSAGE:**
   A. The only way of approach to God the Father is through His beloved Son (Jn. 14:1, 6).
   B. There is no eternal life apart from the Son.
   C. Those who believe enter into a father and son relationship with God.
   D. Faith brings life; unbelief brings death.

8. **OUTLINE:**

I.	The Son of God			Ch. 1:1 - 18
II.	His Public Ministry	To the Jews		Ch. 1:19 - 12:50
III.	His Private Ministry	To the Disciples		Ch. 13 - 17
IV.	His Passion	To the World		Ch. 18 - 21

9. **SUMMARY:**
   The distinctive characteristic of John's Gospel is its appeal to the whole world. Not only does John use the word "world" many times, but he also emphasizes the universal nature of Christ's mediatorship; that Jesus is the only way of salvation for the whole world. Matthew, Mark, and Luke primarily present the outer factual aspects of the Lord's life and humanity, emphasizing His public discourses and Galilean ministry. John primarily presents the inner doctrinal aspects of the Lord's life and person, emphasizing His private discourses and Judean ministry.

10. **CHRIST SEEN:**
    Christ is seen as the Word (1:1, 14), the Son (3:16), the Life (1:4), the Light (1:5), the "I AM" (8:56 - 58), and the only Way of Salvation (14:6).

ACTS

1. **TITLES:**

    A.   The Acts of the Apostles

    B.   The Book of The Holy Spirit

2. **AUTHORS:**

    Written by Luke, a physician, who was a companion of Paul and also wrote the Gospel bearing his name.

3. **DATE:**

    A.   Covers approximately 33 years from the Ascension of Christ to the time when Paul had been a prisoner in Rome for two years.

    B.   Probably written between 61 and 65 A.D.

4. **KEY WORDS:**

    A.   Jew (ess, s) --- 81

    B.   Spirit, Holy Ghost ---------------------------------- 54

    C.   Gentiles, nations (same Greek word) ------------------ 44

    D.   Word (of God) --- 40

    E.   Name (of Jesus, Lord) ----------------------------------- 37

    F.   Pray (ed, er, ers, eth, ing) ---------------------------- 35

5. **KEY VERSE:** 1:8

6. **PURPOSE:**

    A.   To record Christ's continued ministry from heaven of all that He began to do and teach on earth (1:1).

    B.   To give a panoramic view of the birth, formation, and development of the early church.

    C.   To show the pattern by which Christ builds His church.

7. **MESSAGE:**

    A.   The church, as the body of Christ, cannot function apart from the ministry of the Holy Spirit.

    B.   Only by the power of the Holy Spirit can the great commission be fulfilled (Zech. 4:6).

8. **OUTLINE:**

    I.   The Ministry of Peter ---- to the Jews ------------------- Circumcision . . . . Ch. 1 - 12
           Jerusalem / Judea / Samaria

    II.   The Ministry of Paul ---- To the Gentiles -------------- Uncircumcision . . . . . . Ch. 13 - 28
           Uttermost Parts of the Earth

9. **SUMMARY:**

    In the Gospels, Christ is presented in His earthly ministry, but in the Acts He is presented in His heavenly ministry, building His Church, as He promised (Mt. 16:18), through the power of the Spirit. In the Acts we see the order of witness in the great commission being fulfilled; first in Jerusalem, then Judea, Samaria, and the uttermost parts of the earth. The Book of Acts centers basically around two apostles; Peter, the apostle to the Jews and Paul, the apostle to the Gentiles (Gal. 2:8). It sets forth the formation and establishment of the church upon the foundational principles of the apostles' doctrine, and thus it becomes a pattern-book for the church, both universal and local.

10. **CHRIST SEEN:**

    Christ is seen as the Head of the Church, governing, guiding, equipping, and building it by the Spirit.

ROMANS

1. **TITLES:**
   A. The Epistle to the Romans
   B. The Gospel According to Paul (16:25)
   C. The Book of Justification

2. **AUTHOR:**

   Written by Paul, the apostle to the Gentiles.

3. **DATE:**

   Probably written between 55 and 58 A.D. during Paul's second visit to Corinth.

4. **KEY WORDS:**

   A. Law --- 78
   B. Righteousness (42); Justification (22)
   (related Greek words) ------------------------------------- 64
   C. Faith (39); Believe (21) (same Greek root) -------------------- 60
   D. Sin (ned, ner, s) --- 57
   E. Grace -- 24
   F. Imputed (reckoned, etc.) (one Greek word) ----------------- 19

5. **KEY VERSE:** 1:16, 17

6. **PURPOSE:**

   A. To answer the age-old question, "How can a man be just before God?" (Job 9:2).
   B. To give a clear doctrinal exposition of God's method of justification by faith.
   C. To show that both Jew and Gentile are only acceptable to God through the New Covenant in Christ.

7. **MESSAGE:**

   A. The just shall live by faith (1:17).
   B. All men are under sin and cannot be justified by the works of the law.
   C. The only righteousness God accepts is a faith-righteousness based on His Word.

8. **OUTLINE:**

   I.   Doctrinal: Righteousness Imputed .... Ch. 1 - 8
   II. National: Jew and Gentile .... Ch. 9 - 11
   III. Practical: Righteousness Outworked ...... Ch. 12 - 16

9. **SUMMARY:**

   In his epistle to the Romans Paul outlines the gospel of Christ which sets forth the righteousness of God for Jew and Gentile. In Chapters 1 - 3 he concludes the whole world guilty under sin; the Gentiles without the law and the Jews under the law. Then in Chapters 3 - 8, he presents the Gospel message covering justification (3 - 5), sanctification (6 - 8), and glorification (8:18 - 39). In Chapters 9 - 11 he deals with the election (9), the rejection through unbelief (10), and the restoration (11) of the Jews through faith in Christ. In Chapters 12 - 16, Paul concludes his epistle by pointing out the practical duties of the justified.

10. **CHRIST SEEN:**

    Christ is seen as the Salvation of God, the Righteousness of God (10:3, 4), and the Propitiation for our sin (3:25).

I CORINTHIANS

1. **TITLES:**

    A. The First Epistle to the Corinthians
    B. The Book of Correction
    C. The Book of N.T. Church Order

2. **AUTHOR:**

    Written by Paul, the apostle to the Gentiles.

3. **DATE:**

    Probably written between 53 and 57 A.D. during Paul's stay at Ephesus on his third missionary journey (Acts 19). Later he visited Corinth again (Acts 20:1, 2).

4. **KEY WORDS:**

    A. Body -- 44
    B. Spirit (Greek word) --------------------------------------- 41
    C. Wise (dom, er) --- 31
    D. Tongue (s) --- 22
    E. Prophet, Prophesy, etc. ------------------------------------ 21
    F. Charity, Love (same Greek word) ------------------------ 16

5. **KEY VERSES:** 1:24, 30; 3:10, 11

6. **PURPOSE:**

    A. To answer questions that the Corinthians had addressed to him concerning problems in the church (7:1; 8:1; 12:1; 16:1).
    B. To reprove and correct abuses in the mental, moral, social, and spiritual life of the Corinthian church.

7. **MESSAGE:**

    A. Recognition of the Lordship of Jesus is the solution to division in the body of Christ.
    B. God's church must be built by God's wisdom and power rather than by man's.
    C. To have order in the church we must conform to God's order.
    D. That which edifies the church is sound doctrine and that which motivates the church is God's love.

8. **OUTLINE:**

    I. Corrective Section: Carnalities . . . . 1:1 - 8:13
       Divisions/Immorality/Marriage/Idolatry
    II. Constructive Section: Spiritualities . . . . 9:1 - 16:24
        Ministry/Communion/Spiritual Gifts/Body of Christ
        Love/Resurrection/Collections

9. **SUMMARY:**

    The church at Corinth was founded by Paul, as recorded in Acts 18. It had enjoyed the ministries of Paul, Peter, and Apollos and factions had arisen around these personalities. Other carnalities such as immorality, idolatry, and heresy had arisen. Thus Paul wrote this first epistle to reprove the Corinthians of these and to correct disorders concerning the Lord's Table, spiritual gifts, and the collection. He also answered questions and clarified misunderstandings concerning the resurrection. All of these things are evidence of a lack of spirituality, the essence of which is love.

10. **CHRIST SEEN:**

    Christ is seen as the Power of God (1:24), the Wisdom of God (1:24, 30), our Righteousness, Sanctification, and Redemption (1:30), the Love of God (13), and the Resurrection (15).

II CORINTHIANS

1. TITLES:

   A.   The Second Epistle to the Corinthians
   B.   The Book of Comfort
   C.   The Book of Apostolic Qualification

2. AUTHOR:

   Written by Paul, the apostle to the Gentiles.

3. DATE:

   Probably written between 54 and 57 A.D. during Paul's stay in Philippi on his third missionary journey (Acts 20).

4. KEY WORDS:

   A.   Glory, Boast (same Greek root) ------------------------------------- 31
   B.   Comfort, Consolation, Beseech, etc. (same Greek word) -------- 29
   C.   Glory (of God) (different Greek word from above) -------------- 22
   D.   Minister (ing, ed, s, ry, ration) ------------------------------- 18

5. KEY VERSE: 1:3, 4

6. PURPOSE:

   A.   To defend Paul's apostolic ministry and authority against false ministers trying to destroy his influence.
   B.   To give further instruction concerning the collection for the saints at Jerusalem (9:1 - 5).
   C.   To point out the need for consolation in the case of discipline mentioned in the first epistle (2:5 - 11).
   D.   To show that the New Covenant surpasses the Old Covenant in glory.

7. MESSAGE:

   A.   A true minister of God will glory in the Lord and not in himself.
   B.   The chief purpose of church discipline is restoration rather than condemnation.
   C.   Apostolic ministry is attested to by patience, signs, wonders, and mighty deeds (12:12).

8. OUTLINE:

    I.   The Ministry of Reconciliation .... Ch. 1 - 7
   II.   The Ministry of Distribution (Giving) .... Ch. 8 - 9
  III.   The Ministry of Vindication (of Apostleship) .... Ch. 10 - 13

9. SUMMARY:

   The church at Corinth had responded to Paul's first epistle dealing with certain disorders, particularly in the matter of immorality. This second epistle was written to balance out the discipline they exercised, encouraging them to restore the penitent brother back to fellowship. Whereas the first epistle was written to correct, this second epistle was written to comfort. This second epistle, like Hebrews, contrasts the glory of the New Covenant and its ministers (Christ & the Chruch) with the Old Covenant and its ministers (Moses & the Prophets). In the practical realm Paul reminds and exhorts the church to have the collection for the poor saints in Jerusalem ready. In the remainder of the epistle, Paul vindicates his apostleship by pointing to the fruit of his ministry.

10. CHRIST SEEN:

   Christ is seen as our Comforter, our Sin-offering (5:21), our Apostle, and the Glory of the New Covenant (3, 4).

GALATIANS

1. **TITLES:**
   - A. The Epistle to the Galatians
   - B. The Book of Christian Liberty

2. **AUTHOR:**

   Written by Paul, the apostle to the Gentiles

3. **DATE:**

   Probably written between 48 and 58 A.D. from Antioch, either at the end of Paul's first or second missionary journey (Acts 14, 18).

4. **KEY WORDS:**

A.	Law	32	F.	Life, Live, etc.	13
B.	Faith	22	G.	Gospel	12
C.	Flesh	18	H.	Works	10
D.	Spirit	18	I.	Grace	7
E.	Righteousness, Justified	13			

5. **KEY VERSES:** 3:2, 3, 11

6. **PURPOSE:**
   - A. To prove the authenticity of the Gospel according to Paul.
   - B. To refute the legalism of the Judaizers under the Old Covenant.
   - C. To establish the doctrine of Christian liberty under the New Covenant.
   - D. To show the superiority of the Abrahamic and New Covenants over the Mosaic Covenant.

7. **MESSAGE:**
   - A. True liberty in Christ is neither the legalism of the Law nor the license of the flesh.
   - B. Life and righteousness come only by grace through faith.
   - C. Having received the Spirit we must also walk in the Spirit.

8. **OUTLINE:**

I.	Personal:	Paul's Gospel	Ch. 1, 2
II.	Doctrinal:	Law or Grace	Ch. 3, 4
III.	Practical:	Liberty or License	Ch. 5, 6

9. **SUMMARY:**

   The Judaizers mentioned in Acts 15:1 had followed Paul's ministry among the churches of the Gentiles, having particular success in Galatia. Their teaching was a mixture of law and grace, faith and works, and Moses and Jesus. They said that a sinner was saved by faith plus works, and that the saved were to be perfected through works as they kept the Mosaic Law. The result of this teaching was that the Galatians became entangled again with the yoke of the bondage of the Law. Thus, Paul writes this epistle refuting the perverted gospel of the Judaizers and establishing the truth of his gospel. He takes up the covenant made with Abraham and by allegory he illustrates the two covenants (Mosaic Covenant and New Covenant), using Abraham's two sons, Ishmael and Isaac. Paul closes the epistle by showing that Christian liberty is neither legalism nor license.

10. **CHRIST SEEN:**

    Christ is seen as our Faith, our Righteousness, our Life, our Redeemer, the Seed of Abraham, and the New Covenant Gospel of Grace.

EPHESIANS

1. **TITLES**
   A. The Epistle to the Ephesians
   B. The Book of the Body of Christ
   C. The Book of The Church

2. **AUTHOR:**
   Written by Paul, the apostle to the Gentiles.

3. **DATE:**
   Probably written between 57 and 62 A.D. during Paul's first imprisonment at Rome (Acts 28).

4. **KEY WORDS:**

A.	Love (d, eth)	19	E.	Heaven (ly, s)	8
B.	Grace	12	F.	Walk (ed)	8
C.	Faith, Believe	10	G.	Mystery	6
D.	Body (ies)	10	H.	Will (of God)	6

5. **KEY VERSES:** 1:22, 23; 2:6; 4:1

6. **PURPOSE:**
   A. To strengthen the believers in their love and faith in Christ.
   B. To encourage the believers to put off the old man and put on the new man.
   C. To show the unity of both Jew and Gentile in the one body of Christ.
   D. To set forth the purpose of the mystery of Christ and the church.

7. **MESSAGE:**
   A. The believer as a member of the body of Christ is seated in heavenly places in Christ, but yet is to walk in practical love on earth.
   B. The church is a time manifestation of God's eternal purpose in Christ.

8. **OUTLINE:**
   I. Doctrinal: Heavenly Calling . . . . Ch. 1 - 3
   II. Practical: Earthly Conduct . . . . Ch. 4 - 6

9. **SUMMARY:**
   During Paul's third missionary journey he spent at least three years at Ephesus establishing the church. It soon became the center for the evangelization of Asia Minor. Then while imprisoned at Rome, Paul wrote this epistle. In chapter one he sets forth the eternal purpose of God in Christ and shows the heavenly calling and position of the church. In chapter two the grace of God is seen in the bringing together of both Jew and Gentile into one body through the cross, thus building a spiritual temple for the habitation of God. Chapter three unfolds the mystery of Christ and the church. Chapter four deals with the unity of the members of the body and chapter five deals with the unity of the body with Christ under the figure of marriage. Then in chapter six Paul outlines the church's spiritual warfare. If the church had heeded Paul's admonition to walk in love they would not have received the rebuke of Christ found in Revelation 2:1 - 7.

10. **CHRIST SEEN:**
    Christ is seen as the Fulness of God, the Head of the Church, the Bridegroom, the Giver of Ministries, the Grace of God, and our Peace.

PHILIPPIANS

1. **TITLES:**

   A. The Epistle to the Philippians
   B. The Book of Joy and Rejoicing

2. **AUTHOR:**

   Written by Paul, the apostle to the Gentiles.

3. **DATE:**

   Probably written between 60 and 64 A.D. during Paul's first imprisonment at Rome (Acts 28).

4. **KEY WORDS:**

   A. Joy, Rejoice --- 18
   B. Mind (ed, s) --- 10

5. **KEY VERSE:** 2:2; 4:4

6. **PURPOSE:**

   A. To thank the church for their gifts and to inform them of Paul's intended visit.
   B. To warn them against the Judaizing false teachers.
   C. To exhort them to be likeminded by having the mind of Christ.
   D. To encourage them to rejoice in all circumstances.

7. **MESSAGE:**

   A. The Christian life is one of joy and rejoicing which is independent of all circumstances.
   B. The key to unity (being likeminded) is having the mind of Christ.

8. **OUTLINE:**

   Rejoice In:

   I.   Christ our Life (1;21) . . . . Ch. 1
   II. Christ our Mind (2:5) . . . . Ch. 2
   III. Christ our Goal (3:10, 14) . . . . Ch. 3
   IV. Christ our Strength (4:13) . . . . Ch. 4

9. **SUMMARY:**

   The church at Philippi was founded by Paul and Silas on Paul's second missionary journey (Acts 16). Some of the first converts were gained as a result of Paul's rejoicing while in prison and it is very fitting that Paul while in prison at Rome would write an epistle of joy to this church. The theme of joy and rejoicing can be traced through the epistle as follows; Joy and Prayer (1:4 - 6), Joy and Opposition (1:14 - 18), Joy and Faith (1:25, 26), Joy and Unity (2:2), Joy and Ministry (2:14 - 16), Joy and Sacrifice (2:17, 18), Joy and Victory (2:25 - 29), Rejoicing in the Lord (3:1 - 3), Rejoicing Always (4:4), Rejoicing in All Circumstances (4:10 - 12). It is also interesting to note that faith, love, unity, and humility are seen as being at the root of joy.

10. **CHRIST SEEN:**

    Christ is seen as our Joy, our Life, our Mind, our Goal, and our Strength.

COLOSSIANS

1. **TITLES:**

   A. The Epistle to the Colossians
   B. The Book of The Head Of The Body

2. **AUTHOR:**

   Written by Paul, the apostle to the Gentiles.

3. **DATE:**

   Probably written between 60 and 64 A.D. during Paul's first imprisonment at Rome (Acts 28).

4. **KEY WORDS:**

   A. Body ('s) --- 8
   B. Fulness, Complete (Greek word) ------------------ 7
   C. Wisdom -- 6
   D. Mystery -- 4
   E. Glory (ious)--- 4
   F. Head -- 3

5. **KEY VERSES:**   1:18; 2:9, 10

6. **PURPOSE:**

   A. To warn them against the heresies concerning the person and nature of Christ.
   B. To warn them against ritualism and asceticism.
   C. To present Christ as the Head of the Church in His Deity and Humanity.
   D. To exhort them to put off the old man and to put on the new man.

7. **MESSAGE:**

   A. Christ is in all, through all, and above all. He is the fulness of the Godhead bodily and the Church is complete in Him.
   B. We are to set our affections on things above and not on things on the earth.

8. **OUTLINE:**

   I.   Doctrinal: The Glory of the Head . . . . 1:1 - 2:5
   II. Practical: The Conduct of the Body . . . . 2:6 - 4:18

9. **SUMMARY:**

   There is no record in Acts of Paul's visiting Colosse, and he evidently did not found the church there (2:1). Possibly Epaphras founded the church (1:7; 4:12, 13) which probably met in Philemon's home (4:9 with Phm. 10, 23; Phm. 2 with 4:17). According to Acts 19:10, the church was probably founded while Paul was in Ephesus only 100 miles away. Paul was well acquainted with the progress of the church and the heresies that had arisen. Thus he wrote to refute them. In section one Paul sets forth the glory and pre-eminence of Christ, refuting the heresies concerning the person and nature of Christ; in particular his pre-existence, deity, and humanity. He also exhorts them to recognize the proper position of the Head over the Body. In the second section, Paul exhorts them to the practical application of the doctrine contained in the first section by putting off the old man with his deeds and by putting on the new man. The Church is seen as being complete in Christ apart from asceticism, ritualism and formalism.

10. **CHRIST SEEN:**

   Christ is seen as the Pre-existent, Pre-eminent, Creator, Ruler, Redeemer, Head of the Body who is the Fulness of the Godhead Bodily.

I THESSALONIANS

1. **TITLES:**

   A. The First Epistle to the Thessalonians
   B. The Book of <u>The Second Coming of Christ in Comfort</u>

2. **AUTHOR:**

   Written by <u>Paul</u>, the apostle to the Gentiles.

3. **DATE:**

   Probably written between 50 and 52 A.D. during Paul's stay at Corinth on his second missionary journey (Acts 18).

4. **KEY WORDS:**

A.	Faith, Believe	12	D.	Comfort		6
B.	Joy, Rejoice	7	E.	Coming		4
C.	Love	6	F.	Hope		4

5. **KEY VERSES**   2:19; 4:15 - 18

6. **PURPOSE:**

   A. To correct mistaken views of and to establish the doctrine of the second <u>coming</u> of Christ.
   B. To exhort the believers to display the three chief Godly virtues: <u>faith</u>, <u>hope</u>, and <u>love</u>.
   C. To confirm the purity of Paul's ministry among the Thessalonians.

7. **MESSAGE:**

   A. The <u>coming</u> of Christ for his people is a <u>comfort</u> to those who look for and patiently wait for Him.
   B. The doctrine of the second <u>coming</u> is a great incentive to holiness.
   C. The Lord's return will be as a thief in the night to those that are in darkness, but will not be so to those that are in the light.

8. **OUTLINE:**

   I.   <u>The Waiting Church</u> . . . . Ch. 1 - 3

       A.   Elected . . . . Ch. 1
       B.   Persecuted . . . . Ch. 2
       C.   Afflicted . . . . Ch. 3

   II. <u>The Coming Christ</u> . . . . Ch. 4 - 5

       A.   Revelation . . . . Ch. 4
       B.   Sanctification . . . . Ch. 5

9. **SUMMARY:**

   Paul laid the foundation of the church in Thessalonica on his second missionary journey (Acts 17). He experienced considerable opposition from the Judaizers and did not stay there long, but soon after departing he wrote his epistle to them. The general spiritual state of the church was good but there were several things that needed correction. In chapter <u>one</u>, Paul commends them for being a pattern church. In chapters <u>two</u> and <u>three</u> he reminds them of the persecution and affliction which he and they endured at the hands of the Judaizers. Then in chapters <u>four</u> and <u>five</u> he exhorts them to the practical outworking of their sanctification in spirit, soul, and body. The main theme running through the epistle is the <u>second coming</u> of Christ, references to which are made in each chapter. (1:10; 2:19; 3:13; 4:13 - 18; 5:1 - 11, 23) Also seen throughout the epistle is the abiding trinity of <u>faith</u>, <u>hope</u>, and <u>love</u>.

10. **CHRIST SEEN:**

    Christ is seen as our <u>Sanctification</u> and our <u>Coming Lord</u>.

II THESSALONIANS

1. **TITLES:**

    A. The Second Epistle to the Thessalonians
    B. The Book of The Second Coming of Christ in Judgment

2. **AUTHOR:**

    Written by Paul, the apostle to the Gentiles.

3. **DATE:**

    Probably written between 50 and 52 A.D. during Paul's stay at Corinth on his second missionary journey (Acts 18).

4. **KEY WORDS:**

A.	Faith, Believe	8	D.	Command (ed)	4
B.	Love, Charity (Greek word)	6	E.	Coming	3
C.	Revealed	4			

5. **KEY VERSES:** 1:7 - 10

6. **PURPOSE:**

    A. To give further details concerning the events surrounding the coming of the Lord.
    B. To encourage the believers in the midst of severe persecution.
    C. To command them to continue in their occupation and well-doing until the coming of the Lord.

7. **MESSAGE:**

    A. The coming of Christ is a judgment upon those who know not God.
    B. The spirit of the Anti-Christ is already at work within the world.
    C. In the light of the comings of both Christ and the Anti-Christ, the believer should now walk orderly.

8. **OUTLINE:**

    I. The Christ Avenging . . . . Ch. 1
    II. The Anti-Christ Deceiving . . . . Ch. 2
    III. The Church Working . . . . Ch. 3

9. **SUMMARY:**

    (Refer to this same heading under I Thessalonians for Paul's relationship to this church.) This second epistle was written soon after the first epistle. The first epistle shows that they were concerned about the "dead in Christ" in relation to His second coming. The second epistle shows their concern about the suffering of the living saints in relation to Christ's second coming. In chapter one, Paul comforts them by pointing out that it is far better for them to suffer tribulation previous to Christ's coming than to suffer vengeance at His Coming. In chapter two Paul describes two of the main events that are to precede the second coming; the great falling away and the revelation of the Anti-Christ. Then in chapter three he commands them to wait patiently, to walk orderly, and to work faithfully in the light of Christ's return.

10. **CHRIST SEEN:**

    Christ is seen as the Avenger and the Coming Lord Jesus Christ.

I TIMOTHY

1. **TITLES:**

   A. Timothy = honoring God; honoured of God; worshipper of God
   B. The First Epistle to Timothy
   C. The Book of The Minister -- Qualifications

2. **AUTHOR:**

   Written by Paul, the apostle to the Gentiles.

3. **DATE:**

   Probably written between 61 and 65 A.D. after Paul's first imprisonment at Rome (Acts 28).

4. **KEY WORDS:**

A.	Faith, Believe (1 Greek root) ------------	35	D.	Godliness --------------------------------	9
B.	Good ------------------------------------	23	E.	Doctrine (s) -----------------------------	9
C.	Charge, Command (ing, ment) ----------	11	F.	Teach (er, ers) --------------------------	8

5. **KEY VERSES:**   3:15; 6:11, 12

6. **PURPOSE:**

   A. To warn against false teachers.
   B. To give instruction regarding sound doctrine.
   C. To set forth the qualifications of elders and deacons.
   D. To encourage Timothy concerning his ministry.

7. **MESSAGE:**

   A. The minister that is given to godliness will be good and faithful.
   B. The true minister will teach sound doctrine and will fulfill the charge given him.
   C. The relationship between older ministries and younger ministries is to be a "father-son" relationship.

8. **OUTLINE:**

   I.   Charge Concerning Sound Doctrine . . . . Ch. 1
   II.   Charge Concerning Public Worship . . . . Ch. 2
   III. Charge Concerning Church Officers . . . . Ch. 3
   IV.   Charge Concerning False Teachers . . . . Ch. 4
   V.   Charge Concerning Members of the Congregation . . . . Ch. 5
   VI.   Charge Concerning the Minister Himself . . . . Ch. 6

   (by H. A. Kent)

9. **SUMMARY:**

   This book is one of Paul's four personal epistles, written to individuals rather than to churches. Timothy was probably converted under Paul's ministry at Lystra (Acts 14 with I Tim. 1:2). Seven years later he had matured spiritually so that he was "well reported of", and became Paul's traveling companion (Acts 16). In chapter one, Paul points out the necessity and responsibility of maintaining sound doctrine. Paul's exhortation in chapter two deals with prayer and the roles of men and women in public worship. Chapter three is given to the qualifications of elders and deacons and the importance of maintaining them. Chapter four shows the minister's relationship to false teachers and chapter five deals with the minister's care for the various members of the congregation. Paul closes the epistle in chapter six with a personal charge to Timothy.

10. **CHRIST SEEN:**

   Christ is seen as the Elder (Ruler), the Deacon (Servant), and the Good Teacher who was faithful to the charge given Him.

II TIMOTHY

1. **TITLES:**

   A. Timothy = honouring God; honoured of God; worshipper of God
   B. The Second Epistle to Timothy
   C. The Book of The Minister -- Doctrine

2. **AUTHOR:**

   Written by Paul, the apostle to the Gentiles.

3. **DATE:**

   Probably written between 63 and 68 A.D. during Paul's second imprisonment at Rome. This was his last epistle written.

4. **KEY WORDS:**

   A. Faith, Faithful, Believe (1 Greek root) ----------------- 12
   B. Doctrine, Teach (er, ers) -------------------------------- 8
   C. Words (s) --- 7
   D. Truth --- 6
   E. Ashamed --- 4

5. **KEY VERSES:** 4:1 - 5

6. **PURPOSE:**

   A. To summon Timothy to come to Rome (4:9, 11, 13, 21).
   B. To direct Timothy as to a proper course of action in a time of apostacy.

7. **MESSAGE:**

   A. The true minister of Christ should not be ashamed.
   B. The true minister will be faithful in times of apostacy.
   C. The true minister will be sound in doctrine, teaching and preaching the word of truth.

8. **OUTLINE:**

   I. Charge Concerning the Testimony of Christ . . . . Ch. I
   II. Charge Concerning the Service of Christ . . . . Ch. 2
   III. Charge Concerning Apostacy from Christ . . . . Ch. 3
   IV. Charge Concerning the Word of Christ . . . . Ch. 4:1 - 5
   V. Paul's Farewell . . . . Ch. 4:6 - 22

   (by H.A. Kent)

9. **SUMMARY:**

   This was the last of Paul's four personal epistles, and was written just prior to his death. (Refer to the summary of I Timothy for background information concerning Timothy.) In chapter one Paul exhorts Timothy not to be ashamed of Christ, His Testimony, nor His servants by using himself and Onesiphorus as examples. In chapter two he uses several illustrations to exhort Timothy to be strong in his service. In chapter three he foretells of and explicitly describes the coming apostacy. Then in chapter four he charges Timothy to preach the Word as a true minister of Christ and he closes with personal instructions and greetings. It is also worthy to note that Paul here acknowledges that the end of his life and ministry is at hand (4:6 - 8).

10. **CHRIST SEEN:**

    Christ is seen as the Saviour (1:10), the Seed of David (2:8), the Righteous Judge (4:8), and the Lord of the Heavenly Kingdom (4:18).

TITUS

1. **TITLES:**

    A. Titus = pleasant, honourable, nurse, or rearer
    B. The Epistle to Titus
    C. The Book of The Minister -- Godliness

2. **AUTHOR:**

    Written by Paul, the apostle to the Gentiles.

3. **DATE:**

    Probably written between 62 and 66 A.D. after Paul's first imprisonment at Rome (Acts 28).

4. **KEY WORDS:**

    A. Good --- 11
    B. Work (s) --- 8
    C. Saviour -- 6
    D. Sound -- 5
    E. Doctrine --- 4
    F. Teach (ers, ing) --- 4
    G. Godly (ness, un) --- 3

5. **KEY VERSES:** 2:11 - 14

6. **PURPOSE:**

    A. To give to Titus specific instructions as to the qualifications of elders in the churches of Crete.
    B. To show the life of godliness that is to be lived by God's grace.
    C. To exhort Titus to teach sound doctrine.

7. **MESSAGE:**

    A. The teaching of sound doctrine leads to godliness of character and to good works.
    B. True godliness is embodied not in what we say but in what we are and do.
    C. A true appreciation of the grace of God will provide motivation for good works.

8. **OUTLINE:**

    I.   Godliness in the Church ------------ Qualifications of Ministers .... Ch. 1
    II.   Godliness in the Home -------------- Character of Believers .... Ch. 2
    III. Godliness in the World ------------- Conduct of Believers .... Ch. 3

9. **SUMMARY:**

    This book is one of Paul's four personal epistles, written to individuals rather than to churches. Titus, like Timothy, was Paul's son in the faith and became one of his traveling companions. He is not named in Acts but is referred to several times in the Pauline epistles. Titus had been left in Crete to establish and set in order the churches there (1:5). Thus Paul writes to Titus giving him instructions how to carry out his mission. Chapter one emphasizes church order, giving qualifications for elders. In chapter two, Paul exhorts Titus to teach sound doctrine, showing the godly character it produces, especially in the home. Chapter three deals with the practical realm of maintaining good works and avoiding evil. Also note that this epistle contains more references to Jesus Christ as "God our Saviour" than any other New Testament book! (1:3, 4; 2:10, 13; 3:4, 6).

10. **CHRIST SEEN:**

    Christ is seen as our Saviour (1:3), the Grace of God (2:11), and our Redeemer (2:14).

PHILEMON

1. **TITLES:**

   A. Philemon = friendship
   B. The Epistle to Philemon
   C. The Book of Reconciliation

2. **AUTHOR:**

   Written by Paul, the apostle to the Gentiles.

3. **DATE:**

   Probably written between 57 and 62 A.D. during Paul's first imprisonment at Rome (Acts 28).

4. **KEY WORDS:**

   A. Brother -- 4
   B. Receive --- 3
   C. Love ('s) --- 3
   D. Prisoner (fellow) ------------------------------------- 3

5. **KEY VERSES:**   9, 15, 16

6. **PURPOSE:**

   A. To persuade Philemon to receive Onesimus as a brother in the Lord rather than as a runaway slave.
   B. To inform Philemon that Paul would soon be released from prison and would visit him.

7. **MESSAGE:**

   A. We are to receive one another as Christ also has received us (Rom. 15:7).
   B. Regardless of our social position we are all brethren in the Lord.

8. **OUTLINE:**

   I.   Paul's Commendation of Philemon . . . . v. 1 - 7
   II. Paul's Intercession for Onesimus . . . . v. 8 - 21
   III. Paul's Salutation . . . . v. 22 - 25

9. **SUMMARY:**

   This book is one of Paul's four personal epistles, written to individuals rather than to churches. It centers around three persons:

   Philemon -- The Master
   Onesimus -- The Runaway Slave
   Paul --------- The Intercessor

   Philemon, a wealthy Christian of Colosse, had apparently been robbed by a runaway slave, Onesimus (v. 10, 11, 16, 18). Onesimus fled to Rome and was there led to the Lord by Paul. Paul then intended to send him back to Philemon (v. 12, 15, 16), and wrote this epistle to intercede for him. Onesimus returned with Tychicus, who carried the letters to the Ephesians and the Colossians.

   This epistle presents a beautiful picture of the Gospel of the grace of God. God our master (Philemon) receives His runaway slaves (Onesimus) because of the intercession of the mediator (Paul).

10. **CHRIST SEEN:**

   Christ is seen as our Intercessor, our Advocate.

HEBREWS

1. **TITLES:**

   A. The Epistle to the Hebrews
   B. The Book of Christ's Priesthood

2. **AUTHOR:**

   Uncertain. Suggested authors are Luke, Apollos, Barnabas, and Paul; but the weight of historical and internal evidence points to Pauline authorship.

3. **DATE:**

   Probably written between 63 and 68 A.D. just prior to the destruction of the Temple and its services in 70 A.D. (8:4; 9:6; 10:11; 13:10).

4. **KEY WORDS:**

A.	Priest (s, hood)	37	F.	Perfect (1 Greek root)	14
B.	Faith	32	G.	Eternal, Forever	14
C.	Blood	22	H.	Better	13
D.	Let, Let us	18	I.	Once (for all)	11
E.	Heaven (s, ly)	16	J.	Lest	11

5. **KEY VERSE:** 4:14

6. **PURPOSE:**

   A. To wean Hebrew Christians from Judaism to Christianity and to warn them against apostasy.
   B. To present the Lord Jesus Christ in His absolute pre-eminence as the final and complete revelation of God.
   C. To set forth the Promises, Sacrifice, Priesthood, and Sanctuary of the New Covenant in Christ.

7. **MESSAGE:**

   A. The cure for spiritual relapse and apostasy is a right conception of the Glory and Work of Christ.
   B. Faith in the blood of our eternal, perfect, and heavenly priest is better than that which was shadowed forth in the Old Covenant.

8. **OUTLINE:**

   I. Doctrinal Exposition . . . . Ch. 1 - 10
   II. Practical Exhortations . . . . Ch. 11 - 13

9. **SUMMARY:**

   This epistle was written to Hebrew believers who were under pressure to return to Judaism. Thus it is a book of comparison and contrast, showing the SON to be better than the prophets, the angels, Adam, Moses, Joshua, and Abraham. The New Covenant with its heavenly sanctuary, Melchisedec priesthood and once for all sacrifice is better than the Old Covenant with its earthly sanctuary, Aaronic Priesthood, and continual animal sacrifices. The summary is that all these things that were involved in the earthly Zion and earthly Jerusalem were only the shadow of the heavenly Zion and heavenly Jerusalem. This epistle gives the fullest exposition and interpretation of the sanctuary service set forth in Exodus and Leviticus. Hebrews and Romans stand together as the two great doctrinal epistles of the New Testament.

10. **CHRIST SEEN:**

   Christ is seen as the Word, the Angel of Jehovah, the Last Adam, The Prophet, the True Joshua (Saviour), the High Priest after the order of Melchisedec; Minister and Sacrifice of the New Covenant Sanctuary, and the Author and Finisher of all Faith.

JAMES

1. **TITLES:**

   A. James = supplanter
   B. The Epistle of James
   C. The Book of Faith And Works

2. **AUTHOR:**

   Uncertain. Most scholars ascribe the authorship of this epistle to either James the son of Joseph or James the son of Alphaeus. The weight of evidence leans toward James the son of Alphaeus, who was one of the twelve apostles.

3. **DATE:**

   Probably written between 45 and 53 A.D. thus making it the first of the New Testament epistles to be written.

4. **KEY WORDS:**

   A. Faith --- 16
   B. Work (s) --- 16
   C. Law --- 10

5. **KEY VERSES:** 2:17, 18

6. **PURPOSE:**

   A. To comfort and encourage Hebrew believers who were going through severe trials and temptations (1:2; 5:8).
   B. To correct some disorders and misconceptions among the Hebrew believers' assemblies.
   C. To refute the tendency to divorce faith and works.

7. **MESSAGE:**

   A. True faith is shown by its good works.
   B. Good works are not a means to salvation, but rather are the product of salvation.
   C. Though man is not justified by the law of works, he is justified by the law of faith-works.

8. **OUTLINE:**

   I.   Faith Tested and Shown by our TEMPTATIONS . . . . .1:1 - 21
   II.   Faith Shown by our WORKS . . . . .1:22 - 2:26
   III. Faith Shown by our WORDS . . . . 3:1 - 18
   IV.   Faith Shown by our UNWORLDLINESS . . . . .4:1 - 5 - 6
   V.   Faith Shown by our PATIENCE . . . . 5:7 - 12
   VI.   Faith Shown by our PRAYERS . . . . .5:13 - 20

   (by Robert Lee)

9. **SUMMARY:**

   The apostle James became known as the bishop of the Jerusalem church. He wrote this epistle from Jerusalem "to the twelve tribes scattered abroad" (the Hebrew believers living in other lands). Rather than writing a doctrinal treatise, he wrote an epistle of practical Christian living, showing that in every area the "heart" of the matter is seen by its "fruit". He relates the principle of faith to trial, temptation, works, words, worldliness, patience, and prayers. There is no conflict between Paul and James concerning faith and works as some have suggested. Paul, in Romans, deals with justification by faith, apart from works, before salvation (Rom. 3:27, 28). James deals with justification by works after salvation (Jas. 2:20 - 24).

   NOTE: There is a remarkable correspondence between James and the Sermon on the Mount, and there is hardly a thought that cannot be traced to Christ's personal teaching.

10. **CHRIST SEEN:**

   Christ is seen as the Lord of Glory (2:1), the Judge (4:12), the Lord of Hosts (5:4), the Husbandman (5:7), and the One who demonstrated perfect faith by perfect works.

I PETER

1. **TITLES:**

   A. Peter = stone, rock
   B. The First Epistle of Peter
   C. The Book of Suffering and Glory

2. **AUTHOR:**

   Written by Peter, a fisherman, who was one of the twelve apostles.

3. **DATE:**

   Probably written between 63 and 65 A.D.

4. **KEY WORDS:**

   A. Suffer (ed, ing, ings) ---------------------------------- 16
   B. Glory, Glorify (ied) ------------------------------- 16
   C. Grace (Greek word) ----------------------------- 10
   D. Precious -- 5
   E. Hope (Greek word) ----------------------------- 5

5. **KEY VERSES:** 4:12, 13

6. **PURPOSE:**

   A. To encourage the Christians suffering under persecution.
   B. To prepare the Christians for greater trial ahead.
   C. To show the Christians the hope of glory that lies ahead.
   D. To exhort them to fulfill practical Christian duties.

7. **MESSAGE:**

   A. God will balance out the believer's sufferings with glory and their glories with suffering.
   B. Suffering purifies and proves the believer's faith and character.
   C. Christ is the "pattern-stone" of suffering and glory.
   D. The cause of the believer's suffering should only be his godliness and not his lack of discretion.

8. **OUTLINE:**

   I. Suffering in Relation to Salvation . . . . 1:1 - 2:10
   II. Suffering in Relation to Conduct . . . . 2:11 - 4:11
   III. Suffering in Relation to Attitude . . . . 4:12 - 5:11

9. **SUMMARY:**

   The apostle Peter while a disciple of Jesus had been given the initial revelation of the sufferings of Christ and the glory that should follow in the church. It is upon this experience that the themes of his epistles are built. The theme of this first epistle is glory through suffering. In the first section suffering is seen in relation to salvation, emphasizing the living hope, the living word, the living stone and our reaction to the same. The second section deals with suffering in relation to conduct, covering every area of life and setting forth Christ as the example. The final section concerns suffering in relation to attitudes in both shepherds and sheep. It should be noted that in every context where "suffering" appears "glory" is also to be found.

   NOTE: One good approach to studying the epistles of Peter is to relate his writings to his own life as revealed in the Gospels and the Acts.

10. **CHRIST SEEN:**

   Christ is seen as the Foreordained Lamb, the Chief-Cornerstone, the Stone of Stumbling, the Rock of Offence, the Example, the Chief Shepherd, and the Bishop of our Souls, who experienced the sufferings of the Cross and was crowned with Glory and Honour.

II PETER

1. **TITLES:**

   A. Peter = stone, rock
   B. The Second Epistle of Peter
   C. The Book of True Knowledge

2. **AUTHOR:**

   Written by Peter, a fisherman, who was one of the twelve apostles.

3. **DATE:**

   Probably written between 63 and 67 A.D.

4. **KEY WORDS:**

   A. Know (n, ing, eth), Knowledge ---------------------------- 16
   B. Day (s) -- 12
   C. Righteous (ness) (2 Greek words) ------------------------- 8
   D. Judgment --- 4
   E. Remembrance -- 4
   F. Corruption (Greek word) ---------------------------------- 4

5. **KEY VERSES:** 3:17, 18

6. **PURPOSE:**

   A. To stir the saints to godliness.
   B. To warn them of false teachers and scoffers within.
   C. To contrast true and false knowledge.
   D. To describe the judgments relative to the day of the Lord.

7. **MESSAGE:**

   A. True knowledge is evidenced by growth in godliness.
   B. The believer must remain pure and loyal in days of corruption and apostacy.
   C. All doctrinal and moral corruption will be judged at the day of the Lord.

8. **OUTLINE:**

   I.   The Nature of True Knowledge . . . . Ch. 1
   II.   The Peril of Abandoning True Knowledge . . . . Ch. 2
   III. The Promise in True Knowledge . . . . Ch. 3

9. **SUMMARY:**

   While I Peter is built upon Matthew 16, this second epistle arises out of Peter's experience on the Mount of Transfiguration in Matthew 17. The theme of this second epistle is the contrast between true and false knowledge. In chapter one Peter points out that the nature and character of true knowledge is expressed in Christian growth. Chapter two deals with error; stating its invasion, giving its examples, exposing its activities, and warning of its danger. In chapter three, the promise of the Coming of the Lord is confirmed and explained with emphasis on its being a day of wrath to all those who persist in false knowledge. In contrast the first epistle was written to encourage, the second to warn; the first shows the suffering and glory of the believers, the second the suffering and judgment of the unbelievers; the first emphasizes persecutions from without, the second heresies within.

   NOTE: Much of the material in chapter two is also to be found in Jude and these two passages should be studied in conjunction.

10. **CHRIST SEEN:**

    Christ is seen as the Beloved Son, the Daystar, and the Coming Lord.

I JOHN

1. **TITLES:**

   A. John = gift of God
   B. The First Epistle of John
   C. The Book of Love

2. **AUTHOR:**

   Written by John the Beloved, the author of the Gospel, three Epistles, and the Revelation.

3. **DATE:**

   Probably written between 85 and 90 A.D.

4. **KEY WORDS:**

   A. Love (d, th) --- 46
   B. Know (2 Greek words) ------------------------------ 42
   C. Sin (s, ed, eth) ------------------------------------- 28
   D. World ('s) -- 23
   E. Life -- 15
   F. Abide (th, ing) -------------------------------------- 12

5. **KEY VERSE:** 4:16

6. **PURPOSE:**

   A. To refute the heresy of Gnosticism born out of apostate Judaism and corrupt Paganism.
   B. To exhort the believer concerning his relationship to God, the brethren, the world, and sin.
   C. To show that true knowledge of God involves a personal relationship with Him.

7. **MESSAGE:**

   A. If we truly know God and are in fellowship with Him, then we will not love the world, but will walk in light and walk in love.
   B. If the believer abides in life he will not live in sin.

8. **OUTLINE:**

   I. God is Light . . . . Ch. 1, 2
   II. God is Love . . . . Ch. 3,4
   III. God is Life . . . . Ch. 5

9. **SUMMARY:**

   This epistle was born out of John's intimate relationship with and his personal knowledge of the Lord Jesus as seen in his Gospel. Converts from Judaism and Paganism sought to mingle the theories of their former beliefs with the truth of the Gospel. This eventually led to the rise and development of the deadly heresy of Gnosticism. While admitting the Deity of Jesus they denied His humanity and boasted that they alone as Gnostics ("knowing ones") had the true knowledge. They despised those who maintained true apostolic doctrine. Thus John writes to assure the believers that they are the "knowing ones", having the true knowledge of Christ. In chapters one and two he applies the truth that "God is light and in Him is no darkness at all" to the believer's walk. Chapters three and four show that if a believer has true knowledge of God he will walk in love toward God and the brethren. The key thought in chapter five is "He that hath the Son hath life".

10. **CHRIST SEEN:**

   Christ is seen as the Word, the Son, our Advocate, our Propitiation, the Christ, the Light, Love, and Life.

II JOHN

1. **TITLES:**

   A. John = gift of God
   B. The Second Epistle of John
   C. The Book of Truth -- Doctrinal

2. **AUTHOR:**

   Written by John the Beloved, the author of the Gospel, three Epistles, and the Revelation.

3. **DATE:**

   Probably written between 85 and 90 A.D.

4. **KEY WORDS:**

   A. Truth ('s) --- 5
   B. Commandment (s) ------------------------------- 4
   C. Love --- 4
   D. Doctrine --- 3
   E. Walk (ing) -- 3

5. **KEY VERSES:** 9,10

6. **PURPOSE:**

   A. To warn against the deceivers that come in the spirit of the Anti-Christ.
   B. To instruct against receiving such deceivers.
   C. To encourage them to abide in the doctrine of Christ.

7. **MESSAGE:**

   A. The believer is to walk in the commandment of love and abide in true doctrine.
   B. The believer is not even to be hospitable to deceivers and transgressors of the doctrine of Christ who are anti-christs.

8. **OUTLINE:**

   I.   Walking in True Doctrine . . . . v. 1 - 6
   II. Falling from True Doctrine . . . . v. 7 - 13

9. **SUMMARY:**

   This second epistle of John is either a personal epistle written to a Christian lady and her children or a church epistle written to a local church and its members. In either circumstance the truth of the epistle is intended for all believers. In the first section of the epistle John emphasizes walking in true doctrine, keeping the commandment of love. The second section gives warning concerning those who transgress true doctrine, showing that they are deceivers and anti-christs. He exhorts them not even to show hospitality to those false brethren. The basic principles in this epistle arise from the teachings of Christ found in John's Gospel.

10. **CHRIST SEEN:**

   Christ is seen as the Truth, the Son, and the Christ who is come in the flesh.

III JOHN

1. **TITLES:**

   A. John = gift of God
   B. The Third Epistle of John
   C. The Book of Truth -- Practical

2. **AUTHOR:**

   Written by John the Beloved, the author of the Gospel, three epistles, and the Revelation.

3. **DATE:**

   Probably written between 85 and 90 A.D.

4. **KEY WORDS:**

   A. Truth, True --- 7
   B. Receive (th) --- 3
   C. Walk (est) --- 2
   D. Love (th) -- 2

5. **KEY VERSE:** 3

6. **PURPOSE:**

   A. To encourage Gaius in his reception of the brethren.
   B. To assure Gaius that John himself would deal with the arrogant Diotrephes when he next visited the church.
   C. To bear record of Demetrius' good report in the truth.

7. **MESSAGE:**

   A. Believers must be willing to receive the brethren and show hospitality to them.
   B. Any leader who desires to have the pre-eminence will by his deeds bring himself under divine discipline.
   C. Christianity is a practical walk in truth and love.

8. **OUTLINE:**

I.	Exhortation ----------	Gaius . . . . v. 1 - 8
II.	Condemnation --------	Diotrephes . . . . v. 9 - 11
III.	Commendation ------	Demetrius . . . . v. 12 - 14

9. **SUMMARY:**

   This third epistle of John is a personal epistle written to Gaius. In the early church there were various believers called to itinerant ministry. Having no guarantee of material support they were dependent on the hospitality of the Christians in the cities in which they ministered. John had sent certain brethren and had written to the church to receive them, but Diotrephes, a leader in the church, refused to receive them. He manifested an arrogant domineering spirit by threatening with excommunication any members who would receive them. Thus John writes concerning this situation commending Gaius for receiving them and assuring him that he would deal with the matter personally upon his arrival. This epistle centers around three men, showing their relation to truth and love:

Gaius ------------	well-beloved, kind, generous, hospitable
Diotrephes ----	arrogant, autocratic, domineering
Demetrius -----	well-reported, commendable

   While II John warns against receiving false teachers who deny the doctrine of Christ, III John warns against refusing to receive those who are true ministers of Christ.

10. **CHRIST SEEN:**

    Christ is seen as the Truth.

JUDE

1. **TITLES:**

    A. Jude = praise
    B. The Epistle of Jude
    C. The Acts of the Apostates
    D. The Book of The Apostates

2. **AUTHOR:**

    Uncertain. Most authors ascribe the authorship of this epistle to either Jude the son of Joseph or Jude the son of Alphaeus. The weight of evidence leans toward Jude the son of Alphaeus, who was one of the twelve apostles and the brother of James (See James).

3. **DATE:**

    Written probably between 67 and 80 A.D.

4. **KEY WORDS:**

    A. Ungodly --- 6
    B. Kept (Greek word) ---------------------------- 5
    C. Eternal, Forever ------------------------------- 4

5. **KEY VERSE:** 3

6. **PURPOSE:**

    A. To exhort believers to contend for the faith.
    B. To warn them of apostate teachers and to expose their character, doctine and deeds by example and illustration.
    C. To comfort them in view of apostacy.

7. **MESSAGE:**

    A. True believers in the midst of apostacy must contend for the faith.
    B. All the ungodly will be brought to eternal judgment by fire.
    C. God is always faithful to keep his elect from falling.

8. **OUTLINE:**

    I.   Contending For the Faith . . . . v. 1 - 4
    II. Apostacy From the Faith . . . . v. 5 - 16
    III. Keeping the Faith . . . . v. 17 - 25

9. **SUMMARY:**

    Jude opens his epistle by commenting that he had intended to write concerning "the common salvation" but that he was constrained by the spirit to write concerning a different matter. False teachers had crept in, denying the faith and giving birth to apostacy in the church. Jude, then, exhorts the believers to contend for the faith. He exposes the false teachers by using examples from history and illustrations from nature and then he foretells of their certain judgment at the Lord's coming. Lastly he exhorts and encourages the believers concerning their remaining steadfast in the faith.

    NOTE: This is the only book that refers to the contention over the body of Moses and the prophecy of Enoch.

    NOTE: Much of the material in Jude is also to be found in II Peter 2 and these two passages should be studied in conjunction.

    NOTE: This epistle is made up of triads.

10. **CHRIST SEEN:**

    Christ is seen as the Coming Lord, the Judge and "The Only Wise God, our Saviour".

REVELATION

1. **TITLES:**

    A. The Revelation
    B. The Apocalypse
    C. The Book of Ultimates

2. **AUTHOR:**

    Written by John the Beloved, the author of the Gospel and three epistles.

3. **DATE:**

    Probably written between 90 and 96 A.D.

4. **KEY WORDS:**

A.	Angel (s 's)	76	H.	King (s, dom)	30
B.	See, saw (est)	65	I.	Book (s)	30
C.	Seven (th)	59	J.	Lamb ('s)	29
D.	Hear (d, eth)	46	K.	Spirit (s)	22
E.	Throne (s)	40	L.	Church (es)	20
F.	Name (s, 's)	36	M.	White	19
G.	Twelve, Twenty-four	30			

5. **KEY VERSE:**   1:19

6. **PURPOSE:**

    A. To give a revelation of the Lord Jesus Christ in the glory of His varied offices.
    B. To give instruction, encouragement and rebuke to the seven local churches in Asia.
    C. To give to the universal church a prophetic panorama of events from the First to the Second Coming of Christ.
    D. To bring into focus the ultimate conclusion of the plan of redemption which was begun in Genesis, the book of Creation.

7. **MESSAGE:**

    A. The Kingdom of God will ultimately and completely triumph over all evil.
    B. Those who overcome the world, the flesh, and the devil will receive everlasting rewards.
    C. A true witness must be able to testify of that which he has seen and heard.

8. **OUTLINE:**

I.	Things Seen	The Glorified Christ	Ch. 1
II.	Things Which are	The Ministering Christ	Ch. 2, 3
III.	Things Hereafter	The Triumphant Christ	Ch. 4 - 22

9. **SUMMARY:**

    John was in exile on the Isle of Patmos. There, while caught up in the spirit, he was given a series of visions showing the progressive unfolding of events from the First Coming through to the New Heavens and New Earth. The first three chapters show Christ's relationship to His church, local and universal. The remainder of the book deals with the following subjects; the seven-sealed book (Rev. 4 - 7), the seven trumpets (Rev. 8 - 11), the tribulation (Rev. 12 - 14), the seven vials (Rev. 15, 16), Mystery Babylon (Rev. 17, 18), the Second Coming, the Kingdom and the New Heavens and New Earth (Rev. 19 - 22). All that began in Genesis pertaining to the Old Creation, finds its consummation in Revelation which then introduces the New Creation.

10. **CHRIST SEEN:**

    Christ is seen as the Head of the Church, the Lamb, the Lion of the Tribe of Judah, the Jehovah Angel, the Bridegroom, the Word, and the King of Kings and the Lord of Lords.

HISTORICAL BACKGROUND - FROM THE OLD TESTAMENT THROUGH THE NEW TESTAMENT

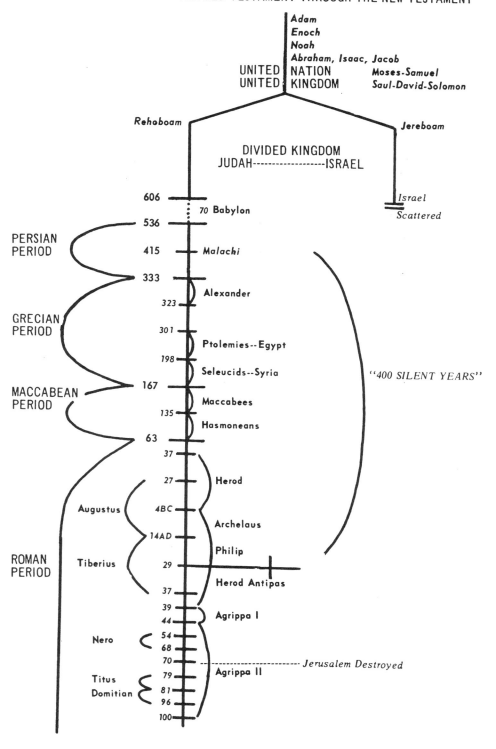

Adam
Enoch
Noah
Abraham, Isaac, Jacob
Moses-Samuel
Saul-David-Solomon

UNITED NATION
UNITED KINGDOM

Rehoboam

Jereboam

DIVIDED KINGDOM
JUDAH------------------ISRAEL

606

70 Babylon

Israel
Scattered

PERSIAN
PERIOD

536

415   Malachi

333

Alexander
323

GRECIAN
PERIOD

301

Ptolemies--Egypt
198

Seleucids--Syria

"400 SILENT YEARS"

MACCABEAN
PERIOD

167

Maccabees
135

Hasmoneans

63

37

27   Herod

Augustus

4BC

Archelaus
14AD

Philip

ROMAN
PERIOD

Tiberius

29

Herod Antipas

37

39

Agrippa I
44

Nero

54
68

70   ------------------------ Jerusalem Destroyed

Titus
Domitian

79   Agrippa II
81
96
100

THE AUTHORS OF THE NEW TESTAMENT

NATIONALITY	AUTHOR	MINISTRY OCCUPATION	BOOK
JEW	MATTHEW	APOSTLE TAX-COLLECTOR	MATTHEW
JEW/ROMAN	MARK	MISSIONARY DISCIPLE OF PETER	MARK
GREEK	LUKE	DISCIPLE OF PAUL PHYSICIAN	LUKE ACTS
JEW	JOHN	APOSTLE FISHERMAN	JOHN I JOHN II JOHN III JOHN REVELATION
JEW	JAMES	APOSTLE?	JAMES
JEW	JUDE	APOSTLE?	JUDE
JEW	PETER	APOSTLE FISHERMAN	I PETER II PETER
JEW	PAUL	APOSTLE TENTMAKER PHARISEE	ROMANS I CORINTHIANS II CORINTHIANS GALATIANS EPHESIANS PHILIPPIANS COLOSSIANS I THESSALONIANS II THESSALONIANS I TIMOTHY II TIMOTHY TITUS PHILEMON HEBREWS?

BACKGROUND FOR PAULINE EPISTLES

BACKGROUND FOR	CITIES	ACTS REFERENCE
GALATIANS	ANTIOCH, ICONIUM, LYSTRA, DERBE	ACTS 13:14-14:28
PHILIPPIANS	PHILIPPI	ACTS 16:11-40
I & II THESSALONIANS	THESSALONICA	ACTS 17:1-9
I & II CORINTHIANS	CORINTH	ACTS 18:1-16
EPHESIANS	EPHESUS	ACTS 19:1-41; 20:17-38 20:17-38

BOOK	WHERE WRITTEN	ACTS REFERENCE
GALATIANS	ANTIOCH	ACTS 14
I & II THESSALONIANS	CORINTH	ACTS 18
I CORINTHIANS	EPHESUS	ACTS 19
II CORINTHIANS	MACEDONIA	ACTS 20:1,2
ROMANS	CORINTH	ACTS 20:2
COLOSSIANS		
PHILEMON	ROME	ACTS 28:30
EPHESIANS		
PHILIPPIANS		
I TIMOTHY		
TITUS		
II TIMOTHY	ROME AFTER "ACTS IMPRISONMENT"	
HEBREWS		

THE UNFOLDING REVELATION IN THE EPISTLES

In the New Testament we find that the epistles are built upon the foundation of the gospels and Acts. The purpose of this supplement is to point out how the key subjects of the epistles find their basis in the four gospels. Through the gospels we come to know Christ after the spirit. While the gospels declare historical facts, the epistles interpret those facts in setting forth doctrine.

GOSPELS

Christ after flesh
Declare
History

EPISTLES

Christ after spirit
Interpret
Doctrine

EPISTLE	KEY SUBJECTS	GOSPEL BASIS
Romans	Justification By Faith	Jn.3:16
I & II Cor.	N.T. Church Order	Mt.16:18
Galatians	Law & Grace; Liberty	Mk.14:24;Jn.8:36
Ephesians	The Body;Church-Eternal Purpose	Mt.16:18
Philippians	Joy & Rejoicing	Jn.15:11
Colossians	The Head (Majesty of Christ)	Mt.28:19,20
I & II Thess.	2nd Coming; Anti-Christ	Jn.14:1-3
Tim.;Titus	Pastoral Epistles;Elders & Deacons	Lk.11:49;Mt.23:34
Philemon	Reconciliation	Mt.5:24;18:15
Hebrews	Christ's Priesthood;Perfection	Mk.10:45;Mt.5:48
James	Faith & Works	Mt.5-7
I Peter	Suffering & Glory; Church	Mt.16:18,21,27
II Peter	2nd Coming;False Prophets	Mt.24
I,II,III John	Love,Light,Life;Anti-Christ	Jn.1,6,11,13
Jude	The Acts of the Apostates	Mt.24
Revelation	2nd Coming; Ultimates	Lk.19:11-27;Jn.5:29

"But the Word of the Lord was unto them precept upon precept, line upon line, here a little, and there a little." Isaiah 28:13

"I have yet many things to say unto you, but ye cannot bear them now...when the Spirit of Truth is come, He will guide you into all Truth..." John 16:12,13

Cacti and Succulents in Habitat

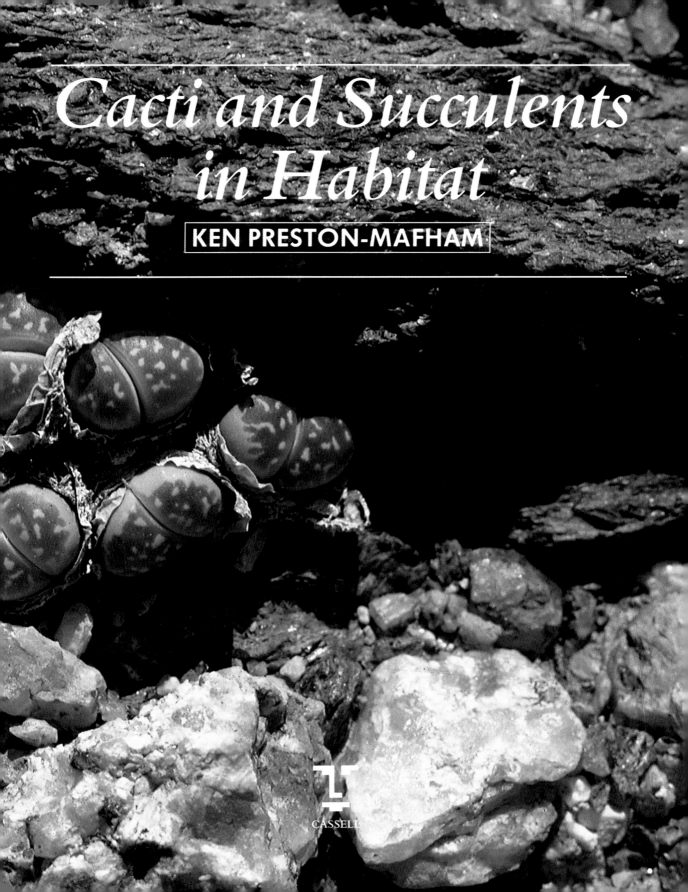

Cacti and Succulents
in Habitat

KEN PRESTON-MAFHAM

CASSELL

Authors note: to help the reader identify the plant illustrated, the scientific names of these plants have been set in bold type

A CASSELL BOOK

First published in the UK
1994 by Cassell
Wellington House
125 Strand
London
WC2R 0BB

First Paperback edition 1995
Reprinted 1995

Distributed in the United States
by Sterling Publishing Co., Inc.
387 Park Avenue South, New York, NY 10016-8810

Distributed in Australia
by Capricorn Link (Australia) Pty Ltd
P.O. Box 665, Lane Cove, NSW 2066

ISBN 0-304-34551-2

A catalogue record for this book is
available from the British Library

Typeset by Litho Link Ltd., Welshpool, Powys.

Printed and bound in Singapore by Kyodo Printing Co Ltd

Page 1: *Lobivia lateritia*
Title page: *Lithops Olivacea*

CONTENTS

INTRODUCTION

The main aim of this book is to illustrate how surprisingly easy it is to find cacti and succulents in their natural habitats. At the same time, by portraying (where it is helpful) more than one plant from a single locality, I have been able to convey something of the perplexing variation in appearance exhibited by many species, especially in the Cactaceae. This variation can include the shape and the colour of the body; the length, flexibility, number and colour of the spines; and the colour of the flowers, along with the shape of the petals and the length of the tube. In the past this has led many workers to single out one or more noticeably aberrant specimens from a single population for description as separate varieties or even separate species. Although such oddballs may look very different from their neighbours, their elevation to anything more than cultivar status cannot be justified. Such behaviour is, after all, on a par with picking out the most unusual-looking people from a crowd on the basis of characteristics such as height, hair colour and length of noses, and then flattering them with specific names!

By showing some of the natural variations which occur in the wild, I hope to give readers a better understanding of why so many cactus names have disappeared over the last few years, sinking into synonymy with earlier species. This has happened more and more of late, due to a gradual realization that many of our recent 'novelties' are just familiar old-stagers thinly disguised with fancy new names.

The chief difference between the present work and the numerous excellent and comprehensive travelogues which have appeared over the years in the specialist journals is in its use of *colour* throughout. This enables the full beauty of the plants to be appreciated to an extent which is impossible with the mainly black-and-white pictures used in the specialist literature. We have also chosen to have our pictures a much larger size, thus increasing the amount of detail which can be seen. The illustrations are substantially more attractive and useful in generally depicting plants in flower too. As the main flowering time (at least in the South American cacti) coincides with the rainy season, the pursuit of plants in bloom is far more difficult and hazardous. However, the results are certainly worthwhile when compared with the pictures of shrivelled, sterile plants which result from journeys made under the more favourable travel conditions of the dry season.

Bolivia

I spent December 1986 in Bolivia, having travelled for the previous nine months through Costa Rica, Panama, Venezuela, Bonaire and Brazil. Bolivia boasts a wide range of cactus habitats, from the high Altiplano of the Andes to the tropical lowlands of the Yungas. This spectacular land is the sole home of that most popular of genera *Sulcorebutia*, but also hosts a plethora of other highly collectable species in the genera *Lobivia, Weingartia, Rebutia, Echinopsis* and *Parodia*. For lovers of the taller-growing cacti, there are splendid examples of *Oreocereus, Cleistocactus* and *Trichocereus*, as well as the endemic *Neocardenasia*.

The photographs in the section on Bolivia were all taken during the remarkably brief period of just under two weeks. The first fortnight of my stay was wasted because of money-exchange problems, which were finally solved only through the generous assistance of Jim Solomons of Missouri Botanic Gardens. Jim was living in La Paz in order to work on the Bolivian flora, and without his kindness and his trust in a complete stranger who shared an interest in plants I would not have been able to make the trip. In a mere thirteen days I managed to make a hectic journey from La Paz down as far south as Tarija, via Cochabamba, Sucre, Potosi and Camargo. For most of the time the weather was quite appalling. Day after day of heavy rain had turned most of the rivers into dangerous, swirling torrents which, given the lack of bridges on most Bolivian roads, made progress both slow and difficult. Sometimes a queue of vehicles had to wait for up to ten hours before it was safe for them to nose cautiously through the rushing – but now less threatening – waters as they gradually subsided. Given this constant hindrance to progress, it is truly amazing how many cacti I managed to see. This success was partly due to the fact that in Bolivia cacti are often common roadside plants which occur in their hundreds of thousands, making it unnecessary to step more than a few metres from the road in order to photograph a plant in flower. However, it was also thanks to Edgar Aguilar, who accompanied me from his home town of Cochabamba as far as Culpina. He was a fluent English-speaker and a fount of knowledge about the precise localities for many of the choicest Bolivian cacti. As well as coping with the stresses of driving under appalling conditions, Edgar was also able to point out a few of the more localized species which I should otherwise certainly have missed (for example, *Parodia occulta*). The fact that flowers were often present also made the plants conspicuous against the murky backdrop which prevailed most of the time, and indeed only the terrible weather prevented us from seeing an even greater variety of species along our route.

When choosing which plants to illustrate I have plumped almost exclusively for those that we saw in flower. I am mindful of the fact that non-flowering plants of most species of *Lobivia*, *Rebutia* and *Sulcorebutia* are not particularly attractive. In habitat this is compounded by their frequent habit of submerging themselves so thoroughly below the ground that only the top is visible. Colour pictures of such plants would be rather an extravagant waste of space, so although I have generally mentioned them in passing in the text, they have mostly been omitted from the plates. The few exceptions are species which stand on their own visual merits even without flowers (for example, *Gymnocalycium pflanzii*).

South-west United States

The same general comments apply to the section on the south-west United States. I spent three weeks during April and early May 1985 travelling through Arizona, north-western New Mexico, south-east Utah and north-west Colorado, with a brief foray into California. Sadly, during the year of my visit there had been an unusually dry winter and spring, so the display of annual flowers was rather sparse, and although the cacti flowered in normal quantities, the start of blooming was rather earlier than normal. This had the unfortunate consequence of making me miss one of my main aims: to photograph all the *Pediocactus* species in flower. This is one genus where expert assistance really is essential if a first-time visitor is going to find even a single species during a short trip. In my case expert guidance was on hand in Farmington, New Mexico, in the person of Ken Heil, the well-known authority on American cacti. However, it is worth emphasizing that even a tyro in the art of tracking down cacti in habitat would certainly have an enjoyable and rewarding time in this part of the world, where some of the most beautiful species are common roadside plants.

Southern Africa

In 1984 I spent nearly eight months driving my car around South Africa and Namibia. My main object in being there was to photograph the abundant animal life, anything from spiders and insects to lions and elephants. As a sideline to this, I allocated a small amount of time to the photography of the remarkably rich succulent flora of the region. However, in view of the secondary nature of plant photography on this trip, I had not taken along any notes about the best localities for succulents, so for most of the time I was dependent on finding them by chance. Despite this I managed to see a breathtaking diversity of species. Once or twice I was lucky enough to be shown the best spots, as at Pofadder, whose fabulous natural rockeries of succulent plants are depicted in the following pages. During my time in southern Africa I covered so much ground, from the Transvaal to Namibia, that I have had to restrict the coverage in the present volume to those species photographed during just two weeks in Namaqualand.

BOLIVIA

'Bolivia boasts a wide range of cactus habitats, from the high Altiplano of the Andes to the tropical lowlands of the Yungas. This spectacular land is the home of some of the most popular of genera.'

Scale: 0 50 100 km / 0 20 40 60 80 100 miles

Contours: 10,000 ft

PERU

■ LA PAZ
Viacha

Y u n g a s

Cochabamba ● ● Tiraque
● Cliza ● Epizana

Oruro ●

Rio Caine
Rio San Pedro
● Aiquile
Rio Mizque

Puente Arce
Rio Grande

Sucre ● ● Zudanez
● Tarabuco

Rio Grande

Potosi ● Millares
● Cuchu Ingenio

BOLIVIA

Camargo ●
● Culpina

CHILE

Tupiza ● Iscayache
● Tarija

Rio Pilcomayo

PARAGUAY

ARGENTINA

▷ *Trichocereus* species and *Oreocereus celsianus* dominate this Andean landscape at Cieneguillas.

△ Although Bolivia's capital, La Paz, is not situated in the richest zone for cacti, lying as it does at an altitude of over 3,000 metres (10,000 ft), even the immediate environs of this great city can still boast a number of interesting species. Indeed, the slim, almost spineless stems of *Trichocereus bridgesii* can be seen sticking up from roadside banks even within the city limits.

Just below the city lie the spectacular eroded clay hills of Moon Valley. The valley itself is not prime cactus habitat, but a few rather bedraggled specimens of *Oreocereus pseudofossulatus* do manage to cling precariously to the bare clay, along with the odd, rather sad representatives of *Echinopsis bridgesii*. Both are, however, much more abundant and healthy on flatter areas nearby. Behind the clay hills in this picture it is possible to discern some less

heavily eroded slopes covered in short, wiry grass. This is the kind of habitat favoured by a cactus endemic to the La Paz area, *Lobivia backebergii*.

▷ Just below Moon Valley thousands of **Oreocereus pseudofossulatus** thrive in the alluvial soils of the valley bottoms. This species is characteristic of the La Paz region, spreading southwards mainly along the gorge of the La Paz river. Spine colour varies from ginger to pale straw, and although many plants are adorned with the abundant hair which is so familiar (and expected) on our cultivated plants of this species, there are also numerous specimens which are virtually bald. By December flowering had ceased and most plants bore numerous large yellow fruits.

△ *Oreocereus pseudofossulatus* is usually accompanied by **Echinopsis bridgesii**. These were in full flower in mid-December, but as many of the plants also bore ripe fruits, the first flowers must have begun to appear as early as November, when the plants would be in an extremely shrivelled state. This dual flowering effort applies to numerous Bolivian cactus species, as I often found ripe fruits and young flower buds on the same plant. This indicates two bursts of flowers, separated by around six to eight weeks, with the first appearing at the height of the dry season in October–November, followed by another during the rains in December–January. The flowers on these *E. bridgesii* plants are beginning to wilt in mid-afternoon after opening the previous evening. The plants are still in a very shrivelled state, the long, dry season having been broken by heavy rain only the day before. This species is part of a complex which includes *E. cochabambensis* and *E. sucrensis*. Some people suggest that these (and several other names) should all be included in *E. huotii*. This would represent a single variable taxon distributed widely over the Bolivian highlands, with each superficially distinctive population grading gradually into the next.

▷ Not far from Moon Valley, is the herbarium established by the University of La Paz. Close behind a cluster of buildings, some only half finished (at least in 1986) because of financial constraints, lies a steep slope leading up on to gently rolling hills covered in small stones and a thatch of short, wiry grass. On the flat area at the base of the slope I found **Corryocactus melanotrichus**. Many of the plants were damaged and trampled by cattle and goats, but at least they stood in full, glorious flower. This species is widespread, and I was to see it later in many more localities – around Cochabamba, for example.

▽ I had no idea what might be hidden among the grass at the top of the slope, not having been given any localities for cacti in the La Paz area. Fortunately, a well-worn goat track beckoned, so I proceeded steeply upwards, despite the ominous flashes and deep rumblings which heralded the arrival of a huge thunderstorm which was already battering the nearby city. Half-way up the slope I came across this tiny **Opuntia teres**, with its sumptuous red flowers. The chance to see such a species in bloom is particularly valuable, as flowers are rarely produced in Britain. It was interesting to see how several bright red fruits had rooted where they had fallen and were growing into new plants.

△ It was now a race against time to find out what grew at the top of the slope before the approaching thunderstorm curtailed my search. The answer was revealed as soon as I stepped on to the grassy sward at the summit. Nestled among the grass lay a **Lobivia backebergii**, its flowers still wide open despite the premature darkness brought on by the storm. In frantic haste I scoured a wide area for more plants, finding a few dozen, every one in a desiccated state and shrunken tightly into the ground, making them difficult to spot unless betrayed by their small but attractive flowers. In the typical manner of the cactus family, these plants would no doubt respond rapidly to the impending deluge, becoming plump and green within twenty-four hours or so.

Most of the plants were rather small, with between one and four heads. The flowers varied only slightly, from bright red to reddish-pink, and were noticeably smaller than those in the other lobivias from this region, such as *Lobivia pentlandii* and *L. hertrichiana*. *L. backebergii* is rather locally distributed around La Paz, yet I had found it at my first try and without prior knowledge of the locality. This serves to highlight the main theme of this book – that cacti are not necessarily as elusive as the average home-based collector might sometimes think.

▷ From La Paz I made a pleasant day trip to Oruro by bus. Oruro is surrounded by hills rich in cacti, but I had been advised that the easiest places to search were the slopes behind the university. The altitude here is over 4,000 metres (13,000 ft) – considerably higher than La Paz city and quite cold when the inevitable afternoon thunderstorm drenched me in stinging rain driven hard before a stiff wind. The most prominent cactus in this area is the heavily spined **Lobivia formosa** var. **bertramiana**. A little more effort is needed to distinguish the bleached tufts of tough dry grass from the wild thatch of straw-coloured spines which clothe the hundreds of *L. ferox* scattered across the rocky slopes. The form which grows here – its type locality and also its most northerly station (it ranges down into Argentina) – is the smallest of all, and had already finished flowering. The *L. formosa* var. *bertramiana* were also mostly in fruit, but a few plants still bore their pale yellow, rather unattractive blooms.

△ The third cactus at Oruro, **Lobivia pentlandii**, still yielded a few flowers, although most plants were covered in ripe fruits. Here was an object lesson in how a whole bunch of 'new' species can be created (by Backeberg) merely on the variation between individuals in a single population. As in humans, no two *L. pentlandii* plants in this botanical crowd were exactly alike: spine length ranged from less than 1 centimetre (½ in) to around 7 centimetres (3 in); flowers varied from different shades of pink to yellow, orange, red and almost pure white. In fact, plants which I later raised from a *single* seed pod collected at Oruro exhibited the full range of flower colours and spine lengths – five Backebergian 'species'.

▷ After an overnight bus trip to Cochabamba, during which I passed through a lot of good cactus habitat cloaked in darkness, I spent an afternoon at the highest point on the road from Cochabamba to Chapare at 3,600 metres (11,800 ft). The habitat here consists of a mosaic of cultivated fields and rough grassy areas. Among the grass occurs the most variable known population of *Sulcorebutia steinbachii*, in which the flower colours range from pure yellow (described by Cardenas as a separate species, *S. tuberculata-chrysantha*), through orange to red and magenta; bicoloured forms also occur. The only other cacti were a few small, non-flowering clumps of *Lobivia caespitosa*. A short distance away some sulcorebutias with purely magenta flowers were in bloom. This form of *S. steinbachii* is the one we know and cultivate as *S. glomerispina*.

The range of flower colours in the population of **Sulcorebutia steinbachii** at this locality was striking, bearing in mind that in the original description the flower was given as 'red'. The plants themselves exist in two forms: 'juvenile', with numerous small heads and short spines; and 'adult', with a much larger body which remains solitary or else clumps only sparingly. The latter form is usually covered in a dense and striking array of black, dagger-like spines. Had it not been for the presence of flowers, I would probably have been looking for some time before I noticed even the largest clump – 30 centimetres (12 in) or more across – of the 'juvenile' form, due to a major error in my search image. I was looking for the mounds of heads several centimetres high which we see in our cultivated specimens, with the individual heads tending to grow at different heights so as to form an uneven surface. I was not prepared for the fact that in habitat all clump-forming sulcos grow flush with the ground, so that the tops of the heads are the only part of the plant visible at the soil surface. This means that you can easily walk over a plant the size of a dinner plate without seeing it.

◁ Next day we took the road from Cochabamba to Epizana and Sucre. Not far from Cochabamba, at Angostura, the low hills beside the road are covered in limestone rubble. The vegetation consists of small clumps of low trees and bushes, accompanied by many large plants of white-flowering *Roseocereus tephracanthus* and plenty of *Cleistocactus parviflorus*, with their small, red tubular blooms in untidy ranks up the stems. The latter is a wide-ranging and unusually variable species which has managed to acquire a substantial inventory of extra names at the species level.

On the flatter slopes among grass and limestone rubble we found the object of our quest, **Lobivia acanthoplegma** var. **roseiflora**, described from here by Walter Rausch. A few of the plants were beginning to flaunt their beautiful pink flowers, but most simply bore dozens of unopened buds. The scattered clumps of *Echinopsis cochabambensis* were only in early bud, just as they had been on a small hill in the middle of Cochabamba, right in front of my hotel.

△ A few miles further on we left the main road and turned into the village of Cliza. This is situated on flat alluvial land which is almost completely under cultivation – not the most promising-looking habitat for cacti. However, Edgar Aguilar knew what he was doing, for this unlikely place is the chosen home of **Lobivia acanthoplegma** var. **patula**, discovered here by chance by Roberto Vasquez and described by Rausch. Alas, this striking variety, with its large, flat, bright green body and brilliant flowers, is now all but extinct, buried under a tide of cultivation and house-building – human activities which tend to favour the same flat, easily worked terrain as the lobivias. We found fewer than 100 plants, mostly scattered in the open grassy areas which had been left between the buildings. The flowers were mainly a rich crimson, but a few were orange, and some even bordered on a rich egg-yolk yellow.

Beyond Cliza the road starts to climb seriously into the hills, past the rock-strewn slopes of Cuchu Punata. This is a rich locality for cacti, including the now familiar *Cleistocactus parviflorus*, *Corryocactus melanotrichus* and *Echinopsis cochabambensis*. The last had shorter, fatter heads than back in Cochabamba, already beginning to exhibit that confusing plasticity of appearance so typical of the family. Edgar was anxious to show me a population of the wide-ranging **E. obrepanda**, which was of particular interest because plants with white, magenta, salmon-pink or red flowers could all be found growing together. As a host of 'species' had been described by Cardenas mainly on the basis of flower colour (for example, *E. callichroma*, *E. calliantholilacina*, *E. toralapana*, *E. calorubra*, *E. roseolilacina*), the presence of all the known colours within a single population was of particular interest in stressing the folly of placing too much emphasis on a single characteristic.

▷ The most abundant cactus at Cuchu Punata, and then high up into the hills beyond, is **Lobivia acanthoplegma** var. **oligotricha**. Backeberg also coined the names *L. pseudocinnabarina* and *L. neocinnabarina* for the same plant. Here it grew alongside tiny non-flowering plants of *Sulcorebutia kruegeri* var. *hoffmanniana*, almost buried in the ground. Down at Cuchu Punata the *oligotricha* plants are small, rather cylindrical and densely covered in a very sharp, generally dark spination.

△ We also found a few **Parodia schwebsiana** – my first parodia and in full flower. In reality this name probably encompasses a whole group of 'species', ranging across the highlands to Sucre and beyond, and currently rejoicing in a number of names, including *P. backebergiana* Brandt, *P. firmissima* Brandt, *P. idiosa* Brandt, *P. otuyensis* Ritt., *P. quechua* Brandt, *P. stereospina* Brandt, *P. yamparaezi* Card. and *P. tuberculata* Card. We were later able to see the innate variability in these plants at a locality near Sucre.

▽ What a difference a few kilometres can make! Along the same road near Tiraque, at a slightly higher elevation, where the plants were nestling among bright green turf between cultivated fields beside the road, we found a quite different form of **Lobivia acanthoplegma** var. **oligotricha** with a much larger, flatter body and more open, paler spination. Also near here in a similar short-turf habitat, but not in flower, we found clumps of Rausch's *Sulcorebutia steinbachii* var. *horrida* within a few metres of the road.

◁ After Tiraque the road began a long, winding descent which took us down into an enveloping shroud of cloud and rain. Near Kayrani and Toralapa a brief search beside the road turned up **Sulcorebutia steinbachii** var. **polymorpha**. The grass had recently been burned, and although this had not generally harmed the sulcos, which were almost buried in the soil, the accompanying plants of *Echinopsis obrepanda* (= *E. toralapana*) had been badly singed, although probably not fatally so. By now it was raining hard – and was to continue thus in varying degrees for the next three days!

▽ Contrary to what could be expected from its name, **Sulcorebutia tiraquensis** is not found around Tiraque, but further along the valley near Epizana and Monte Puncu. It lives in one of the wettest areas colonized by any cactus, subject to almost constant cloud and mist from the tropical forest of the Yungas below. This stimulates prolific growth of ferns and mosses, among which the cacti nestle. The plant illustrated is var. **'bicolorispina'**, which is restricted to just a few prominent, steeply sloping slabs of rocks which sweep upwards above the road near Epizana. It has suffered sadly at the hands of ruthless commercial collectors, who have virtually exterminated the population. The dense spination and small magenta flower shown here are typical of the variety, but plants exhibiting these characteristics are also found among other populations mixed with 'normal' plants.

▷ A short distance away, on the drier opposite side of the valley, restricted to just a few rocky outcrops, grows Backeberg's var. **electracantha**, typified by its yellow spines and clear orange flowers. However, as a few *bicolorispinas* occur alongside the *electracanthas*, it clearly makes better sense to regard them as forms rather than varieties, with purely cultivar status in our greenhouses.

◁ On the outskirts of Aiquile it is easy to spot the main habitat for *Sulcorebutia mentosa*. In fact, you can step straight out of the car and on to the plants. Unfortunately, the goats which roam across the site seem to regard a juicy *S. mentosa* as a special delicacy, and nibble the tops off the heads. The plants respond by clumping ever more prolifically and hugging the ground as tightly as possible among the green sward of mosses, liverworts and clubmosses. Although most of the cacti were in bud, the incessant drizzle from a leaden sky prevented even a single flower opening.

▽ This picture shows a typical **Sulcorebutia mentosa** near Aiquile, which forms the centre of distribution for a whole group of sulcorebutias, such as *S. flavissima*, *S. albissima*, *S. swobodae* and *S. santiaginiensis*. These all grow on the exposed hilltops around Aiquile, up to a distance of 30 kilometres (18 miles) or so, and are probably just forms of *S. mentosa*. We did not have time to confirm this at first-hand ourselves, but continued on down the main road towards the valley of the Rio Chico. We made two brief and positively electrifying stops (lightning struck deafeningly close several times as I stood, the highest object in a treeless landscape, on the bare open ground) to view *S. oenantha* and *S. pampagrandensis* in their roadside localities. Most of the plants bore ripe fruits and half-grown flower buds, pointing to a twin flowering period.

◁ South of Aiquile the road follows the valley of the Rio Chico, seen here from a point near Puente Arce, with a *Trichocereus* species in the foreground.

▷ The climate along the valley of the Rio Chico is hotter and drier than anywhere on our route so far. Unfortunately, this seems to result in a change in seasonal flowering: the cacti in this valley produce their blooms at a different time from those on the highlands nearby. Along the Rio Chico we therefore saw many thousands of cacti, yet few bore buds, only one or two were in flower, and none was in fruit. The most prominent cactus of this almost subtropical area is the stately **Neocardenasia herzogiana**, which occurs in thousands along the lowermost parts of the valley. On the very steep slopes above the road, often growing in the shade of open woodland, was a whole succession of interesting yet non-flowering cacti. There were plenty of large, handsome specimens of *Gymnocalycium pflanzii* var. *zegarrae* and a whole series of Ritter's *Weingartia* 'species', such as *W. riograndensis* (forming large clumps right beside the road) and *W. lanata* (single). On the steep, winding climb out of the balmy valley back up on to the cool, rainy highlands we saw *W. longigibba* and *W. sucrensis* growing fully exposed on amazingly bare, eroded rock beside the road. In mid-December none of these weingartias yielded either flower buds or seeds. All are merely forms of *W. neocumingii*.

▷ The steep sun-baked cliffs above the Rio Chico are also home to **Parodia ocampoi**. It sometimes forms densely packed masses on rock faces beside the road, with the plants almost close enough to touch by reaching out of the car window. Despite the thousands of plants present, this was the only one we found in flower.

◁ Further along the Rio Chico valley occur these impressive and beautiful mounds of **Parodia compressa**. It is probably best regarded as a variety of *P. ocampoi*, differing mainly in its red flowers, which unfortunately were not on display in December. Many fine clumps were growing in the dense shade of trees, along with large plants of *Weingartia lanata*, a plant which disappointed and confused me in habitat by being anything but woolly, as the name *lanata* indicates it ought to be.

▽ As we headed southwards down the Rio Chico we had to cross numerous rivers flowing out of small gullies to our left. These were all swollen after the heavy rains in the highlands, and Edgar had to handle the pick-up with great care in order not to become stuck in the loose, slippery gravel. After negotiating our way across several of these, Edgar stopped at the mouth of a particularly narrow gully to show me **Blossfeldia liliputana** jammed into cracks in the vertical rock face. They were accompanied by a few plants of a parodia similar to *Parodia compressa* but with substantially different spination (possibly Vasquez's *P. zecheri*).

◁ After emerging from the warm river valley on to the cool highlands near Sucre, we stopped briefly to look at a clumping, heavily spined parodia (probably *Parodia tuberculata*) growing with a form of *Echinopsis obrepanda*. A short distance from there we stopped to search for *Sulcorebutia canigueralii* in a well-known roadside site, but alas there was no sign of either flowering or fruiting. After a miserable rainy night in Sucre, during which I was kept awake by the water from my hotel's gutters splashing noisily on to the flagstones below, we headed next morning for Zudanez, soon running into large populations of the plant illustrated here, for which the earliest name seems to be **Parodia otuyensis**. It then accompanied us on the roadside banks for much of the way from Tarabuco to Zudanez. Within a single population the spines could be either hooked or straight, some taller-bodied, others shorter and broader, some light green, some almost purplish. Such a degree of variability is to be expected, and does nothing to excuse the seven or so extra specific names given to this one species along a single, fairly short stretch of road. It is obvious to anyone with botanical sense that only a single species must be present.

◁ Growing abundantly with the parodias all the way to Zudanez were large plants of **Lobivia cinnabarina**. Most of these were covered in buds, but the few flowers which did manage to open in the depressing drizzle did not expand to their full extent. Even this easily recognized plant, so obviously a single species, has managed to spawn several 'species' names, such as Cardenas's *L. zudanensis* and *L. prestoana*, and Knize's catalogue names *L. sucrensis* and *L. tarabucensis*.

35

Near Tarabuco Edgar stopped beside a large tilted rock to show me my first members of the genus *Rebutia*. We immediately found several small plants of *R. fiebrigii*, each bearing at most one or two flowers, peeping out of damp, shady clefts in the rocks and snugly seated in a bed of mosses, liverworts, clubmosses and small ferns. These damp, shady spots are the preferred habitat for most members of the genus. Harder to pick out, due to an absence of flowers, were the few specimens of Rausch's *R. brunescens*, their small, dark bodies hardly projecting above the black humus-rich earth which had collected in the cracks. Although they were multi-headed, the scattered plants of *Sulcorebutia verticillacantha* var. *aureiflora* were also well hidden, scarcely peeping out of the loose sand and humus which had been washed across them by the recent rain. This variety was established because of its golden-yellow flower and rather miniature mode of growth. However, plants with either red or magenta flowers have recently been found. Indeed, plants from a *single* seed pod which I collected bear either golden-yellow or brilliant flame-coloured blooms. The latter are similar to those of the *S. canigueralii* back near Sucre; they are obviously one and the same species.

Zudanez proved to be a washout, with the local river in spate, barring access to the mountain on which grew our chief goal, *Sulcorebutia rauschii*, which I had hoped would be in flower. Near the village we did see plenty of *Cleistocactus tominensis*, with dense masses of short, golden spines and both red and green flowers on the same stem. Right beside the road were big clumps of a short, densely spined trichocerceus covered in huge flower buds, and in grassy meadows on the edge of Zudanez, huge plants of *Echinopsis obrepanda*.

△ So it was back to Sucre, and then onwards towards Potosi. While still on the outskirts of town we had to make an unscheduled stop for an urban cactus. On a small patch of stony waste-ground surrounded by houses, numerous handsome mounds of **Echinopsis sucrensis** mounted a brave display of rather bedraggled, rain-soaked flowers. This plant is widespread in the region, where it often grows in open thorny woodland.

▷ As we finally left Sucre behind we began to pass hundreds of **Trichocereus tacaquirensis**, poking their heads up through the woodland which skirted the edge of the valley, their enormous white, rain-spattered flowers standing out starkly against the sombre green background. This is one of the most abundant members of the genus, occurring over a wide area in central Bolivia (Cardenas's *T. taquimbalensis* is the same plant).

◁ The journey from Sucre as far as Millares was a nightmare. The incessant rain of the last few days had transformed the normally dry, dusty surface of the road into a slick skid-pan which made driving on black ice in a British winter seem tame by comparison – several trucks lying at drunken angles in the roadside ditches bore testimony to the hazards of being on the open road in the Bolivian 'summer'. At Millares the sun finally came out and shone brightly off the slaty slopes, which glittered above the swollen torrent which was the Rio Pilcomayo.

△ Millares is certainly cactus country, and the two most common species grow in masses on the roadsides. The most abundant is the small-flowered form of **Weingartia lanata** subsp. **pilcomayoensis**, known to many collectors as *W. platygona*. In places it was difficult to walk without treading on one, and a few were even in flower – the only weingartia flowers seen on the whole trip.

◁ Millares is the type locality for **Gymnocalycium pflanzii** var. **millaresii**. Most plants, some of which were the size of a human head, bore ripe fruits and buds, but alas there were no open flowers.

▽ Beyond Millares the rain began again in earnest, forcing us to make only the odd brief stop as we headed across the high, cold Altiplano towards Potosi. One particular grassy, rock-strewn slope seemed to me to be so absolutely 'right' for cacti that I asked Edgar to stop. Sure enough, I was confronted by thousands of large *Lobivia cinnabarina* var. *walterspielii*, which were covered in half-grown flower buds. They would be quite a sight when they all opened in the middle of January. The only fully open flowers belonged to a dwarf opuntia, probably the widespread and variable **Opuntia (Tephrocactus) pentlandii**. The actual colour varied from yellow to an attractive brick red.

△ In gathering darkness my eye was drawn to a splash of red on the roadside. It turned out to be **Opuntia vestita** in full flower. This species was one of the first cacti I ever acquired as a teenager, yet until that moment I had never realized how gorgeous were its blooms, so shy is it of producing them in Britain.

As darkness cut short further exploration, the road finally wound down into Potosi, where we spent a long night luxuriating beneath half a dozen blankets in a cheap but clean hotel which was patronized mainly by truck drivers. We were interested to learn that we were not alone in suffering the dreary effects of incessant rainfall: in Potosi it had not stopped raining for six days!

▷ From Potosi the road to Camargo winds gradually downwards off the Altiplano, visible here behind the white, hairy stems of **Oreocereus trollii**. The increasing frequency of the oreocerei marked our arrival at Cucho Ingenio. It is a famous haunt for many different kinds of cacti, several of which lurk inconspicuously among the tufts of grass and stones visible beyond the oreocereus here. Another rewarding habitat consists of ledges on a rockface which rises directly above the road (on the right), providing the favoured ecological conditions for some of the best plants, such as *Lobivia versicolor*.

◁ What cactus enthusiast would not make a pilgrimage to Cuchu Ingenio, just to marvel at the spiniest lobivia of them all, Rausch's **Lobivia versicolor**, for which Cuchu Ingenio is the type locality? Fortunately, this species flowers over an extended period, so both ripe fruits and open flowers were available in mid-December. Unlike many lobivias, the flower colour is very uniform, varying little from a bright, clear, lemon-yellow. The plants are easy to spot, bristling boldly from the top of the rocks right beside the road. At Cuchu Ingenio I also made my first acquaintance with the most widespread and abundant of the parodias, *Parodia maasii*. This highly successful species ranges from north of Potosi way down into northern Argentina. With so many separate populations spread over such a wide area, it is not surprising that each one tends to have evolved its own particular combination of body size, spination and flower colour. Even so, there is scant excuse for the creation of at least *nineteen* separate 'species' to cover these variations; they are all just *maasii* by another name. The plants at Cuchu Ingenio fall into an 'average' size-band, with pale-orange flowers and rather open, straw-coloured spination.

◁▷ This far south the local form of **Lobivia formosa** is the red-flowered var. **tarijensis**. At Cuchu Ingenio the spination varies from relatively soft and wavy to straight and more needle-like, much as exhibited by the familiar *Neoporteria nidus* in Chile. These red-flowered var. *tarijensis* are apparently pollinated (at least partly) by birds. I watched hummingbirds delicately probing the flowers on throbbing wings, while oriole-like birds flopped rather clumsily around in the flowers, becoming well dusted with pollen.

△ The smaller cacti, which are some of the gems of Cuchu Ingenio, are much harder to find than the statuesque *Lobivia formosa* var. *tarijensis*, and indeed are extremely elusive save when in flower. The plant illustrated here is one of the many forms of the wide-ranging **Rebutia pygmaea**. Many of the forms have received specific names, but the variation is really relatively minor, mostly consisting of flower colour and size, and small details of spination and body size. Most 'species' have now been reduced to varieties, and rightly so. This, my first wild specimen, really impressed upon me the major differences which often exist between a plant pampered in our greenhouses and one subject to the rigours of life in the wild. A good 'show bench' *R. pygmaea* will fill a 30-centimetre (12-in) pan with a multitude of heads, swathing itself in a carpet of flowers with an exuberance which I had always taken to be the norm for this species. In the harsh conditions of its Bolivian highland home, however, matters are very different, and anyone who expects (as I did) to have an easy task locating large clumps of this plant is going to be disappointed. Most specimens (and I saw many more in several places later in the trip) can manage to produce only a single tiny head, and even this scarcely dares to expose itself to the elements, huddling down instead in the ground or moss, leaving only the very apex of the stem visible to betray its presence. As for flowers, two is a veritable extravagance, one the norm, and even this often has to push its way to the surface through the surrounding soil.

▷ Any comments which apply to *Rebutia pygmaea* apply almost equally to **R. steinmannii**, also normally a tiny single-headed plant with but a single flower. The form illustrated from Cuchu Ingenio was originally described by Rausch as *Digitorebutia cincinnata*, but he has since reduced it to a variety of *steinmannii*, under *Lobivia*, though, rather than *Rebutia*.

◁ Further south the bleak, inhospitable rockscape of the Pampa de Lecori is covered in carpets of **Parodia maasii** – hundreds of thousands of them, stretching off into the far distance like thistles in a neglected English pasture. They tended to be rather flatter than at Cuchu Ingenio, with more open spination but similar flowers.

▽ The *Parodia maasii* hordes are accompanied by large, handsome plants of **Weingartia lecoriensis**, which is probably just a large form of *W. westii*. Although attractive in themselves, with their dense spination, the lack of flowers reduced the appeal somewhat, especially as the rain was driving fiercely down before a gusty wind. Intermixed with these was a medium-sized form of *Lobivia ferox*, with long, twisted, straw-coloured spines, described (superfluously) by Cardenas as *Echinopsis lecoriensis*. Just south of here I had my first view of *Oreocereus celsianus* – thousands of them – viewed with difficulty through cascades of water streaming untidily down the car windows in the semi-darkness of a violent thunderstorm.

△ **Parodia maasii** abounds throughout the region between Cuchu Ingenio and Camargo. In one population south of the Pampa de Lecori the flowers were smaller, scarcely opening beyond the spines, and of a deeper orange. The spination is usually long and curling, but may be straight, as seen in the plant at top right. This emphasizes the folly of basing 'new' species on minor details of spination, especially when plants are received second-hand from another collector and described in Europe without full knowledge of their variability in the wild.

Near the gorge of the Rio Honda we found a *Parodia maasii* population in which the plants looked quite different from those either to the north or to the south, being densely covered in quite short, straight, glassy, hedgehog-like spines. On the shady cliffs above the river we found large non-flowering plants of Rausch's *Rebutia raulii* (reduced by him later to *Lobivia atrovirens* var. *raulii*). On the rocks there were plenty of fine specimens of a much smaller form of *Weingartia westii*, with heads only 3–4 centimetres (1–1½ in) across, tightly wedged in cracks in full sun.

▷ Not far north of Camargo I noticed what appeared to be foxes' tails sticking up out of the roadside bushes. They turned out to be **Cleistocactus tupizensis** a long way from the type locality of Tupiza. In reality this splendid plant is much more widespread than the infrequent mention of Tupiza in the books would have us believe.

Growing with it was a giant barrel-shaped form of *Parodia maasii*, with golden spines but no flowers, and unfortunately there was no fruit.

◁ A short distance from the outskirts of Camargo I spotted a likely looking habitat for rebutias a few hundred metres from the road. It was a shady cliff with rocks arranged in tilted planes, and it is in the damp clefts of just such rock formations that rebutias thrive, in a soft bed of mosses and liverworts. Sure enough, even from a distance I spotted small patches of red which, as I walked closer, turned out to be the bright, lustrous flowers of a ginger-spined form of **Rebutia fiebrigii**. Edgar ferreted around among the mosses and discovered several sterile *R. pygmaea* plants. These two often live together in similar habitats over a wide area of Bolivia and Argentina, and it is certainly not vital to have prior knowledge of a specific locality in order to find them easily enough. The spination of *R. fiebrigii* varies enormously from one population to another, and even within a population, but it has relatively uniform flowers. *R. pygmaea* varies greatly in flower colour (white, pink, orange, red, red-violet), and to a lesser extent in spination, body size and body colour.

△ South of Camargo the road follows the western bank of a river which was in full spate due to the constant rain. For much of the way between Camargo and the turn-off to Culpina at Puente San Pedro the road sits on a ledge cut out of the cliff above the tumbling waters. Still, wherever the road meanders away from the river, leaving an intervening stretch of open ground, there is a chance for low-spreading clumps of the dwarf **Trichocereus camarguensis** to become established. In December they were adorned with their large white flowers. On the steeper, rocky roadsides there were plenty of *Parodia maasii* (described from here by Ritter as *P. camarguensis*), often forming large clumps of ginger-spined heads.

△ In contrast to the ginger-spined **Parodia maasii** found along the rocky roadsides above the western bank of a river south of Camargo, the huge mounds of *P. maasii* on the other side of the river, just a few metres away, are notable for their beautiful dense mantle of shining white spines. Ritter described this splendid form as var. **albescens** and then later described what is probably the same species as *P. roseoalba* var. *australis*. In fact, the spines start out as a light brown, but soon turn greyish white. The pale orange flowers are unusually small. From a distance it is difficult to distinguish the *albescens* mounds from the similar-looking mounds of *Weingartia cintiensis* which occur with them, although the latter were not in flower. *W. cintiensis* is a particularly handsome member of the genus, and certainly forms the largest clumps.

▷ The slope in the foreground strewn with limestone rubble is a superb habitat for hundreds of splendid *Lobivia lateritia* (later described by Cardenas as *L. cintiensis*) on the eastern bank of the river near Puente San Pedro. Accompanying flora include the jatropha seen bottom left, and hundreds of mounds of *Parodia maasii* var. *albescens* and *Weingartia cintiensis*. On the far side of the river on reddish sandstone rocks the *P. maasii* have ginger spines.

▽ The flower colour of **Lobivia lateritia** is very variable. I was doubly fortunate in reaching this population just when most of the plants were ready to burst into flower, and precisely on the first day when there was sufficient sun to allow this to happen. Examples are shown in the picture below and on pages 56-7. Both *L. lateritia* and *L. cintiensis* were originally described as having a crimson flower, without any mention of the kaleidoscopic range of colours which was so brilliantly evident in the magnificent display I was privileged to witness on that very memorable day. It is small wonder, then, that collectors are often given a fixed idea about how a species 'should' look and behave. If a plant does not fit the original description, which is often based upon a single plant, then it is assumed that the 'wrong' species has been supplied.

At Puente San Pedro most of the **Lobivia lateritia** plants grow under, or at least close to, small bushes such as the jatropha, but some grow in the open, where they are well protected by their dense spination. This is just as well, as goats pose a threat to the future of this population through trampling.

At the top of the pass between here and Culpina I subsequently found a more squat plant with long, black spines and purely red flowers. This probably corresponds to Ritter's *Lobivia horrida*, more positively known as *L. lateritia* var. *rubriflora* (Bkb.) Rausch.

▷ By the time I arrived at this location near Culpina I thought I 'knew' the kinds of habitat preferred by Bolivian cacti, so I was puzzled when Edgar brought the car to a halt beside these hostile-looking bare flats. Fortunately for me, he knew that this unlikely spot was the *only* habitat in which the smallest of the parodias can thrive. *Parodia occulta*, a tiny gem of a plant, was found in this improbable place by Ritter, and it occurs only in one or two similar spots between Mal Paso and Culpina.

▽ **Occulta** means 'hidden' and it is doubtful if anyone would spot these tiny – up to only 2 centimetres (less than 1 in) broad – plants camouflaged among the fine gravel were they not betrayed at this particular season by their flowers. At any other time it would be possible to walk over hundreds of plants without ever suspecting their presence. The rather small flowers vary from brick red to sulphur yellow.

△ Growing with *Parodia occulta*, never cheek by jowl in the same bare, open substrate but rather in adjacent deeper soils, is this form of **P. maasii**, which probably corresponds with Ritter's *P. suprema* (he mentions that they grow together). The habitat preferences of the two plants is an object lesson in plant ecology. The *suprema* is restricted to the better, deeper soils which are found in shallow gullies among the bare gravel, and also the edge of the gravel plains. These richer soils can support grass, herbs and even small woody plants as well as *P. suprema*.

By contrast, the only plants which seem capable of surviving on the gravel plains themselves are the *P. occulta*, a superb example of adaptation to a hostile environment which a specialist can monopolize because potential competitors are unable to become established there. The two parodias flower at the same time, yet they do not hybridize, presumably because there is some fertility barrier between them. Despite this, some 'lumper' will no doubt go ahead and submerge *occulta* as a variety of *maasii*. Such a fate has already befallen (with equally scant justification) another perfectly distinct species from this area, *P. subterranea*.

▷ **Parodia subterranea** occurs in several places between Culpina and Salitre. I spent a rain-sodden morning pacing impatiently back and forth on the hills beside the river at Incahuasi in the hope that the sun might eventually break through and persuade a few *P. subterranea* buds to open. The plants throng the slopes in hundreds, mainly growing in distinctive grey pebbles on flat natural terraces directly above the river. The black spines can be either hooked or straight, and in habitat the plants remain small, flat and very neat, and do not develop the grotesquely inflated proportions seen in cultivation. The accompanying cactus flora is highly interesting. The plants illustrated in the next two pictures occur beside the parodias, while near the river, in deeper soils, grows a large, distinctive echinopsis. It has been linked to the widespread and variable *Echinopsis obrepanda*, but the differences between the two are far greater than those between other forms of *obrepanda*. The habitat is also isolated and the Culpina plant flowers a month or two earlier than any *obrepanda* form, and already has ripe fruits when most *obrepanda* have only small buds.

Tucked away inconspicuously among the bare, flat, sloping rocks above the river cliffs we also found numerous tiny single-headed plants of *Rebutia albopectinata*. These had fruits but no flowers, as did the tiny plants of *R. pygmaea* (= *R. friedrichiana*) nestled among the moss on the shady rocks below the cliffs. The area around Culpina is one of the richest and most exciting cactus habitats in Bolivia, boasting at least fifteen distinct species, plus a whole host of varieties. This botanical treasury includes a huge black-spined form of *Lobivia ferox* which grows in bushy, flatter areas among the cultivated fields, and the very distinctive, locally endemic *L. rauschii*, which we did not have time to locate.

▷ Accompanying *Parodia subterranea* in the same kind of grey pebbles were scattered plants of **Lobivia pugionacantha** var. **culpinensis**. These almost always grew nine-tenths buried in the ground, with only the flowers betraying their presence. However, in deeper soils near the road the plants were much bigger, although also scarcer. I saw only red flowers, but Rausch reports yellow as well.

▽ Growing on the same slopes as the last two species, but restricted to the sides of small gullies covered in dense tufts of grass, were a few specimens of **Echinopsis mamillosa** var. **hystri-choides**. Most plants bore one or two flowers, which could be either pink or white. Originally described as a species in its own right, this plant is nowadays regarded as a form of the solely white-flowered plant found widely around Tarija (where it even crops up commonly among the factory buildings to the south of town) and down into northern Argentina. The droplets of water prominent on the flower in the picture give some idea of the constant soaking we received in our two days at Culpina. The prolonged bouts of rain and unpleasantly cool daytime temperatures typical of the Bolivian summer (the locals refer to summer as *el invierno Boliviano* – the Bolivian *winter*!) probably explain why in cultivation lobivias and rebutias seem to thrive on abundant water, and start to struggle when the thermometer in the greenhouse soars above 40°C (104°F).

△ Edgar left me in Camargo and returned to his family for Christmas. I hitched a ride in the back of a truck to this spectacular locality at Cieneguillas, on the road to Iscayache and Tarija. It was a typical Andean journey. I stood in the back of the truck, clinging desperately to the sides as we jolted along the appalling roads, rubbing shoulders with Indian families decked out in colourful

clothes. With a familiarity typical of Bolivia, we all huddled down together for warmth as we made our way with agonizing slowness up across the high, cold mountain pass, before gently easing back down again to the blessed warmth of the valleys.

Bright sunlight illuminating the serried ranks of **Trichocereus werdermannianus** and **Oreocereus celsianus** which dominate the scene at Cieneguillas beckoned me down from my uncomfortable station. Even so, the sun proved as unreliable and ephemeral as ever, and it was with half my mind concentrated on a thunderstorm which was brewing ominously on the horizon that I hurried to snatch a few pictures of the cactus flora of Cieneguillas.

◁ **Oreocereus celsianus** is abundant here and was in both flower and fruit. The bright pinkish-red flowers of *Lobivia formosa* var. *tarijensis* also made a fine show, but the taller-stemmed *Trichocereus werdermannianus* produces its large white flowers at a different season.

▽ The most conspicuous 'globular' cactus at Cieneguillas is **Parodia maxima**. Juvenile plants resemble *P. maasii* in that the central spines are more or less hooked at the tip, but these become straight and dagger-like on older plants. *P. maxima* had flowered and fruited well before the accompanying form of *P. maasii*, which was in full flower during my visit. The two plants cannot therefore cross and no hybrids seem to be present. Despite this, the 'lumpers' have reduced *maxima* to a variety of *maasii*, although by definition two varieties of a single species should be capable of interbreeding if they meet together. The form of *P. maasii* at Cieneguillas is broadly similar to that found at Cuchu Ingenio. Admittedly, red-flowered plants were common at Cieneguillas, but the spination is similar in both localities and Ritter's name of var. *intermedia* for the Cieneguillas plant seems hardly justified.

△ Accompanying the parodias were a few mainly quite small plants of **Lobivia ferox** var. **longispina**. Because of the incipient rain I had time to observe only pink flowers. However, Rausch has found plants which bloomed yellow, red, orange and white. This was the last shot I managed to snatch before a cold squall of rain hit me, and I was fortunate to hear a truck grinding my way. I spent an unusually comfortable journey perched up in a cab beside the friendly driver as he heaved his heavy load of cement bags up across the high passes to Iscayache. We chatted about my objectives in Bolivia, my interest in the cacti and his prospects for selling his cargo at a good profit in Tarija. Despite the fact that he owned the vehicle, which was his sole source of income, and that paying for truck rides in Bolivia is quite normal (the trucks in effect act as unofficial 'stop anywhere' buses), he refused my proffered 'fare' as I disembarked at Iscayache. This was not the first time that I had experienced the generosity of the Bolivian people.

▷ This is the scene that greeted me on Christmas Day 1989 just outside the little hamlet of Iscayache, which lies at the foot of the looming cloud-capped bulk of the Cuesta de Sama. After a Christmas dinner comprising two fried eggs, eaten alone in my spartan and almost deserted little 'hotel', I strode off up the road towards the Cuesta. Even at Iscayache the altitude is over 3,000 metres (10,000 ft), so I was breathing rather laboriously as I scrambled up the rocky hillside to view the landscape spread out below me. On my way up the road I had already passed hundreds of plump plants of *Lobivia chrysochete* var. *tenuispina*, growing among stones and sparse grass on the flats around the village. They were all covered in seed pods, but there was not a single flower (these are large and golden yellow).

The most interesting feature of this photograph is the slope opposite, at top right, where it is just possible to see layers of tilted rocks forming a miniature cliff face. This is typical rebutia habitat.

◁ Another kilometre of walking up the winding road on to the lower slopes of the Cuesta de Sama brought me to this small gully. Note how the clefts in the rocks are inclined almost vertically – classic rebutia habitat. This particular gully turned out to be most exiting, harbouring four good *Rebutia* species. One of these, *R. deminuta*, was particularly interesting, as it occurred in a bewildering variety of very different-looking forms, many of which correspond to 'species' described by various authors from this general area of Bolivia.

▷ The rebutias tend to squat inconspicuously among the rocks in deep shade, well camouflaged among a soft, damp bed of mosses, liverworts and ferns. The largest species in this locality is **Rebutia fiebrigii** of which I found no two plants precisely alike. This form, with its long ginger spines, probably corresponds with the plant distributed by K. Knize as *R. aureispina*.

▷ Almost cheek by jowl with the plant depicted in the above photograph grew this quite different-looking specimen, whose soft, white spination resembles that of *Rebutia muscula*, itself no more than a form of **R. fiebrigii**. Here at the Cuesta de Sama the small bees which brave the cool, wet conditions fly indiscriminately from flower to flower, regardless of the type of spination, pollinating all the different plants at random and presumably giving rise to a full set of forms in the next generation.

△ In the same rock cleft as the last two plants I found this third form of **Rebutia fiebrigii**, with shorter, brownish spines and a darker flower.

▷ This is the rebutia which presented me with a puzzling situation in the gully on the Cuesta de Sama. It occurred in such profusion and variety that it was difficult at first to assign a correct name to it. Previous visitors to this area have chosen the 'splitter's' route of selecting one or two of the most distinctive-looking specimens to honour with the title of 'species'. As this so-called 'species' has on occasion comprised but a single plant, carefully singled out just because it happens to look different from its neighbours (as in Ritter's *Rebutia minutissima*), a situation arises which is both ridiculous and unacceptable. After all, the total natural population of a species can hardly be one!

It seemed to me much more likely that the mixed bag of plants seen in these populations

could be explained by the existence of a single, highly plastic species. In my opinion, the first valid name for these plants would be **Rebutia deminuta**, although others would no doubt prefer to maintain the current hotchpotch of 'species' names such as *R. spegazziniana* Bkb., *R. kupperiana* Boed., *R. fulviseta* Rausch, *R. pseudodeminuta* Bkb., *R. wahliana* Rausch, *R. vulpina* Ritt., *R. tamboensis* Ritt., *R. cajasensis* Ritt., *R. nitida* Ritt., *R. robustispina* Ritt., etc., etc., etc. Perhaps the reader can decide on the correct solution to this problem by studying the next four pictures, which give but a small idea of the variation within this single population. First of all, though, make a note of the particular characteristics of the plant illustrated here: dense, rather glassy spination, allied to a small, rather orange-red flower.

▽ This plant, with its long, ginger spines and pale orange flower, corresponds to the plant distributed as **Rebutia maxima**.

△ With its black body and short, dense, black spination, allied to a tiny, deep red flower, this must surely be a candidate for the sobriquet 'new' with regard to species, although it is clearly similar to Rausch's **Rebutia fulviseta**.

△ Bright green body, short, ginger spines at apex, small orange-red flower: this is Ritter's **Rebutia vulpina**.

▷ This is a sight I thought I would never see: a big clump of **Rebutia deminuta** (or *R. kupperiana*, if you prefer) just as smothered in flowers on the side of the gully on the Cuesta de Sama as it would be in the cosy, pampered conditions of a greenhouse. In fact, appearances are misleading. This is not a large multi-headed plant but a mass of single-headed plants which had germinated and prospered on a ready-made seed bed caused by a small rockfall.

▷ The third, and rarest, of the rebutias in the gully tends to avoid detection unless given away by its flowers. This is yet another form of **Rebutia pygmaea**, with the usual tiny, single head boasting at most two flowers. It probably corresponds to Rausch's *R. iscayachensis*, and I eventually tracked down quite a few of them, peeping out of the moss at the bases of the grass tufts or lurking in damp clefts among the rocks.

▽ The fourth species in the gully seems to be identifiable as **Rebutia ritteri**, typified by its rather broad, black body and pure orange flower. Surprisingly enough, although numerous plants of *R. fiebrigii*, *R. deminuta*, *R. pygmaea* and *R. ritteri* were all in flower at the same time and are visited by the same bees, no obvious hybrids seemed to be present.

△ The more open rocks above the 'rebutia gully' provided a much harsher environment, alternately roasted by the hot sun and lashed by the summer's winds and rain. This was the preferred habitat for hundreds of small specimens of **Parodia maasii**, a local form having either brown or black spines and deep red flowers – the so-called *P. escayachensis.* They were accompanied by a few rather small, fat-stemmed, semi-prostrate plants of *Oreocereus trollii,* which were in flower.

▽ After a long and tiring walk, with my head pounding from the altitude and my breath coming in laborious pants, I finally reached a spot high on the Cuesta de Sama which I thought might provide a suitable habitat for **Sulcorebutia tarijensis**. With raindrops driven before a biting wind stinging my face, I finally tracked it down on an exposed grassy hillside grazed by sad-looking cattle, veiled in an almost constant chill shroud of swirling cloud and mist. This is by far the most southerly member of the genus, and I was fortunate to find a few plants in flower, despite the prevailing conditions of semi-darkness and perpetual rain. Unless they had flowers, the plants were very difficult to find, as their dark bodies merged imperceptibly into the equally sombre-coloured rocks and earth. In fact, the form illustrated has a particularly dark body, coupled with a deep red flower.

▷ Tarija lies in a warm valley, and I arrived there from Iscayache in the usual way – on the back of a truck. On the eastern side of Tarija, on the road to Narvaez, lies the Condor Pass. This area is home to several exciting cacti, including **Cleistocactus strausii**.

In Tarija I climbed aboard a truck heading for this area, then climbed off again when I saw this cliff covered in *C. strausii*, banging hard on the cab roof in the time-honoured manner of gaining the driver's attention. One of the attractions of this particular locality was the orange-flowered begonia which shared the small cliff with the *C. strausii*, along with a *Trichocereus* species.

△ On the same cliffs as shown on the previous page, growing in full sun among ferns and lichens, was this rebutia, with its very grass-green body and pale orange flowers. Is this another **Rebutia deminuta** form?

▷ I stopped at two places on the road to the Condor Pass and in both found **Lobivia cardenasiana** in flower in full sun on exposed rocky slopes. The original description called for purely magenta flowers from populations west of the Condor Pass, but nearer to Cajas red-flowered plants occur. Growing with it I found diminutive plants of *L. tiegeliana* which had recently finished flowering and bore unripe fruits.

◁ This is the typical landscape near the Condor Pass. Most of the flatter, less stony ground has been cultivated and turned into fields. Cacti can therefore survive only on the steeper slopes, which are too rocky to allow easy cultivation. On the gentle slope in the foreground I easily found *Lobivia cardenasiana* (the magenta-flowered plant depicted on pages 78-9) and *L. tiegeliana*. However, I had to search much more carefully to find the plant in the next picture, *Rebutia heliosa* var. *condorensis*, first turning up several tiny, well-camouflaged, sterile plants before I moved across to an area in which they were in flower. Note the open, sun-drenched, rocky nature of the site – a far cry from the usual damp, shady habitat preferred by most species of *Rebutia*. Perhaps this explains why the various *R. heliosa* forms are more difficult to cultivate than other members of the genus, and more likely to rot off at the roots if kept too damp.

▽ On that day in late December I was lucky: the **Rebutia heliosa** var. **condorensis** were in full flower. This is not the impressive display seen in cultivation, as each tiny, single-headed plant never boasted more than one bloom. How different from the multi-headed monsters we proudly grow in our greenhouses! The flower was variable in that the tips of the petals could be either pointed or rounded, but in this population the colour was invariably the clear orange seen here. I was fortunate indeed to be able to photograph the flowers fully expanded, as minutes later the warm sunshine was replaced by a violent thunderstorm as premature darkness enfolded the mountains.

SOUTH-WEST UNITED STATES

*'An enjoyable and rewarding part of the world, where some of even the
most beautiful species are common roadside plants.'*

▷ Here in Utah the rock has formed a natural and breathtaking bridge.

◁ This is a typical early April scene in the Sonoran Desert on the edge of the Santa Catalina Mountains near Tucson, Arizona. The dominant cactus is the saguaro, **Carnegiea gigantea**. Apart from a few opuntias, the only other cacti I found here were a few small *Mammillaria milleri* (= *M. microcarpa* Eng.), a species which comes into flower later in the summer.

▽ In the fairly flat desert where Tucson itself is situated, the soils are deeper and less rocky, with a scattering of small trees such as mesquite, *Prosopis juliflora*, and palo verde, *Cercidium microphyllum*; there is also a great deal of creosote bush, *Larrea tridentata*. The most abundant cactus in such areas is usually the chain-fruit cholla, **Opuntia fulgida**, often accompanied by the barrel cactus, *Ferocactus wislizenii* – another species which flowers late in the summer. Here and there among the thorny scrub I found large mounds of *Escobaria vivipara* var. *bisbeeana*, yet another summer bloomer.

△ The typical hedgehog cactus of the desert flats, even surviving within the outer boundaries of Tucson itself, is **Echinocereus fendleri** var. **fasciculatus**. It forms quite large clumps, which in their adult state closely resemble some forms of *E. engelmannii*; however, the seedlings look quite different. Dr Pierre Fischer, the well-known American cactus specialist, took me to see this particularly fine colony and helped me considerably during my stay in Tucson.

◁ **Echinocereus nicholii** often grows with **E. fendleri** var. **fasciculatus**, seen here as the smaller plant on the right (note how the plants in this population had much paler flowers than those in the picture above). The combination of long, golden spines and small, pale pink flower characteristic of *E. nicholii* makes it the most easily recognizable of all the hedgehog cacti of the area. This species used to be regarded as a variety of *E. engelmannii*, but it is now established as a good species in its own right. Spotting such plants in flower is not difficult: I saw these from the road as I drove towards Tombstone.

◁ A number of large-growing agaves occur throughout the area, of which **Agave parryi**, with its neat arrangement of leaves, is probably the most attractive.

▽ Pierre Fischer had given me details of a locality for **Echinomastus intertextus** north of Tombstone. Although this species is widespread in the south-western deserts, it is very scattered. After considerable searching I finally found my plants growing on flat, well-drained areas at the base of a rocky, tree-covered slope, and fortunately almost all of them were in flower. Admiring these handsome plants in their natural habitat, I was saddened to contemplate the fate of the thousands of beautiful specimens which have been ripped out of the desert over the years and sent to quick and certain death in the greenhouses of Europe. Imported specimens of this species are notoriously difficult to establish, so all these plants will have been sacrificed to commercial gain and the selfish desire to own habitat-collected plants.

△ **Mammillaria macdougalii** is another widespread plant, and was growing close to some large, spectacular specimens of *Echinocereus rigidissimus* which were just coming into bud. These were a chance find when I just happened to stop the car to stretch my legs.

▷ My eventual destination was the famous Organ Pipe Cactus National Monument on the Arizona–Mexico border. The teddy bear cholla, **Opuntia bigelovii**, is the dominant plant in this picture, which was taken near the main campsite. This cholla prefers stony, well-drained, slightly sloping ground and is absent from the flatter areas with deeper alluvial soils. Also visible in this picture are a few single-stemmed *Carnegiea gigantea* and some small, multi-stemmed organ pipe cacti. Within 100 metres (325 ft) of the campsite I easily found dozens of *Mammillaria milleri* and *Echinocereus nicholii*, although in April only the latter was decorated with its pale pink blooms. *Ferocactus emoryi* is also quite common in the vicinity, while two more barrel cacti occurring in the park are *F. wislizenii* and *F. cylindraceus*. I did not have time to visit the localities for *Lophocereus schottii* or *Echinomastus acunensis*, which hails from the Acuna Valley within the park.

△ The thickets of **Opuntia bigelovii** were covered in their attractive green-centred blooms, which are pollinated by small bees. In these western deserts there are a number of such bees (for example, *Perdita opuntiae*) whose females feed solely on flowers of various opuntias. Such is the extravagance of their pollen-supply that a female bee can often collect a full load from just a single flower. The males utilize the flowers as trysting sites, lying in wait on a bed of pollen until a foraging female shows up.

▷ The jumping cholla, **Opuntia acanthocarpa**, is one of the commonest of the thirteen species of opuntia resident in the Organ Pipe Cactus National Monument. It prefers the deeper soils, and is interesting in having two flower colours, ochre and rust red. One of the great advantages of making a visit to the south-west United States is the opportunity it gives you of actually seeing flowers on the plethora of opuntias which occur in the region. Few people cultivate opuntias because of their size, so it is only by seeing them in habitat that the beauty of their blooms can be appreciated.

◁ After a rapid drive back to Tucson I made a day trip to the Dragoon Mountains with Pierre Fischer. The geology of these mountains is interesting, as they are partly granite (seen here in the foreground) and partly limestone (visible as the white slopes in the background).

▽ Growing on the sandstone beside the dirt road which led up into the mountains were a few plants of **Echinocereus coccineus** var. **arizonicus**. This variety has larger, more robust stems than the type and has thicker spines. The stems are also fewer in number, so that the dense clumps of crowded heads typical of var. *coccineus* are not formed. The var. *arizonicus* is restricted to the southern part of Arizona and New Mexico, occurring in rather scattered localities, such as the Dragoon Mountains.

△ Here and there on areas of flat sandstone rubble we found a few specimens of **Echinocereus fendleri** var. **rectispinus**. The small, often solitary stems differentiate this variety from var. *fasciculatus*, while the straight, perpendicular central spine sets it apart from var. *fendleri*, with its upwardly curving central spine.

▽ It was in a specific quest for **Epithelantha micromeris** that we had headed for the Dragoon Mountains. The plant is rather rare in Arizona and it took us quite a time to locate the first one. We had to scramble across great sloping slabs of limestone to find each tiny plant, wedged inconspicuously into cracks in the rocks. It grew only on the limestone, never straying to the nearby sandstone.

▷ After again returning to Tucson, I started off alone on a trip up to the north-west towards Globe. Along Highway 77 I passed regiments of large, stately *Ferocactus cylindraceus* ranged across the open rocky hillsides. Alas, I had to admire them from the shelter of the car, as the hills were shrouded in dense cloud and rain. Between Winkelman and Globe the sun came out, brilliantly illuminating the rain-soaked magenta blooms of hordes of *Echinocereus fendleri* var. *bonkerae*. It is along this road that this spectacular variety, with its almost pectinate spination, reaches its peak densities, although it is also found in the Santa Catalina Mountains quite near Tucson.

▽ The flowers of **Echinocereus fendleri** var. **bonkerae** are a notably striking shade of purple. The length of the central spines (between one and three in number) varies greatly, but does not normally exceed 1 centimetre (½ in). Short-spined plants resemble *E. pectinatus* to a surprising degree.

▽ Not far away, along the same stretch of highway, *Echinocereus fendleri* var. *bonkerae* is replaced by **E. fendleri** var. **boyce-thompsonii**. This variety is noted for its beautiful dense, curly spination, which is usually whitish, while the lowermost central spine may occasionally attain the remarkable length of 10 centimetres (4 in). I was fortunate that echinocereus flowers do not close up in poor light, for the weather was gloomy and overcast, with frequent squalls of cold rain. I made a detour up the good but winding road into the Pinaleno Mountains, easily locating numerous plants of the rare *E. ledingii* and widespread *Mammillaria wilcoxii*. The former tended to grow on rocky outcrops in full or part sun among the oaks and pines, while the *Mammillaria* grew partly buried in a dense carpet of leaves in deep shade beneath the oaks, rooted in rich humus. Both species bore small flower buds, so would probably not bloom until much later in May.

▷ Having returned to Tucson once more, I headed west for a lightning three-day trip into California, mainly to visit the Joshua Tree National Monument. The higher part of the park, above 1,000 metres (3,250 ft), is situated within the Mojave Desert system, and it is here that the park's namesake plant grows. The Joshua tree, **Yucca brevifolia** (seen here in the background), dominates the landscape over much of this sector of the park. It is often in company with the smaller **Yucca schidigera**, known as the Mojave yucca, seen here in the foreground.

◁ Scattered among the Joshua trees and visible from a considerable distance when in flower, were numerous impressively large mounds of **Echinocereus triglochidiatus** var. **mojavensis**. In this locality most of the plants bear the twisted spines that tend to be regarded as 'typical' for this variety, but, according to Dave Ferguson, who is well acquainted with the plants of this area, there is great variation and in some localities the plants have much straighter spines.

▷ The Joshua Tree National Monument is also home to **Echinocereus engelmannii**, a species which is spread over a wide area of the south-west United States and nothern Mexico, where it crops up in a bewildering variety of forms, in a fashion reminiscent of *Parodia maasii* in Bolivia and Argentina. The form illustrated seems to correspond to var. **variegatus**, one of the diagnostic characteristics of which is the noticeably small, dark flower seen here.

▽ The most beautiful opuntia in this region is **Opuntia basilaris**, the beavertail cactus, which flowers in springtime. The commonest cholla in the park is *Opuntia ramosissima*, which has pencil-thin stems and attractive needle-like spines.

◁ We now make an abrupt change in location, to a typical stretch of landscape near Farmington, New Mexico. The most characteristic feature of the flora in this region is the Utah juniper, *Juniperus osteosperma*, seen in the background, along with the grey-leaved sage-brush, *Artemisia tridentata*. In the foreground **Echinocereus triglochidiatus** is in flower. This is the form often called var. gonacanthus, although in reality it differs in no significant way from var. **triglochidiatus**, as the spination is very variable in every population. Around Farmington these cacti usually seem to occur as widely scattered individuals, often partly hidden beneath sage-brush and junipers, making them very inconspicuous unless in flower.

△ Throughout much of this area **Sclerocactus parviflorus** var. **intermedius** is probably the commonest of the 'globular' cacti, growing both among the junipers and out in full sun on open stony hillsides. The cacti which inhabit this high plateau – around 1,700 metres (5,500 ft) – are a hardy bunch. Winter temperatures are low, and a light powdering of snow covered the ground when I was there in April. The cacti sit wet at the roots in winter and early spring, and dry throughout the summer – the reverse of what we give them in cultivation. The large plant illustrated, with its spectacular garland of flowers, was growing with many others on a stony vacant lot almost in the centre of Farmington itself, along with non-flowering plants of several other species of cacti.

◁ A short distance to the east of Farmington, on the road to Bloomfield, a stony slope just above the road was home to not only plenty of *Sclerocactus parviflorus* var. *intermedius* but also dozens of the delightful plant illustrated, **Echinocereus fendleri**; most of these were in flower. This is var. **fendleri**, which has rather a small body and often forms low clumps of a few heads. In spring these are dwarfed by superb flowers, which are among the most beautiful in the Cactaceae.

△ The same slope was home to a few scattered plants of **Escobaria vivipara** var. **arizonica**, which were just coming into flower. Despite its name, this rather small-growing variety is found in Utah, Colorado and New Mexico as well as Arizona.

▷ There then followed a whirlwind three-day tour in Ken Heil's jeep to some of the pediocactus habitats. My aim was to photograph the plants in flower, but in this I was thwarted because most of them had flowered earlier than normal and I had missed them.

Our first stop was near the canyon of the Little Colorado River near Holbrook, Arizona. The object of our quest here was the grama grass cactus, *Pediocactus papyracanthus*, which grows on the ledges above the river.

◁ Arriving in mid-morning we discovered that most of the **Pediocactus papyracanthus** plants bore buds which were obviously not destined to open until later in the afternoon, too late for us to see them. By walking up and down and peering at the ground with the utmost concentration, we found dozens of plants without much trouble. They were beautifully camouflaged among the grama grass clumps, the papery grey spines of the cactus exactly mimicking the shrivelled dry blades of grass. I know that other cactophiles (many in large groups) have searched this self-same area for hours without managing to detect a single one of these amazingly well-hidden plants! In another locality near Holbrook we painstakingly searched the low alkaline conglomerate hills for *Pediocactus peeblesianus*. Unfortunately, they had finished flowering and all we found were two or three plants shrunk into the ground, where they were all but invisible.

▽ Growing with the *Pediocactus papyracanthus* plants we turned up a number of tiny specimens of an escobaria which seems to be a remarkably diminutive form of the very widespread **Escobaria missouriensis**. The full-grown plants were only around 1 centimetre (½ in) across and were dwarfed by the flowers, which themselves were much smaller than those in any of the named varieties.

△ Heading northwards through spectacular desert scenery towards Marble Canyon, we passed through several areas where clumps of **Echinocactus polycephalus** var. **xeranthemoides** could easily be spotted growing on rocks near the roadside. This species flowers later in the summer, but with its wild and dense spination even a sterile plant makes a fine sight. Unfortunately, we also saw piles of dead plants dumped by the roadside, where unscrupulous commercial collectors had left their illegal haul to be collected later and then failed to return for them. Such is the price paid for access to habitat-collected plants, a price which is doubly high when one considers that this species is virtually impossible to re-establish in cultivation in Europe.

▷ At the north-east end of the Grand Canyon lies the Vermilion Cliffs area of Marble Canyon. Ken knew where to look for *Pediocactus bradyi* but had scant reward for his efforts, for the tiny plants had already shrunk down into the soil after their brief show of blooms a mere week or two earlier. This is the first member of the genus to flower, often at the end of March, and by the end of April the shrivelled plants are almost impossible to detect among the flakes of Kaibab limestone among which they grow on ledges above the river.

◁ The red soils at Vermilion Cliffs are home to one of the more attractive dwarf yuccas of the area, **Yucca harrimaniae**.

△ Another rather local species of the Colorado Canyon area is the prostrate-growing **Opuntia nicholii**. Fortunately, its beautiful pink flowers were fully open when we arrived.

△ Nor far to the west of Marble Canyon lies House Rock Valley. Here we searched for a rather dwarf form of **Sclerocactus whipplei**, with a very small, pale yellow flower. The plants were widely scattered and hard to find among dense sage-brush. We also spent over an hour searching for *Pediocactus paradinei* here, but without success.

▷ Although we drew a blank for **Pediocactus paradinei** in House Rock Valley, we found plenty of them just a little higher up, where the road climbs through the juniper-pinyon woodlands on the Kaibab Plateau at an altitude of 2,100 metres (7,000 ft). Here the plants grew abundantly in large colonies in open gravel among pines close to the road. Many of the plants had flowered earlier in the day, but we arrived too late in the afternoon to see them, and by now the buds had closed. The only associated cacti were a few small, non-flowering specimens of the locally endemic *Escobaria vivipara* var. *kaibabensis*.

◁ Our next stop was the gypsum hills near Fredonia. The traveller speeding through the pinewoods on the Kaibab Plateau suddenly emerges from the forest and looks down on these dramatic bare hills below – a spectacularly sudden change in habitat and geology.

△ This bare eroded gypsum would seem to be innately inimical to any form of plant life, and yet it is in this environment that the locally endemic **Pediocactus sileri** thrives (it is also abundant on adjacent areas of red sandstone-based soils). We arrived too late in the evening to see the yellow flowers, which had just closed up on many of the plants. Despite this, the plants themselves are probably the most handsome in the genus, with their dense thatch of white spines. It is incredible how even large plants manage to cling to the bare, almost vertical, gypsum slopes, and yet more amazing to see the numerous small seedlings which somehow contrive to establish themselves on the hard-packed earth. The paucity of competing vegetation is noticeable, presumably because few plants can work the miracle of surviving in such an environment, so *P. sileri* has the field almost to itself.

◁ Our destination next day was Capitol Reef National Park, one of the driest and most barren cactus habitats in the whole of the United States. Just beyond the park Ken pointed out a large colony of a tall, robust, non-flowering *Sclerocactus* species thronging the arid roadsides. The only cactus able to prosper on the bare alkaline hills of the Navajoan Desert depicted in the picture is the tiny *Pediocactus winkleri*. Unfortunately, these had also flowered early, and we had missed them by a good fortnight. The plant in flower is the cliff-rose *Cowania stansburiana*.

▽ Once it has finished its brief burst of flowering, the tiny **Pediocactus winkleri** is virtually impossible to find. In common with the other dwarf members of the genus, the plants swiftly shrink back into the soil for protection against the rapid onset of summer, with its uncomfortably high temperatures up to 40°C (104°F) and week after week of desiccating sunshine. By contrast, environment there is virtually no other vegetation to compete with the cacti.
apparently takes in its stride. We spent hours tracking down just a few specimens of this elusive and extremely localized plant, most of which bore seed pods which were already almost ripe. (We had similarly bad luck with *P. despainii* next day on the San Rafael Swell; all had finished flowering and shrunk into the soil.)

△ In another part of the Capitol Reef park we had better luck with **Sclerocactus wrightiae**, which was at the peak of its blooming, yielding plenty of flowers which were either white or pale pink. This is one of the rarest members of the genus, with a very restricted distribution in Utah. The plant depicted is rooted in a soil composed of fine silt mixed with millions of fossilized sea shells which litter the surface. In such a hostile environment there is virtually no other vegetation to compete with the cacti.

▷ Next day we headed back towards Farmington on US 163, making a brief detour along a dirt road into the Abajo Mountains. The vegetation consists of ponderosa pines, *Pinus ponderosa*, mixed with oaks. Winters are cold and the last snows would only have melted a few weeks earlier.

◁ The Abajo Mountains west of Monticello are one of several similar locations in Utah and adjacent Colorado where the local form of **Echinocereus triglochidiatus** var. **mojavensis**, known as 'inermis', is found. Although in its most extreme, spineless, form it has often been distributed as *E. inermis*, it should be obvious to anyone who visits the habitat that it is very far from being a discrete species. Not only do large clumps of fully spined plants occur alongside those which lack spines, but the degree of spination can even vary on a single plant, so that some heads may be naked while others are quite well armed. In these cool mountains the plants were mostly in advanced bud only by the middle of May, but fortunately a few had begun to open their first flowers.

△ In another part of the same range Ken Heil showed me dozens of handsome **Pediocactus simpsonii** rooted in leaf-mould under oaks. This species is incredibly widespread, ranging way up into the states of Oregon and Washington. However, even in the Abajo Mountains the plant colonies tend to be restricted to small areas, and are absent from superficially similar spots close by. It apparently prefers south-facing slopes, with rocky, well-drained soils which are also rich in humus – often oak leaf-mould. The stamens are sensitive and rapidly move inwards to clasp the style when stroked.

SOUTHERN AFRICA

'A remarkably rich succulent flora and breathtaking diversity of species flourish in fabulous natural rockeries.'

▷ Two Hartmann's Mountain zebra appear in this South African desert landscape at Springbok.

◁ The Knersvlakte is situated close to the town of Vanrhynsdorp, approximately 300 kilometres (180 miles) due north of Cape Town. The landscape is renowned for its sweeps of gleaming white quartz pebbles strewn across an almost flat, featureless terrain. The area lies within the winter rainfall regime, and it is during the cool, mist-drenched winters that most of the succulents come into flower. When I arrived in April it was well into autumn and there were few plants in flower. It is hard to credit that there are thousands of succulents in this photograph, receding far into the distance. However, many of the plants which grow here are such perfect mimics of the quartz pebbles that the average person could walk across the whole of the Knersvlakte without ever realizing that many of the 'stones' being scrunched underfoot were alive and growing.

▽ The most abundant quartz-mimics are **Argyroderma pearsonii**, seen here, and the rather more convex-topped *A. delaetii* and *A. subalbum*. In many places these are so densely packed that it is impossible to avoid treading on them (although they do not seem to suffer any harm from such treatment). When the winter rains have been generous, the whole area is transformed into a carpet of purple and yellow argyroderma flowers. Another common species, *A. fissum*, is much easier to see as its greenish, upright, two-fingered stems do not mimic their surroundings. The most highly visible succulent all over the area is *Dactylopsis digitata*, which forms mats of soft, grey, finger-like stems.

△ The pale pinkish-purple flowers of **Conophytum pillansii** betray the presence of the tiny plants, which in April still bear their sheaths of dead skin. The species is so common and widespread in the region that whenever I stopped the car to examine a quartz outcrop, I could rely on finding this pretty little plant in flower.

◁ **Conophytum pearsonii** tends to grow on slightly raised quartz hummocks and is another common species.

◁ Heading north towards Springbok I passed numerous large plants of **Euphorbia schoenlandii** growing in flat, sandy desert near the road. This is a local species restricted to the area, and sadly it has suffered a lot at the hands of rapacious commercial collectors.

▽ There are not many places in South Africa that fail to boast at least one example of a succulent euphorbia. The local representative on the Knersvlakte is **Euphorbia tuberculatoides**, which prefers the sandy areas that crop up here and there as islands in the sea of quartz pebbles. A dwarf thick-stemmed form of the common *Crassula lycopodioides* often grows with it.

◁ Further north, approaching Springbok, the drab countryside is suddenly brightened by thousands of **Cheiridopsis candidissima** accompanied by the almost ever-present *Euphorbia mauritanica* bushes. No doubt those hills in the background harbour a far greater variety of succulents, such as conophytums, but on the sandy desert flats it is only *C. candidissima* which seems to thrive.

▽ The small town of Springbok lies within the region commonly known as Namaqualand, a name synonymous with succulents. Namaqualand covers a huge area, so tracking down many of the choicer species without the help of a guide is difficult unless you have plenty of time. As I was mainly in South Africa to photograph animals, not plants, I had to make do with whatever succulents were easily available near the roads. Fortunately, my campsite at Springbok itself boasted a number of succulents, including two small *Cheiridopsis* species which were in their shrunken state of winter dormancy. However, the most exciting species was the bare 'bush' in this plate, which is actually a fine specimen of **Euphorbia filiflora** growing just in front of my tent. This species is very rare in collections, hardly ever being offered in the trade, although it was common enough on my campsite and on similar flat, sandy ground thereabouts.

◁ The most obvious characteristic of **Euphorbia filiflora** is the long peduncles which cover the plant, lending it the appearance of a small bush which has long ago given up the unequal struggle against the desert's rigours and died. This specimen is growing within the protective embrace of an *E. mauritanica* bush.

▽ Many of the large bushes of **Euphorbia mauritanica** which dot the flat, sandy areas around Springbok provide both board and lodging for the bush Karoo rat, *Otomys unisulcatus.* This particular individual had set up home within a bush in the Hester Malan Nature Reserve at Springbok, and was busy performing its morning ablutions when I took its picture. The phrase 'eating itself out of house and home' could apply literally to this rat, whose favourite food is the stems of its home. Before tucking into a meal, the rat first sniffs and grades each stem for quality. Then the diminutive gourmet bites one off and holds it in its front paws like a stick of celery as it nibbles delicately away. As there is seldom any sign of white, milky sap oozing out, it seems that the preliminary sniffing may serve to select only those stems which are low in sap content.

△ While driving northwards along the Springbok 'bypass' I could scarcely fail to notice the many fine specimens of one of the best of all the aloes, **Aloe melanacantha**, perched up on the rocky cutting. Even without its red flowers, this is a very striking plant, due to its tightly packed, spiny leaves and miniature growth form.

△ Throughout this area **Cotyledon eckloniana** is a frequent sight on the roadsides, often growing with *C. reticulata*. In April all the plants had dropped their leaves, revealing the neat spiral arrangement of the podaria up the silver-grey stems.

▷ The leaves of the widespread **Cotyledon orbiculata** are incredibly varied in shape and colour. The plant is common to the north of Springbok, as I found when heading towards the border with Namibia. Note the shrivelled state of the leaves after an extended period without rain.

◁ The tree aloe or quiver tree, **Aloe dichotoma**, can hardly be missed and is common over a wide area in Namaqualand. It is particularly splendid when covered in its bright yellow flowers. Unfortunately, in some places whole forests of this species are dying, due to a catastrophic lowering of the water table, probably because of abstraction for human uses.

▽ As I approached Vioolsdrif, on the border with Namibia, I started to see the occasional specimen of the small, handsome *Aloe pearsonii* jutting up above the rocks, its leaves neatly stacked in layers up the stem, like a Chinese pagoda.

Just before Vioolsdrif I stopped to examine the rock-strewn hillsides near the road, which were covered with thousands of **Euphorbia virosa**, many of which were in flower. This is a common species in the area and superficially resembles *E. avasmontana*.

◁ I had been given a locality near Vioolsdrif for *Pachypodium namaquanum*. My instructions were to turn off eastwards along a dirt road which led into the flat desert through a gate in the roadside fence. The first plant I saw as I carefully negotiated the track was one of the weirdest-looking euphorbias of all, **Euphorbia namaquensis**. It rather resembles something that has been put together from the odd spare parts of other plants. It was present only on the flat areas of deeper alluvial soils, and was not to be found on the numerous small outcrops of quartz which dotted the desert hereabouts. These were in themselves interesting as, no matter how small – often only the size of a kitchen table – they almost always harboured a few specimens of a small yellow-flowered conophytum.

▽ Just past the last specimen of *Euphorbia namaquensis* my attention was riveted by a spectacle which must be among the most breathtaking on offer in this dry region with its sparse vegetation. Hundreds of huge mounds of **Hoodia gordonii** lay scattered across the desert, each plant extravagantly swathed in veritable canopies of flowers. I seemed to have timed my arrival to perfection, for every single plant was in full flower, and yet, as there were few buds, within a day or two the whole amazing display would be finished.

A strong smell of sweaty feet hit me as I squatted down to take my pictures. I was just about to go back to the car for a fresh pair of socks when it dawned on me that the hoodia flowers were the culprits. Although unpleasant to my nostrils, their powerful aroma attracted several bright-green muscid flies with bulbous orange eyes. Presumably these would be effective operators of the complex pollination mechanism.

▷ With my VW Beetle threatening to become stuck in the rather sandy soil, I had to abandon my quest for the main colony of **Pachypodium namaquanum**. However, I did manage to locate a few scattered outliers growing on the rocks which jutted up from the plain. The Afrikaans name for this weird plant, 'halfmans', seems singularly appropriate.

◁ I headed back to Springbok and then turned eastwards. My route went through some of the richest country for succulents in the whole of South Africa, but with time short and no knowledge of the best local habitats, I aimed straight for Pofadder. There I knew I could rely on a guide, the local doctor, to show me the best plants and so save a lot of time. Like almost everyone in South Africa, the good doctor received me – a complete stranger – with heartwarming hospitality. Within minutes of my knocking on his door, we were out gazing across the rather uninspiring terrain shown in the picture, on the very edge of town. I had mentioned that my greatest ambition was to see lithops in habitat, and I was surprised to find that this could be achieved merely by popping round the corner from the doctor's house.

▽ My first lithops, lovely plants of **Lithops julii** subsp. **fulleri** var. **fulleri**, were well camouflaged among the small quartzite pebbles which littered the red sandy soil. We spent an hour or so pacing up and down, backs bent, tracking down the best specimens, which were scattered over a wide area. We then went across to the other side of town to visit Pofadder Common, whose quartzite rocks must surely support the best assemblage of succulents on earth. The next ten pictures depict but a selection of these riches.

△ When not in bloom this conophytum would no doubt take quite some finding, as only the tips of succulent bodies emerge level with the soil surface. However, in warm sunshine the masses of pink flowers make it the most conspicuous plant of all. It belongs to the subgenus *Ophthalmophyllum*, in which the rather soft, squashy bodies resemble little sacks of water. It appears to correspond to **C. praesectum**, which is endemic to Pofadder.

▷ For me, the most exciting plant on Pofadder Common was also one of the most numerous: **Lithops olivacea**. This particular species is not a good mimic of the surrounding quartzite rocks, and in fact the clumps of heads were quite easy to distinguish. When this picture was taken in May, the plants were in a sterile state. However, when I paid a brief return visit to Pofadder Common in late June (on the way back from Etosha Pan in northern Namibia), there had been a midwinter downpour. In response to the deluge the *L. olivacea* plants had budded up, flowered prolifically and fruited – all in the space of just six weeks.

◁ Unlike the *Lithops olivacea*, **Lapidaria margarethae** is a creditable mimic of a lump of quartz, and so is not easy to spot unless betrayed by the large yellow flowers. Like most of the best plants on Pofadder Common, this species was restricted to the areas of loose quartz pebbles. I later found it on small outcrops of similar rocks further north on the way to Namibia.

◁ **Dinteranthus puberulus** was another excellent mimic of its surroundings, and like *Lapidaria margarethae* was difficult to distinguish unless given away by its large yellow flowers.

◁ Pofadder Common was remarkably rich in species of *Anacampseros*, of which **A. papyracea** was the largest. Unfortunately, none of them was in flower during May.

▽ Growing alongside the *Anacampseros papyracea*, and sometimes difficult to distinguish except by the slimmer, neater stems, were hundreds of **A. albissima**.

△ In places it was difficult to walk without treading on a plant of **Anacampseros alstonii**, although as the leaves scarcely protrude above the ground, it would probably come to no harm. Note the lovely silvery hue of this specimen in habitat, perfectly matching the surrounding quartz both in colour and in texture. These beautiful, tight little plants show little resemblance to the unhealthy, often flaccid and overly tall green plants usually seen in cultivation. In habitat the plants hug the ground closely in a manner typical of most of these small mimicry succulents, giving protection from not only heat and drought but also the ravages of hungry goats and rabbits, and the small steenbok antelopes which manage to glean a living from the meagre resources available in these deserts.

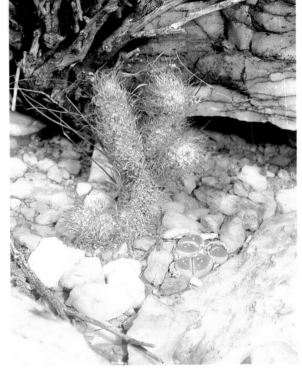

▷ **Anacampseros baeseckii**, which usually lurks in the shade at the bases of small bushes, was not abundant on Pofadder Common. This specimen was accompanied by a small *Lithops olivacea.*

△ Succulents grew so thickly on Pofadder Common that it was often difficult to exclude 'extraneous' species from a photograph. This flowering specimen of **Trichocaulon pictum** has a small *Lithops olivacea* plant at its base. The *T. pictum* were rather rare, being concentrated in one small area on a quartz ridge.

▷ The common haworthia around Pofadder is the miniature **Haworthia venosa** subsp. **tessellata**. These tiny plants usually grow wedged in clefts in the rock where some soil has collected and there is a degree of shade from the roasting sun. Peeping out from behind the rearmost plant there is a single specimen of the rather small, squat form of *Crassula lycopodioides,* which occurs hereabouts, while in front there is a seedling of *Anacampseros papyracea.* I found several quite attractive species of *Crassula* on Pofadder Common, but as I have not been able to name them reliably, I am not including them here.

△ My friend the doctor suggested that I visit a farm to the south-west of Pofadder to see one of the most magnificent plants of the region, the rare **Dinteranthus vanzijlii**. I was taken by the farmer in his jeep to a slope strewn with quartz pebbles, so often the best habitat for unusual succulents. After more than twenty minutes of pacing slowly up and down the slope, peering closely at the ground, I finally spotted the first specimen sitting almost invisibly among the quartz pebbles, where it very much resembled an outsize lithops. We managed to turn up only two more specimens, one of which was given away from a distance by its big yellow flower. The plants were excellent mimics of their surroundings, and much harder to spot than *Lithops olivacea* or *L. julii* subsp. *fulleri*.

▷ This attractive specimen of **Anacampseros recurvata** was the only succulent of note accompanying the *Dinteranthus vanzijlii* on their rubble-strewn slope.

▷ After a hectic and enjoyable day on Pofadder Common, with my afternoon's excursion to the arid home of *Dinteranthus vanzijlii*, I headed north towards Namibia on a dirt road leading towards Karasburg. On sandy flats just outside Pofadder I spotted numerous plants of **Euphorbia confluens**. As there had recently been a heavy but very localized shower, the plants still bore their narrow red leaves, while a few annuals such as this yellow daisy had quickly sprouted and come into flower.

△ All along the road there were small outcrops of quartz, often only a few metres across and rising up a mere 30 centimetres (12 in) or so above the sandy soils of the surrounding plain. Many of these outcrops yielded *Lapidaria margarethae*, while one produced yet another species of *Anacampseros*, which appears to be **A. lanigera**.

◁ A long search of a much flatter area of red sand, thinly veiled with a silvery top-dressing of quartz pebbles, yielded just a few precious specimens of a particularly beautiful form of **Lithops julii** subsp. **fulleri**. The *Batrachornis perloides* grasshopper hunching down along-side is an adult. Although it blends in quite well with its surroundings, it cannot bear comparison with its juvenile, wingless, stage, in which it mimics perfectly a quartz pebble. However, this particular 'pebble' has a habit of suddenly sprouting six legs and jumping away. It is no coincidence that both plant and animal employ the same survival strategy of mimicking the surrounding quartz – in such an open habitat few other options are available.

▽ Almost as difficult to spot among the quartzite pebbles were these tiny plants of **Crassula mesembryanthemopsis** – the largest individuals I could find. Compare them with the monsters we grow in our greenhouses and you have a repeat of the situation with *Rebutia pygamaea* and *R. heliosa*. All these plants are miniature in habitat yet form bizarrely huge mounds in cultivation, grotesque giants which bear no resemblance to the wild plant.

SPECIES INDEX

Accepted names for cacti and succulents are indicated by an asterisk (★).
Page numbers on which illustrations occur are indicated by **bold** type.

◁ *Lobivia acanthoplegma* var. *patula* at Cliza.

PLACE NAMES

THE NAME GAME

This seems an appropriate point at which to discuss in rather more detail one of the avowed aims of this book – to show why the natural variability of cacti and, to a lesser extent, succulents in habitat has led to the creation and subsequent disappearance of so many species names over the years.

This is certainly not a matter to be dismissed lightly. The constant instability displayed by so many names obviously causes considerable annoyance to many people who grow cacti and succulents. The 'lumping' of dozens of familiar and well-loved names into a lesser number of species even incited one American (writing in a 1993 edition of the US *Cactus and Succulent Journal*) to call for the return of Backeberg (of *Cactus Lexicon* fame) on the pretext that each and every species should receive a name. This is fair enough comment. But just how many names do the hobbyists want for a single species? If you follow the philosophy adopted by Backeberg (and several other well-known experts) you will end up growing the same plant under a veritable array of different 'species' names that are biologically meaningless. The only real difference, in fact, will lie in the spelling on the labels.

I have already referred briefly to such a highly artificial and plainly ridiculous situation under *Lobivia pentlandii* on page 18. Backeberg himself, on one of his rare visits to the actual plant habitats, visited the area around Oruro in Bolivia where this plant is very common. From this single population he extracted and named as species a number of individuals that differed in certain minor aspects such as flower colour and the length and number of spines. Ever since hobbyists have been happily cultivating these 'species' under names such as *Lobivia argentea*, *L. brunneo-rosea*, *L. raphidacantha*, *L. varians* and *L. wegheiana*. No doubt when the Austrian lobivia expert Walter Rausch 'lumped' all these lovely names into *Lobivia pentlandii* many people felt both surprised and cheated. After all, in the greenhouse the 'differences' were plain for all to see.

The trouble is that all these differences can be exhibited by plants raised from just a single seed pod, as I myself have proved. This is hardly surprising, as

Backeberg took several of his 'new' species from a single hillside, where the plants would all be closely related to one another as part of a single 'family group'.

Therefore, it is preposterous to consider these as separate species, however great their individual differences. Yet that is exactly what Backeberg (and others) have done over and over again. It is inevitable, therefore, that such baseless names must disappear, especially those that are based mainly on such unstable and unimportant characteristics as flower colour, which can vary enormously even within a single population (see pages 24–5 and 55–6).

So why does it cause so much consternation and outrage when 'species' are duly put to the sword? The answer seems to be that most people like to have as many different names as possible decorating their greenhouses. There is, too, an element of snob value when it comes to 'species', with mere varieties or forms being regarded with considerable disdain.

There is also the problem of familiarity, which leads to a reluctance to change long-held views about the status of familiar plants. Take the example of another species illustrated in the preceding pages, *Echinocereus fendleri*. There are several illustrations showing this widespread cactus, including varieties *bonkerae*, *boyce-thompsonii*, *fasciculatus* and *rectispinus*. Most people are perfectly happy to purchase plants and seeds bearing these names under *E. fendleri*. Yet all of these forms, now so unquestioningly accepted as mere varieties, were originally described as species in their own right. Their specific status was based on the rather scanty knowledge available at the time concerning the distribution and variability of these plants in habitat.

Our knowledge of North American plants has grown rapidly in the last 25 years, and it has become obvious that these 'species' are in reality all so closely related that they must more properly be regarded as varieties of a single, variable and widespread taxon, for which the earliest name is *Echinocereus fendleri*. The ignominious demotion to varietal status probably upset quite a lot of people at the time, yet because most people who grow the plants today have only seen them listed under *E. fendleri*, they are happy to accept them as varieties without complaint. (A similar situation has arisen in many lithops such as *L. fulleri*, now a subspecies of *L. julii*, pages 141 and 150.)

In the case of most South American cacti sufficient information about the true situation on the ground has been forthcoming only in more recent times. As a result, the same ruthless 'lumping' jobs that were performed long ago on many North American cacti are now having to be performed on their southern brethren.

An apt South American parallel to the situation in *Echinocereus fendleri* occurs with *Parodia maasii*. Like its northern cousin, *P. maasii* is also a common plant, being spread over a wide area of the Andes from central Bolivia to just south of the Rio Yacoraite in Salta Province of Argentina. I have seen dozens of populations over the whole of this vast and wild area and can vouch for the perplexing variability that exists from one to another. Some of this will be evident from the illustrations on the preceding pages. A given specimen of *P. maasii* can be short and squat, barrel-shaped, tall and cylindrical, small, large, solitary or form large clumps. The spines can be straight, bent at the tip or even hooked; glassy coloured, whitish, straw-coloured, dark brown, grey or black; so densely covering the plant-body as to conceal the body beneath or so open that the body is clearly visible. The flowers can be yellowish-orange, orange-red or deep red; they can be large or small. In some cases several of these variations – straight or hooked spines, red or orange flowers, for example – occur within a single population, while others exist only as uniform characters peculiar to widely separated populations. In the past plants from at least 19 of these populations have been considered to represent discrete species. However, in most cases the differences between these 'species' are less than those that exist between the various varieties of *Echinocereus fendleri* or even between varieties of *E. engelmannii*.

It is also important to note that most of the *Parodia maasii* populations and its species-segregates are not really isolated but run into one another. There is, in consequence, a continuous range of variability, making it impossible to define where one 'species' ends and another begins, and this applies to many other cacti. The title of 'species' is, therefore, totally inappropriate for such plants, and variety or even mere form is all that they deserve in terms of recognition for greenhouse purposes.

Unfortunately, one factor that has contributed greatly to the creation of a plethora of superfluous names is the inaccessible nature of much cactus habitat. The absence of roads that could enable us to inspect plants in the intervening areas can lead to false assumptions about whether or not a species-population really is isolated, or is only apparently so. In some localities, however, the situation is so confusing that it is difficult to be sure exactly what is being seen. For example, at Puente San Pedro south of Camargo (page 54) parodias occur in large mounds on both sides of the river. On the western side the plants have quite an open spination, which is normally a gingery-brown shade. On the eastern side, just 100 metres (100 yards) away, some plants have a similar spination to this, while others are blessed with a very decorative dense white spination, and the spination of still others is intermediate between the two. As I stood and looked at these magnificent specimens I was not sure whether I was seeing local forms of two distinct species – i.e., *Parodia maasii* (the ginger, more open spination) and *P. roseoalba* (dense white spination and smaller flower) – or merely two forms of *P. maasii*. The presence of numerous intermediates is not in itself helpful, indicating as it does the possibility either of hybrids between two distinct species, or the intergrading of one subspecies of *P. maasii* into another. Without some more detailed work on the ground this sort of problem is difficult to solve, yet there are hundreds of similar examples within the succulent families.

Another important reason for the sudden demise of familiar species names is the fact that they were inadequately described in the first place so that we are not sure exactly what was meant. The situation is made much worse when no precise locality was given in the original description.

We can forgive Rausch and Ritter for describing so many superfluous 'new' species, because they at least gave precise localities for them. This has enabled subsequent workers to find and recognize the plants and make their own decisions about their true status. Rausch himself made the brave decision to 'lump' the majority of his 'new' species and produced a most sensible revision of the genus *Lobivia*.

Unfortunately, however, our ability to make sense of the chaos of names created by Backeberg is severely limited by his failure to cite localities for many of his 'new' species. In most cases he himself simply did not know and just went ahead with his descriptions without the remotest knowledge of the relationships of his 'new' species to any others in the area. In most cases, when these plants have been (after a great deal of trouble) finally nailed down to a locality, they have proved to be no more than local forms or (far worse) merely singular individuals plucked from a single variable population of a long-known species.

Backeberg was not hampered by this lack of the proper data in his apparent frantic haste to create as many 'new' names as possible. The fact that we have been so eager to hang on to these names and so reluctant to abandon them is merely indicative of the eagerness of most collectors to amass as many 'species' as possible – and I have been as guilty of this as anyone in the past. It will undoubtedly take a long time for this 'stamp-collector' mentality to fade out of the cactus world, and until then there will no doubt be other calls to bring back the likes of Backeberg. Fortunately, this is unlikely to happen, as a more sensible and integrated approach to the subject is now becoming commoner. There are still some, alas, who consider that if a plant looks even marginally different from one already described, and grows around the next bend in the road, then there is sufficient justification for leaping into print with a 'new' name. Even so, I am confident that within ten years we shall be enjoying a stability in naming – unseen for many years – helped in part by the widespread and accepted use of cultivar names for many of today's 'species'.